This book may be kept

CHRISTMAS IS HERE

Lucas Cranach. Rest on the Flight into Egypt

CHRISTMAS IS HERE

*A Catholic Selection of
Stories and Poems*

Edited by
ANNE FREMANTLE

STEPHEN DAYE PRESS
NEW YORK

COPYRIGHTS AND ACKNOWLEDGMENTS

The editor and the publishers express their appreciation to the authors and publishers listed below for permission to reprint various selections, including copyrighted material. Every effort has been made to trace all copyright owners; if any acknowledgment has been inadvertently omitted, the publishers will gladly make the necessary correction in the next printing.

George Allen & Unwin, Ltd. and The New American Library: for the selection from *The Meaning of the Glorious Koran*, an explanatory translation by Mohammed Marmaduke Pickthall.

Chatto and Windus, Ltd.: for "Christmas Eve" by Nicolai Gogol from his *Evenings on a Farm near Dikanka*, translated by Constance Garnett.

The Clarendon Press, Oxford: for permission to quote from *The Book of James* translated by M. R. James.

The Commonweal and Harper & Brothers: for Bernard Raymund's "The Last Christmas" reprinted from *The Commonweal Reader*, copyright 1949 by *The Commonweal*, published by Harper & Brothers.

Edward Fenton: for his story "The Broken Christmas," first published in *Mademoiselle*.

S. Fischer Verlag, Frankfurt: for permission to translate especially for this volume "Die heiligen drei Könige von Totenleben" by Alexander Lernet-Holenia, from the author's *Die neue Atlantis*.

Verlag Herder, Freiburg: for permission to translate especially for this volume "Die Ernte ohne Saat" by Ruth Schaumann, from the author's *Der Weihnachtsstern*.

Chr. Kaiser Verlag, Munich: for permission to translate especially for this volume "Das Mütterchen" by Otto Bruder from the author's *Die Weihnachtshirten*.

Arnoldo Mondadori Editore, Milan: for permission to include a translation of "La croce d'oro" by Grazia Deledda.

William Morris Agency and Jo Pagano: for "Signor Santa" by Jo Pagano, copyright 1935 by The Atlantic Monthly Company.

New American Library and Philip Booth: for "Twelfth Night" by Philip Booth, from *New World Writing, No. 8*, copyright 1955 by New American Library of World Literature, Inc.

iv

Copyrights and Acknowledgments

Pantheon Books: for "Bethelehem" (editor's title) reprinted from *The Mystery of the Charity of Joan of Arc* by Charles Péguy, translated by Julian Green, copyright 1950 by Pantheon Books, Inc.

Eric Posselt: for the use of his translations, "The Golden Crucifix" and "The Carpenter's Christmas."

Random House, Inc.: for permission to reprint "The Vision of the Shepherds" (editor's title) and the final selection in the volume from *For the Time Being* by W. H. Auden, copyright 1944 by W. H. Auden.

Charles Scribner's Sons: for "Dulce Domum" reprinted from *The Wind in the Willows* by Kenneth Grahame; copyright 1908, 1933 by Charles Scribner's Sons; and for "Old Folks' Christmas" from *Round Up* by Ring Lardner; copyright 1929 by Charles Scribner's Sons, both used by permission of the publishers.

The Viking Press, Inc.: for the two stories by Saki from *The Short Stories of Saki* (H. H. Munro), copyright 1930 by The Viking Press, Inc.

Naomi Royde Smith: for her translation of "The Ox and the Ass at the Manger," published by Hollis and Carter, Ltd., London.

Leskov's "The Clothes Mender" is from his *The Musk-Ox and Other Tales*, translated by R. Norman and published by George Routledge, London, 1944.

The selection from *The Gospel According to St. Luke* from the translation by Monsignor Ronald Knox is reprinted by permission of His Eminence the Cardinal Archbishop of Westminster and the publishers, Sheed and Ward.

ILLUSTRATIONS

All woodcuts and engravings in this volume are reproduced through the courtesy of The Metropolitan Museum of Art, New York. We are grateful for the cooperation of the Museum's Department of Prints.

Contents

Contents

Illustrations

About Christmas

So MUCH has been written about Christmas that sometimes it is possible to forget the most important thing about it at all—that it is *here*. And now. For although the first Christmas happened at a very precise moment (though no one is quite sure which) in the reign of Herod, in the town of Bethlehem, in Judea, yet the fact of the Incarnation, which occurred there once, in time, is here and now occurring, and will continue occurring, until the Second Coming of Christ. Before the Gospel, nothing was Gospel; since the Gospel, everything is Gospel —is the Good News. And the ways in which that news is received are as many as there are human beings by whom it is received: it is received, as is every gift, according to the capacity of the receiver. And one of the ways it is received is by being rejected: for to receive is not necessarily to accept; one receives a blow, or a warning; one does not necessarily always accept either.

So, too, with Christmas. It is here, on this planet, and we must face it, this and every year. This anthology, like other Christmas anthologies, is a collection of stories about how people received Christmas, what they did about its being *here.* The stories are therefore of many kinds, and from many countries; there are some comic, some sentimental, some sad, with distinctions of climate and custom. But the focal point in every story is that the real difference is the one that Christmas has made. So the book begins, as it must, with the Gospel itself, with the true story of what really happened. It has been sometimes thought that St. Luke must have been told the story by Our Lady, for there was no one else (except One, the Holy Ghost) who could have told him so much. And then comes the story as it stands in one of the so-called Apocryphal Gospels, probably written down early in the second century, and called the Book of James. This shows, if nothing else, how the instinct to embroider, to re-tell, not to leave well enough alone, is with us all.

Next, I have included the testimony of one who never, all his life, met a Catholic—the Arab Muhammad. He could neither read nor write, and in his book, the Koran, he relates how the angel Gabriel appeared to him and told him to read, and he said "I can't read" and the angel reiterated "Read: in the name of thy Lord Who createth!" And so Muhammad read. The Koran is regarded as divinely inspired by 400,000,000 Muslim (= those who have surrendered themselves to God) as the followers of Muhammad are called. Their religion is called Islam (the Surrender to God) and all Muslim believe in the Immaculate Conception and in the Virgin Birth, as well as that Jesus is Ruh Allah, the Spirit (or breath) of God. Muslim girls fast each year for two days of the month of *rajab*, to imitate Our Lady in the Temple before the Annunciation. But Muslims deny that Jesus is God, Son of God, and declare that God "begetteth not nor is begotten," so the Islamic receiving of Christmas is a rejection, and I have called this witness the "Testimony of the Paynim."

Next in order I have placed a modern French phantasy, based on St. Paul's statement that the whole of Creation groans and travails until Christ's coming, and is, through man, implicated also in the Incarnation. For the charge over Creation made to man in Genesis is for all time, and as, through man, all creation was involved in the Fall (cursed be the earth for thy sake, said God) so, through man also, the Redemption reaches all creatures.

Fiona MacLeod was a nineteenth-century Scotsman, named William Sharp, who collected the folklore of the West of Scotland. Here the Reformation never came, and the Catholic faith is still held by the Gaelic-speaking people, in all the simplicity of the time of the Saints, Patrick, Columba and their friends.

St. Bride, or Bridget, belongs to that golden age, and her story is beautifully retold.

William Sharp, even under his *alias* of Fiona MacLeod, could not, and never did, accept the "Faith of our fathers," and, for all its nostalgic charm, there is a lack of reality about his story—he might be telling a lovely fairy tale. But the Carmelite, Jessica Powers, living today in America, gives us reality with a vengeance, so to speak: God never was comfortable, never is, and never will be, as the next two tales, "The Little Old Woman" and "The Golden Crucifix," also show. After the grim "Three Wise Men of Totenleben" I have given two Victorian children's stories from the delightful *Aunt Judy's Magazine*, that English precurser of the American *St. Nicholas*. May Probyn, a Catholic poet of the nineteenth century, wrongly neglected, wrote the best poem to St. Joseph I know, and several lovely Christmas carols, of which this is one. Wystan Auden is as American as T. S. Eliot is English, and it is one of the nicest results of lend-lease that we have traded, or bartered, our two best religious poets each for the other without loss to either England or these United States. Auden's "The Vision of the Shepherds" is part of his *For the Time Being*, a Christmas oratorio that is annually performed by Columbia University. Raymund's "The Last Christmas" was first published in *The Commonweal*, and was included in their anthology *The Commonweal Reader*; "Fleur-de-Blé" is part of a collection of Christmas stories by a Belgian writer of last century.

Nicolai Gogol brings us a taste of the Eastern Christmas, as does Leskov. It is very important to remember that "the constitution of the Catholic Church remains what it has always been, not one patriarchate with one rite, but the union of East and West, differing in rites . . . but united in the profession of the same faith" and the fact that "vast numbers of the members of the Eastern patriarchates have gone out of the Church altogether, distressing as it is, does not affect the legal position" (Dr. Adrian Fortescue: *The Uniate Eastern Churches*).

Kenneth Grahame's lovely "Dulce Domum" comes, of course, straight out of *The Wind in the Willows,* loveliest and most enduring of all children's tales. The two stories by Saki (that wry, serio-tragic young writer, Hector Monro, killed in World War I) are for the young as well as for grown-ups. Edward Fenton's "The Broken Christmas" is, like François Coppée's "The Baron's Two Francs" a "receiving by rejection." Coppée, by the way, wrote this story after his return to the Church, with a charming preface in which he asked to be excused if, after so long a lack of practice, his Catholic hand was not yet "in," so to speak. This, and all the German stories, are specially translated, for the first time, for this anthology.

"Tom a' Tuddlams" is a morality story from the depths of the English countryside, by a High Church Anglican parson, whose Bishop objected to his use of a Cross in Church. Subsequently, when the said Bishop arrived to administer Confirmation, the Reverend Sabine Baring-Gould met him processionally at the church door singing:

> Onward, Christian soldiers
> Marching as to war,
> With the Cross of Jesus
> Left behind the door.

Wystan Auden's ending points up perfectly the title of this collection: *Christmas Is Here,* for while we are here "for the time being," "the Spirit must practice his scales of rejoicing" once annually more loudly, on the 25th of each December.

Great pains were taken to find illustrations that tallied with the ideas underlying this anthology. They are all masterpieces from the early days of engraving. The contrast between the severe splendor of the Byzantine "Our Lady of the Sign" with the incipient rococo of the Cranach "Rest on the Flight into Egypt" tells in a few simple lines as much about the breadth of the appeal of these stories as does the text itself.

A.F.

The Gospel According to St. Luke

WHEN the sixth month came, God sent the angel Gabriel to a city of Galilee called Nazareth, where a virgin dwelt, betrothed to a man of David's lineage; his name was Joseph, and the virgin's name was Mary. Into her presence the angel came, and said, Hail, thou who art full of grace; the Lord is with thee; blessed art thou among women. She was much perplexed at hearing him speak so, and cast about in her mind, what she was to make of such a greeting. Then the angel said to her, Mary, do not be afraid; thou hast found favour in the sight of God. And behold, thou shalt conceive in thy womb, and shalt bear a son, and shalt call him Jesus. He shall be great, and men will know him for the Son of the most High; the Lord God will give him the throne of his father David, and he shall reign over the house of Jacob eternally; his kingdom shall never have an end. But Mary said to the angel, How can that be, since I have no knowledge of man? And the angel answered her, The Holy Spirit will come upon thee, and the power of the most High will overshadow thee. Thus that holy thing which is to be born of thee shall be known for the Son of God. See, moreover, how it fares with thy cousin Elizabeth; she is old, yet she too has conceived a son; she who was reproached with barrenness is now in her sixth month, to prove that nothing can be impossible with God. And Mary said, Behold the handmaid of the Lord; let it be unto me according to thy word. And with that the angel left her.

In the days that followed, Mary rose up and went with all haste to a city of Juda, in the hill country where Zachary dwelt; and there entering in she gave Elizabeth greeting. No sooner had

1

Elizabeth heard Mary's greeting, than the child leaped in her womb; and Elizabeth herself was filled with the Holy Ghost; so that she cried out with a loud voice, Blessed art thou among women, and blessed is the fruit of thy womb. How have I deserved to be thus visited by the mother of my Lord? Why, as soon as ever the voice of thy greeting sounded in my ears, the child in my womb leaped for joy. Blessed art thou for thy believing; the message that was brought to thee from the Lord shall have fulfilment.

And Mary said, My soul magnifies the Lord; my spirit has found joy in God, who is my Saviour, because he has looked graciously upon the lowliness of his handmaid. Behold, from this day forward all generations will count me blessed; because he who is mighty, he whose name is holy, has wrought for me his wonders. He has mercy upon those who fear him, from generation to generation; he has done valiantly with the strength of his arm, driving the proud astray in the conceit of their hearts; he has put down the mighty from their seat, and exalted the lowly; he has filled the hungry with good things, and sent the rich away emptyhanded. He has protected his servant Israel, keeping his merciful design in remembrance, according to the promise which he made to our forefathers, Abraham and his posterity for evermore.

Mary returned home when she had been with her about three months; meanwhile, Elizabeth's time had come for her childbearing, and she bore a son. Her neighbours and her kinsfolk, hearing how wonderfully God had shewed his mercy to her, came to rejoice with her; and now, when they assembled on the eighth day for the circumcision of the child, they were for calling him Zachary, because it was his father's name; but his mother answered, No, he is to be called John. And they said, There is none of thy kindred that is called by this name, and began asking his father by signs, what name he would have him called by. So he asked for a tablet, and wrote on it the words, His name is John; and they were all astonished. Then, of

2

a sudden, his lips and his tongue were unloosed, and he broke into speech, giving praise to God; so that fear came upon all their neighbourhood, and there was none of these happenings but was noised abroad throughout all the hill country of Judaea. All those who heard it laid it to heart; Why then, they asked, what will this boy grow to be? And indeed the hand of the Lord was with him.

Then his father Zachary was filled with the Holy Ghost, and spoke in prophecy: Blessed be the Lord, the God of Israel; he has visited his people, and wrought their redemption. He has raised up a sceptre of salvation for us among the posterity of his servant David, according to the promise which he made by the lips of holy men that have been his prophets from the beginning; salvation from our enemies, and from the hand of all those who hate us. So he would carry out his merciful design towards our fathers, by remembering his holy covenant. He had sworn an oath to our father Abraham, that he would enable us to live without fear in his service, delivered from the hand of our enemies, passing all our days in holiness, and approved in his sight. And thou, my child, wilt be known for a prophet of the most High, going before the Lord, to clear his way for him; thou wilt make known to his people the salvation that is to release them from their sins. Such is the merciful kindness of our God, which has bidden him come to us, like a dawning from on high, to give light to those who live in darkness, in the shadow of death, and to guide our feet into the way of peace.

And as the child grew, his spirit achieved strength, and he dwelt in the wilderness until the day when he was made manifest to Israel.

TRANSLATED BY RONALD KNOX

The Book of James, or the Protevangelium

(SECOND CENTURY)

AND MARY was in the temple of the Lord as a dove that is nurtured: and she received food from the hand of an angel.

And when she was twelve years old, there was a council of the priests, saying: Behold Mary is become twelve years old in the temple of the Lord. What then shall we do with her? lest she pollute the sanctuary of the Lord. And they said unto the high priest: Thou standest over the altar of the Lord. Enter in and pray concerning her: And whatsoever the Lord shall reveal to thee, that let us do.

And the high priest took the vestment with the twelve bells and went in unto the Holy of Holies and prayed concerning her. And lo, an angel of the Lord appeared saying unto him: Zacharias, Zacharias, go forth and assemble them that are widowers of the people, and let them bring every man a rod, and to whomsoever the Lord shall show a sign, his wife shall she be. And the heralds went forth over all the country round about Judaea, and the trumpet of the Lord sounded, and all men ran thereto.

And Joseph cast down his adze and ran to meet them, and when they were gathered together they went to the high priest and took their rods *with them*. And he took the rods of them all and went into the temple and prayed. And when he had finished the prayer he took the rods and went forth and gave them back to them: and there was no sign upon them. But Joseph received the last rod: and lo, a dove came forth of the rod and flew upon the head of Joseph. And the priest said unto Joseph: Unto thee hath it fallen to take the virgin of the Lord and keep her for thyself. And Joseph refused, saying:

4

I have sons and I am an old man, but she is a girl: lest I became a laughingstock to the children of Israel. And the priest said unto Joseph: Fear the Lord thy God, and remember what things God did unto Dathan and Abiram and Korah, how the earth clave and they were swallowed up because of their gainsaying. And now fear thou, Joseph, lest it be so in thine house. And Joseph was afraid, and took her to keep her for himself. And Joseph said unto Mary: Lo, I have received thee out of the temple of the Lord: and now do I leave thee in my house, and I go away to build my buildings and I will come *again* unto thee. The Lord shall watch over thee.

Now there was a council of the priests, and they said: Let us make a veil for the temple of the Lord. And the priest said: Call unto me pure virgins of the tribe of David. And the officers departed and sought and found seven virgins. And the priests called to mind the child Mary, that she was of the tribe of David and was undefiled before God: and the officers went and fetched her. And they brought them into the temple of the Lord, and the priest said: Cast me lots, which *of you* shall weave the gold and the undefiled (the white) and the fine linen and the silk and the hyacinthine, and the scarlet and the true purple. And the lot of the true purple and the scarlet fell unto Mary, and she took them and went unto her house.

[And at that season Zacharias became dumb, and Samuel was in his stead until the time when Zacharias spake *again*.]

But Mary took the scarlet and began to spin it.

And she took the pitcher and went forth to fill it with water: and lo a voice saying: Hail, thou that art highly favored; the Lord is with thee: blessed art thou among women.

And she looked about her upon the right hand and upon the left, to see whence this voice should be: and being filled with trembling she went to her house and set down the pitcher, and took the purple and sat down upon her seat and drew out the thread.

And behold an angel of the Lord stood before her saying: Fear

5

not, Mary, for thou hast found grace before the Lord of all things, and thou shalt conceive of his word. And she, when she heard it, questioned in herself, saying: Shall I *verily* conceive of the living God, and bring forth after the manner of all women? And the angel of the Lord said: Not so, Mary, for a power of the Lord shall overshadow thee: wherefore also that holy thing which shall be born of thee shall be called the Son of the Highest. And thou shalt call his name Jesus: for he shall save his people from their sins. And Mary said: Behold the handmaid of the Lord is before him: be it unto me according to thy word.

And she made the purple and the scarlet and brought them unto the priest. And the priest blessed her and said: Mary, the Lord God hath magnified thy name, and thou shalt be blessed among all generations of the earth. And Mary rejoiced and went away unto Elizabeth her kinswoman: and she knocked at the door. And Elizabeth when she heard it cast down the scarlet (*al.* the wool) and ran to the door and opened it, and when she saw Mary she blessed her and said: Whence is this to me that the mother of my Lord should come unto me? for behold that which is in me leaped and blessed thee. And Mary forgat the mysteries which Gabriel the archangel had told her, and she looked up unto the heaven and said: Who am I, Lord, that all the generations of the earth do bless me? And she abode three months with Elizabeth, and day by day her womb grew: and Mary was afraid and departed unto her house and hid herself from the children of Israel. Now she was sixteen years old when these mysteries came to pass.

Now it was the sixth month with her, and behold Joseph came from his building, and he entered into his house and found her great with child. And he smote his face, and cast himself down upon the ground on sackcloth and wept bitterly, saying: With what countenance shall I look unto the Lord my God? and what prayer shall I make concerning this maiden? for I received her out of the temple of the Lord my God a virgin, and have not kept her safe. Who is he that hath ensnared me? Who

Italian, 17th century. Flight into Egypt

hath done this evil in mine house and hath defiled the virgin? Is not the story of Adam repeated in me? for as at the hour of his giving thanks the serpent came and found Eve alone and deceived her, so hath it befallen me also. And Joseph arose from off the sackcloth and called Mary and said unto her O thou that wast cared for by God, why hast thou done this? thou hast forgotten the Lord thy God. Why hast thou humbled thy soul, thou that wast nourished up in the Holy of Holies and didst receive food at the hand of an angel? But she wept bitterly, saying: I am pure and I know not a man. And Joseph said unto her: Whence then is that which is in thy womb? and she said: As the Lord my God liveth, I know not whence it is come unto me.

And Joseph was sore afraid and ceased from *speaking unto* her (*or* left her alone), and pondered what he should do with her. And Joseph said: If I hide her sin, I shall be found fighting against the law of the Lord: and if I manifest her unto the children of Israel, I fear lest that which is in her be the seed of an angel, and I shall be found delivering up innocent blood to the judgment of death. What then shall I do? I will let her go from me privily. And the night came upon him. And behold an angel of the Lord appeared unto him in a dream, saying: Fear not this child, for that which is in her is of the Holy Ghost, and she shall bear a son and thou shalt call his name Jesus, for he shall save his people from their sins. And Joseph arose from sleep and glorified the God of Israel which had shown this favor unto her: and he watched over her.

Now Annas the scribe came unto him and said to him: Wherefore didst thou not appear in our assembly? and Joseph said unto him: I was weary with the journey, and I rested the first day. And *Annas* turned him about and saw Mary great with child. And he went hastily to the priest and said unto him: Joseph, to whom thou bearest witness [that he is righteous] hath sinned grievously. And the priest said: Wherein? And he said: The virgin whom he received out of the temple of the

Lord, he hath defiled her, and married her by stealth (*lit.* stolen her marriage), and hath not declared it to the children of Israel. And the priest answered and said: Hath Joseph done this? And Annas the scribe said: Send officers, and thou shalt find the virgin great with child. And the officers went and found as he had said, and they brought her together with Joseph unto the place of judgment. And the priest said: Mary, wherefore hast thou done this, and wherefore hast thou humbled thy soul and forgotten the Lord thy God, thou that wast nurtured in the Holy of Holies and didst receive food at the hand of an angel and didst hear *the* hymns and didst dance before *the Lord,* wherefore hast thou done this?

But she wept bitterly, saying: As the Lord my God liveth I am pure before him and I know not a man. And the priest said unto Joseph: Wherefore hast thou done this? And Joseph said: As the Lord my God liveth I am pure as concerning her. And the priest said: Bear no false witness but speak the truth: thou hast married her by stealth and hast not declared it unto the children of Israel, and hast not bowed thine head under the mighty hand that thy seed should be blessed. And Joseph held his peace.

And the priest said: Restore the virgin whom thou didst receive out of the temple of the Lord. And Joseph was full of weeping. And the priest said: I will give you to drink of the water of the conviction of the Lord, and it will make manifest your sins before your eyes. And the priest took thereof and made Joseph drink and sent him into the hill country. And he returned whole. He made Mary also drink and sent her into the hill country. And she returned whole. And all the people marveled, because sin appeared not in them. And the priest said: If the Lord God hath not made your sin manifest, neither do I condemn you. And he let them go. And Joseph took Mary and departed unto his house rejoicing, and glorifying the God of Israel.

Now there went out a degree from Augustus the king that all

that were in Bethlehem of Judaea should be recorded. And Joseph said: I will record my sons: but this child, what shall I do with her? how shall I record her? as my wife? *nay*, I am ashamed. Or as my daughter? but all the children of Israel know that she is not my daughter. This day of the Lord shall do as the Lord willeth. And he saddled the she-ass, and set her upon it, and his son led it and Joseph followed after. And they drew near (unto Bethlehem) within three miles: and Joseph turned himself about and saw her of a sad countenance and said within himself: Peradventure that which is within her paineth her. And again Joseph turned himself about and saw her laughing, and said unto her: Mary, what aileth thee that I see thy face at one time laughing and at another time sad? And Mary said unto Joseph: It is because I behold two peoples with mine eyes, the one weeping and lamenting and the other rejoicing and exulting.

And they came to the midst of the way, and Mary said unto him: Take me down from the ass, for that which is within me presseth me, to come forth. And he took her down from the ass and said unto her: Whither shall I take thee to hide thy shame? for the place is desert.

And he found a cave there and brought her into it, and set his sons by her: and he went forth and sought for a midwife of the Hebrews in the country of Bethlehem.

Now I Joseph was walking, and I walked not. And I looked up to the air and saw the air in amazement. And I looked up unto the pole of the heaven and saw it standing still, and the fowls of the heaven without motion. And I looked upon the earth and saw a dish set, and workmen lying *by it*, and their hands were in the dish: and they that were chewing chewed not, and they that were lifting *the food* lifted it not, and they that put it to their mouth put it not thereto, but the faces of all of them were looking upward. And behold there were sheep being driven, and they went not forward but stood still; and the shepherd lifted his hand to smite them with his staff, and his hand remained up. And I looked upon the stream of the river and saw the mouths of the kids upon *the water* and they drank not. And of a sudden all things moved onward in their course.

And behold a woman coming down from the hill country, and she said to me: Man, whither goest thou? And I said: I seek a midwife of the Hebrews. And she answered and said unto me: Art thou of Israel? And I said unto her: Yea. And she said: And who is she that bringeth forth in the cave? And I said: She that is betrothed unto me. And she said to me: Is she not thy wife? And I said to her: It is Mary that was nurtured up in the temple of the Lord: and I received her to wife by lot: and she is not my wife, but she hath conception by the Holy Ghost.

And the midwife said unto him: Is this the truth? And Joseph said unto her: Come hither and see. And the midwife went with him.

And they stood in the place of the cave: and behold a bright cloud overshadowing the cave. And the midwife said: My soul is magnified this day, because mine eyes have seen marvellous things: for salvation is born unto Israel. And immediately the cloud withdrew itself out of the cave, and a great light appeared in the cave so that our eyes could not endure it. And by little and little that light withdrew itself until the young child appeared: and it went and took the breast of its mother Mary.

And the midwife cried aloud and said: Great unto me to-day is this day, in that I have seen this new sight. And the midwife went forth of the cave and Salome met her. And she said to her: Salome, Salome, a new sight have I to tell thee. A virgin hath brought forth, which her nature alloweth not. And Salome said: As the Lord my God liveth, if I make not trial and prove her nature I will not believe that a virgin hath brought forth.

And the midwife went in and said unto Mary: Order thyself, for *there is no small contention* arisen concerning thee. And Salome made trial and cried out and said: Woe unto mine iniquity and mine unbelief, because I have tempted the living God, and lo, my hand falleth away from me in fire. And she bowed her knees unto the Lord, saying: O God of my fathers, remember that I am the seed of Abraham and Isaac and Jacob: make me not a public example unto the children of Israel, but restore me unto the poor, for thou knowest, Lord, that in thy name did I perform my cures, and did receive my hire of thee. And lo, an angel of the Lord appeared, saying unto her: Salome, Salome, the Lord hath hearkened to thee: bring thine hand near unto the young child and take him up, and there shall be unto thee salvation and joy. And Salome came near and took him up, saying: I will do him worship, for a great king is born unto Israel. And behold immediately Salome was healed: and she went forth of the cave justified. . . .

And behold, Joseph made him ready to go forth into Judaea. And there came a great tumult in Bethlehem of Judaea; for there came wise men, saying: Where is he that is born king of the Jews? for we have seen his star in the east and are come to worship him. And when Herod heard it he was troubled and sent officers unto the wise men. And he sent for the high priests and examined them, saying: How is it written concerning the Christ, where he is born? They say unto him: In Bethlehem of Judaea: for so it is written. And he let them go. And he examined the wise men, saying unto them: What sign saw ye concerning the king that is born? And the wise men said: We saw a very great star shining among those stars and dimming them so that the stars appeared not: and thereby knew we that a king was born unto Israel, and we came to worship him. And Herod said: Go and seek for him, and if ye find him, tell me, that I also may come and worship him. And the wise men went forth. And lo, the star which they saw in the east went before them until they entered into the cave: and it stood over the head of the cave. And the wise men saw the young child with Mary his mother: and they brought out of their scrip gifts, gold and frankincense and myrrh. And being warned by the angel that they should not enter into Judaea, they went into their own country by another way.

Testimony of the Paynim

THE KORAN

(Remember) when the wife of 'Imrân said: My Lord! I have vowed unto Thee that which is in my belly as a consecrated (offering). Accept it from me. Lo! Thou, only Thou, art the Hearer, the Knower!

And when she was delivered she said: My Lord! Lo! I am delivered of a female—Allah knew best of what she was delivered—the male is not as the female; and lo! I have named her Mary, and lo! I crave Thy protection for her and for her offspring from Satan the outcast.

And her Lord accepted her with full acceptance and vouchsafed to her a goodly growth; and made Zachariah her guardian. Whenever Zachariah went into the sanctuary where she was, he found that she had food. He said: O Mary! Whence cometh unto thee this (food)? She answered: It is from Allah. Allah giveth without stint to whom He will.

Then Zachariah prayed unto his Lord and said: My Lord! Bestow upon me of Thy bounty goodly offspring. Lo! Thou art the Hearer of Prayer.

And the angels called to him as he stood praying in the sanctuary: Allah giveth thee glad tidings of (a son whose name is) John, (who cometh) to confirm a word from Allah, lordly, chaste, a Prophet of the righteous.

He said: My Lord! How can I have a son when age hath overtaken me already and my wife is barren? (The angel) answered: So (it will be). Allah doeth what He will.

He said: My Lord! Appoint a token for me. (The angel) said: The token unto thee (shall be) that thou shalt not speak unto mankind three days except by signs. Remember thy Lord much, and praise (Him) in the early hours of night and morning.

And when the angels said: O Mary! Lo! Allah hath chosen thee and made thee pure, and hath preferred thee above (all) the women of creation.

O Mary! Be obedient to thy Lord, prostrate thyself and bow with those who bow (in worship).

This is of the tidings of things hidden. We reveal it unto thee (Muhummad). Thou wast not present with them when they threw their pens (to know) which of them should be the guardian of Mary, nor wast thou present with them when they quarrelled (thereupon).

(And remember) when the angels said: O Mary! Lo! Allah giveth thee glad tidings of a word from Him, whose name is the Messiah, Jesus, son of Mary, illustrious in the world and the Hereafter, and one of those brought near (unto Allah).

He will speak unto mankind in his cradle and in his manhood, and he is of the righteous.

She said: My Lord! How can I have a child when no mortal hath touched me? He said: So (it will be). Allah createth what He will. If He decreeth a thing, He saith unto it only: Be! and it is.

And He will teach him the Scripture and wisdom, and the Torah and the Gospel.

And will make him a messenger unto the children of Israel, (saying): Lo! I come unto you with a sign from your Lord. Lo! I fashion for you out of clay the likeness of a bird, and I breathe into it and it is a bird, by Allah's leave. I heal him who was born blind, and the leper, and I raise the dead, by Allah's leave. And I announce unto you what ye eat and what ye store up in your houses. Lo! herein verily is a portent for you, if ye are to be believers.

And make mention of Mary in the Scripture, when she had withdrawn from her people to a chamber looking East,

And had chosen seclusion from them. Then We sent unto her Our spirit and it assumed for her the likeness of a perfect man.

She said: Lo! I seek refuge in the Beneficent One from thee, if thou art God-fearing.

He said: I am only a messenger of thy Lord, that I may bestow on thee a faultless son.

She said: How can I have a son when no mortal hath touched me, neither have I been unchaste?

He said: So (it will be). Thy Lord saith: It is easy for Me. And (it will be) that We may make of him a revelation for mankind and a mercy from Us, and it is a thing ordained.

And she conceived him, and she withdrew with him to a far place.

And the pangs of childbirth drove her unto the trunk of the palm tree. She said: Oh, would that I had died ere this and had become a thing of naught, forgotten!

Then (one) cried unto her from below her, saying: Grieve not! Thy Lord hath placed a rivulet beneath thee,

And shake the trunk of the palm-tree toward thee, thou wilt cause ripe dates to fall upon thee.

So eat and drink and be consoled. And if thou meetest any mortal, say: Lo! I have vowed a fast unto the Beneficent, and may not speak this day to any mortal.

Then she brought him to her own folk, carrying him. They said: O Mary! Thou hast come with an amazing thing.

Oh sister of Aaron! Thy father was not a wicked man nor was thy mother a harlot.

Then she pointed to him. They said: How can we talk to one who is in the cradle, a young boy?

He spake: Lo! I am the slave of Allah. He hath given me the Scripture and hath appointed me a Prophet,

And hath made me blessed wheresoever I may be, and hath enjoined upon me prayer and alms-giving so long as I remain alive,

15

And (hath made me) dutiful toward her who bore me, and hath not made me arrogant, unblest.

Peace on me the day I was born, and the day I die, and the day I shall be raised alive!

Such was Jesus, son of Mary: (this is) a statement of the truth concerning which they doubt.

Surahs III, XIX

The Ox and the Ass at the Manger

JULES SUPERVIELLE

JOSEPH led the ass who carried Our Lady up the road to Bethlehem: she was a light burden, all her thoughts were with the future within her.

The ox followed by himself.

When they reached the town the travelers took shelter in an unoccupied stable and Joseph lost no time in busying himself for their comfort.

"Men," the ox reflected, "are, after all, wonderful. Look what they can do with their hands and arms! Much more than we can with our hoofs and pasterns. The master has no equal as a Jack of all trades. He can manage to straighten out bent things and twist straight ones and he does it without getting annoyed or depressed."

Joseph left the stable and came back quite soon carrying on his back a load of straw: but such straw! So gleaming and fresh, a miracle in itself.

"What are they up to?" said the ass. "It looks as if they were getting a cradle ready for a child."

"You may be needed tonight," said the Virgin to the ox and the ass.

The creatures looked long at one another, trying to understand her meaning. Then they lay down to sleep.

A faint voice, which seemed nevertheless to come across the firmament, woke them.

The ox rose from the ground and saw a naked child asleep in the manger. Slowly and carefully he breathed over every part of the little body to warm it. The Virgin thanked him with a smiling glance.

Winged beings were flying in and out of the stable. They appeared to be unaware of the walls, for they passed through them.

Joseph came in with swaddling clothes borrowed from a neighbor.

"It's queer," he said in his carpenter's voice, speaking rather loudly considering the circumstances. "It's all of midnight and as clear as day. And up there I've seen three suns instead of one. I grant you they seem to be trying to join together."

At dawn the ox got up again and stepped carefully on his hoofs. He did not want to wake the child; or to crush a heavenly flower; or to hurt an angel. Everything had become wonderfully difficult.

Neighbors began to arrive to look at Jesus and the Virgin: poor people who had little to offer but their radiant faces. One came bringing nuts; another left a flute behind him.

The ox and the ass made way for the visitors. They stood together in a corner and began to wonder what sort of impression they themselves would make on the child, now that he was awake and would see them for the first time.

"We aren't monsters," said the ass.

"Don't you see," said the ox, "our faces aren't in the least like his, nor like his parents' either. We might terrify him."

"The manger and the stable and the beams overhead haven't got faces like his," said the ass, "and he's not afraid of them."

But the ox was not persuaded by this. He remembered his horns and, as he chewed his cud, he said to himself:

"It's really very sad to be unable to go near those we love without seeming to threaten them. I'm always having to be careful not to hurt people: and it's not really in my nature to dislike anyone or anything without provocation. I'm not mischievous or revengeful. But, wherever I go—there I am with my horns. I wake with them in the morning and, even when I am overcome with drowsiness and doze off, there they are—two of

18

them—hard and pointed. They don't ever leave me alone. I feel them in my dreams in the middle of the night."

The ox grew terrified at the thought that he had gone so close to the newborn child when he warmed him with his breath. Suppose he had, accidentally, hurt him with one of his horns!

The ass guessed what was troubling his companion and said:

"You ought not even to think of going near the little one— you'd hurt him. And you might let some of the cud you are always chewing drop on him. That would be a nice thing! I've often meant to ask you why you water at the mouth so much when you are pleased. Control yourself. There's no need to let everyone know your feelings." The ox said nothing.

"I," went on the ass, "I am going to show him my ears. Two of them. You know they move. They can point in any direction: *They* are not bony. They are soft to touch. They frighten and soothe at the same time. They are exactly the thing to amuse a baby—and they are instructive as well, at his age."

"Yes, yes," sighed the ox. "I understand, I've never said the contrary. I'm not stupid."

Then, as the ass was really looking too much pleased with himself, the ox went on:

"But don't you go braying in his face. You'd kill him."

"Clodhopper!" said the ass.

The ass took his station at the left of the manger, the ox on the right. Thus it had been at the time of the Nativity and the ox, being particular in matters of procedure, felt they should keep these places. They stood there respectfully without moving for hours together as though they were posing for some invisible painter.

The child closed his eyelids. He wanted to sleep again. A shining angel waited, just beyond sleep, waited to teach him something—or, perhaps, to be taught by him.

The angel came out of the dream of Jesus and appeared in

the stable. First he bowed to the newborn and then he painted a clear nimbus around the baby's head. When he had finished that one he painted another for the Virgin and a third for Joseph. Then he vanished in a splendor of wings and feathers, so white and rustling as the foam of the tides.

"There was no nimbus for us," remarked the ox. "The angel must have his reasons for this. We don't amount to much, the ass and I. After all, what have we done to deserve aureoles?"

"You've done nothing, I grant you, but you forget me. I carried the Virgin."

The ox asked himself how so lovely and slight a being as the Virgin could have hidden so fine a child within her body.

He may have thought aloud; in any case the ass said:

"There are things you are unable to comprehend."

"Why will you keep on saying that I do not understand? I've lived longer than you have. I've worked on mountainsides and in the valleys and on the seashore."

"That's not the point," said the ass and then added, "it's not only the nimbus. I'm sure, Ox, that you've not so much as noticed that the child is bathed in a kind of wonderful dust, no: it's something better than dust."

"It's much finer," said the ox. "It's like light or a golden mist rising from the baby itself."

"You're only saying that to make me think you've seen it."

"Who says I've not seen it?"

The ox pushed the ass into a corner of the stable. There on the ground lay a twig, delicately surrounded by shining straws. It was a picture of the divine emanation. The ox had arranged this as an act of worship. It was the first shrine. The ox had brought the straws in from the yard. He had not dared to take a single straw from the manger: just because he could have eaten such straw he was afraid of it.

The ox and the ass went out to graze till nightfall. Although, as a rule, stones take a long time to understand anything, a great many of the stones in the fields of Bethlehem knew already.

German, 15th century. The Nativity

One pebble, even, by a slight change of form and color, let them know definitely that it had heard the news. Some of the wild flowers knew, and these could not be cropped. It was quite a business to graze on the common without committing sacrilege. The ox felt that eating was getting to be superfluous. Happiness was enough.

Before drinking, too, he asked himself:

"Does this water know?"

Being uncertain he preferred not to drink from the brook and went farther on toward a muddy pond which clearly knew nothing, so far. As he was in the act of swallowing the water there was a sweetness in his throat and he knew he should not have lapped even in that troubled pool; but it was too late. He hardly dared to breathe; the air seemed holy because it knew. He was afraid he might breathe in an angel.

The ox was ashamed because he felt he was not so clean as he could wish.

"Well! I must be as clean as I can be. Cleaner than I was. I must take care. I must watch my feet."

The ass was not worried about anything.

The midday sun streamed into the stables, and the two creatures vied with one another for the honor of shielding the child from its glare.

The ox though that a little sunshine might not do much harm, but he was afraid of saying so lest the ass should begin once more saying he was stupid.

The child slept a great deal and, sometimes, in his sleep, he frowned as though he were thinking deeply.

One day the ass put down his muzzle and turned the child on its side. The Virgin on the threshold was occupied answering the thousand and one questions put to her by future Christians. Coming back to the crib Mary was alarmed. She could not see her child's face on the pillow as she had left it. When she understood what had happened she explained to the ass that never, never, must the baby be touched or moved about. The ox agreed in a silence of exceptional quality. He knew how to be a mute rhythm, with delicate, almost punctuated shades of meaning. On cold days it was quite easy to follow the course of his reflections by the length of the stream of vapor from his nostrils. A good many things could be learned in this way.

The ox felt himself authorized to render none but indirect services to the child. He attracted all the flies in the stable to himself, going out every morning to rub his back in a comb of wild bees' honey. He also squashed insects against the wall.

The ass kept his ears open for noises from outside, and when any sound seemed suspicious he stood across the doorway. Then the ox would place himself behind the ass to give bulk to the barrier. They made themselves as heavy as possible: they felt as though they had filled their skulls and their bodies with granite and lead. And their eyes flashed with the utmost vigilance.

The ox was astonished to see that the Virgin could make the baby smile, merely by going close to the manger. Joseph, in spite of his beard, could do it too without much trouble, either by his appearance, or when he played the flute. The ox would have liked to play on some instrument.

"Come to think of it," he said, "you've only got to blow."

He did not want to think badly of the master but it seemed unlikely that the good man could, merely by breathing, have warmed the newborn Jesus as he, the ox, had done.

"As for the flute," he said, "let me get a chance to be alone with the child: when I'm alone with him I'm not nervous of him. He's just a little creature who needs protection. And an ox, after all, does feel his own strength."

When they went out to pasture in the fields, the ox would, as often as not, leave the ass.

"Where are you off to?" the ass would ask.

"I'll be back in a second."

"But where are you going?" the ass would insist.

"I'm going to see if he needs anything—one never knows."

"Can't you leave him be?"

But the ox couldn't.

And he would go back to the stable. There was a small round window in its low roof; the kind of window which was, later, to be named *œil-de-bœuf*, just because the ox had looked through it. One day, when he put his eye to the window, he saw that Mary and Joseph had gone out and had left the flute on a bench within reach of his muzzle and not too far away from the crib.

"What am I going to play for him?" asked the ox of himself, feeling that he might, at last, dare to catch the child's ear by means of this musical instrument. "Shall it be a song of the plough, or the war cry of a brave little bull; or the tune sung by the enchanted heifer?"

Often enough oxen are really singing to themselves when they seem to ruminate.

The ox breathed gently into the flute, and we cannot be sure that an angel did not help him to produce such clear notes.

The child raised its head from the straw and looked toward the place from which the music came. But the musician was not convinced by this sign. He thought that no one but himself had heard his playing. He was wrong. He went out quickly so that nobody, especially not the ass, should come in and catch him so near to the little flute.

One day the Virgin said to the ox:—

"Come and look at my child! Why do you always keep away from him now? It was you who breathed so warmly over him when he was a naked baby."

Thus encouraged the ox knelt down close to Jesus who, to put him quite at ease, took the creature's muzzle between his own hands. The ox held his breath: there was no longer any need for its warmth. Jesus smiled at him. The ox was mute with joy. His joy was the same shape as his body, it filled him to the very points of his horns.

24

The Ox and the Ass at the Manger

The child looked at the ox and the ass, one after the other; the ass, a little too sure of himself, and the ox who felt terribly gross near this countenance lit from within. It was as if, through thin curtains, he had seen a lamp carried from one room to another in a very small and distant house.

The ox looked so solemn that the child began to laugh aloud. The poor beast did not quite know what this laughter meant. Perhaps the child was making fun of him. Must he try in future to be more self-contained? Ought he to go away at once?

But the baby smiled at him once more and it was such a luminous and brotherly smile that the ox understood it was right to stay by the manger.

The Virgin and her son often looked closely at one another as though they wondered which of them were more proud of the other.

"It seems to me," thought the ox, "that they ought to be as happy as happy. No one has ever seen so lovely a mother, so

25

beautiful a child. But there are times when they both seem very serious."

One evening the ox and the ass were about to turn homeward toward the stable. After they had looked carefully in case they could be mistaken the ox said:

"Just look at that star moving across the sky! It seems a particularly fine one. It cheers my heart."

"Don't fuss over your heart," said the ass, "it has nothing to do with the great events we have witnessed these last days."

"You can say what you like, Ass. I believe that star is coming our way. Look how low it is in the sky! It looks as if it were making for our stable. It is shining down on three noblemen wearing precious stones."

When they had reached the threshold of the stable the ass asked the ox if he thought something afoot.

"Ass," said the ox, "who can tell? I am content to watch and wait. It's as much as I can do."

"Hurry up!" said Joseph as he opened the stable door. "Can't you see you are getting in the way of these gentlemen?"

The ox and the ass stood aside to let the Magi enter. There were three of them: one was quite black: he represented Africa. At first the ox kept a careful watch on the black one. He wanted to be sure that this Negro had no evil designs on the newborn child.

However, when the black king, who seemed to be a little short-sighted, bent over Jesus in order to see him clearly, his face, shining like a polished mirror, reflected the child's image, and the king knelt there with so much reverence and so great a self-forgetfulness that the ox was filled with delight.

"This must be a very great man," he thought. "Neither of the other two could do that."

A moment later he added:

"He's quite the best of the three."

That was because he had just caught the two white kings

hiding in their baggage bits of straw they had filched from the crib. The black king hadn't tried to take anything.

Side by side, on a mattress lent by the neighbors, the three kings lay and fell asleep.

"How odd," thought the ox, "to wear a crown in bed. So hard an object must be far more uncomfortable than my horns. They can't sleep easily with all those flashing gems round their heads."

But the kings slept on, like three statues lying side by side in a chantry, and their star sparkled over the roof of the stable just above the place where the manger stood.

A little before dawn the three kings got up simultaneously, making identical movements. All three had seen, in their sleep, an angel who warned them to go home at once without letting the jealous Herod know that they had seen the child.

They set out, but the star did not follow them: it remained shining over the stable so that each one of them could be sure that they had been guided to the very place.

The ox was praying:

"Heavenly child, do not judge me by my astonished and uncomprehending mien. One day I may not look so much like a small rock walking.

"As for my horns, please remember that they are more or less ornamental. I will go so far as to assure thee that I have never used them. Wilt thou, Jesus, shed a little of thy light on the weakness and confusion that is in me? Teach me a little of thy perfection, O, thou whose little hands and feet are so delicately joined to thy body. Wilt thou tell me, my little lord, why, one day, I had only to turn my head to see thee whole? How I thank thee that I am able to kneel before thee, thou marvelous child! And to live thus in company with angels and with stars.

"Sometimes I ask myself if there has not been a mistake and if I ought not really to be here at all. Thou mayst not have noticed that I have quite a long scar on my back and that my

27

coat is no longer very good on one side—which is ugly. Even in my own family, far handsomer oxen might have been chosen to be here—my brother and my cousins are much better looking than I am. Or might not the lion or the eagle have been judged more worthy?"

"Shut up," said the ass. "What are you sighing about? Can't you see that you are keeping the child awake? You and your ruminations?"

"The ass is right," thought the ox. "There is a time to be silent even when a creature is so happy he does not know what to do with himself."

The ass also prayed:

"Draught-asses, saddle-asses, life is going to be grand for us and, in green pastures, little asses will be looking for great things. Thanks to thee, little boy, stones will keep their proper place at the side of the road and we shall not stumble over them. Another thing: why should we still have steep slopes, and even mountains on our journeys? Would not a perfect flat world be better for everyone? And why should the ox, who is far stronger than I am, never carry anyone on his back? And why should my ears be so long and should I have no hair on my tail and such small hoofs, and such a narrow chest? And why should my voice sound quite crazy? Perhaps these things might be changed one day."

During the next few nights one star or another stood on guard and sometimes a whole constellation watched. A cloud covered the place where the absent stars usually shone. This was a heavenly secret. It was miraculous to see the infinitely far make themselves quite small as they took their places over the manger and draw into themselves their excess of luminosity and heat, shedding only enough to warm and light the stable, and reduce their gigantic spheres in order that the child might not be afraid. Oh, those first nights of Christianity! Then the Virgin and

28

The Ox and the Ass at the Manger

Joseph, the Child, the Ox and the Ass were extraordinary to themselves. Their very appearance, which was a little vague in daylight and seemed rather nervous to the ordinary people who came to see the child, concentrated itself and became sublime and confident as soon as the sun had gone down.

Through the good graces of the ox and the ass some of the lower animals asked to be allowed to see the Child Jesus. So, one fine day a horse, known to be at once swift and gentle, was selected by the ox, with Joseph's consent, to assemble all those who wished to come.

The ass and the ox were uncertain about allowing wild beasts to enter the stable and could not be quite sure whether dromedaries, and camels and elephants and other creatures with humps or long noses, or too much bone or flesh should not be kept out.

There was also the problem of poisonous reptiles; scorpions, tarantulas, vipers, creatures whose glands secrete venom all day and all night long, and even at dawn when the rest of the world is pure.

The Virgin decided for them.

"You may let them in. My child is as safe in his crib as he would be in the very height of Heaven."

"But only one by one," said Joseph, almost like a sergeant-major. "I won't have the animals coming in two by two. It would make no end of muddle."

They began with the poisonous creatures, feeling that by so doing they made them some amends. It was noted that all the serpents showed tact in avoiding the Virgin's eye and in gliding past as far as possible from her. And they went out as calmly and with as much self-possession as though they had been watch-dogs.

Next came the little creatures so tiny that it was hard to know if they were there at all. One hour was allowed for these mites to come in and march round the crib. Their time being up,

Joseph, although he could feel by a slight pricking of his skin that some of them were still about, gave the next group of animals the word to enter.

It was impossible for the dogs to hide their astonishment: none of them had been allowed to live in the stable, as the ox and the ass were doing, so they were stroked by everyone to make up for this. Then they went out full of a visible gratitude.

You may say what you like, but when the ox and the ass scented the approach of the lion they were far from comfortable; the more so as the wild odor made its way through that of the myrrh and frankincense which the three kings had so lavishly spread about them.

The ox admitted the nobility of Joseph and Mary in placing full confidence in the lion, but how could they allow so ethereal a being as the child to lie side by side with a creature whose very breath might blow out the delicate flame!

Both the ox and the ass grew more and more nervous as they found themselves absolutely paralyzed before the King of beasts. They could no more dream of attacking him than they could of opposing thunder and lightning. Also the ox, weakened by fasting, felt that it would be easier to float on air than to fight.

The lion came in; his mane had never been brushed except by the desert wind; his melancholy eyes said: I am the lion— what can I do about it? I am only the king of animals.

It was clear that he was bent on taking up the least possible room in the stable and this was no easy matter. He did his best to breathe without blowing things about and to keep his talons sheathed and his muscular jaws under control. He stepped forward with lowered eyelids, covering his shining teeth as though they were signs of some shameful disease. He behaved so modestly that any one might see he belonged to the family of those lions who would, on a day still to come, refuse to devour Saint Blandine. The Virgin was sorry for him and tried to re-assure him with the particular smile she kept for her little son.

But the lion looked straight in front of him and seemed to be saying, in an even more dejected way than ever:

"What have I done to be so great and so strong? You must know what I never eat except when I am hungry: it's living in the open air that sharpens my appetite. And you do understand that, sometimes, it's my cubs. We have all tried to be herbivorous. But grass was never intended to be our food. We can't digest it."

Then, his huge head, looking like an explosion of yellow hair, bent down and lay sadly on the bare ground while the bunch at the end of his tail seemed to be almost as much overcome as his mane. Everyone was sorry for him in the silence of the stable.

When the tiger's turn came he flattened himself on the floor until he made himself into a veritable bedside rug. He might have been practicing the most austere mortifications. In a few seconds, however, he gathered himself together again with unexpected elasticity and left the stable without more ado.

The giraffe did not come in: he stood in the doorway showing his front legs and everyone decided unanimously that this did quite as well as if he had marched right round the manger.

They felt the same about the elephant who limited himself to kneeling on the threshold and swinging his trunk to and fro like a censer. This touch was deeply appreciated by the spectators.

A tremendously woolly sheep wanted to be shorn on the spot; but they sent him and his fleece away together with many thanks for the offer.

The mother kangaroo was quite tiresome with her insistence that Jesus should accept one of her own babies. She said she made the sacrifice more than willingly; that she was not depriving herself; that she had plenty more little kangaroos at home. But Joseph did not see things her way and she had to take her child with her when she went.

The ostrich was luckier: she took advantage of the fuss the

kangaroo was making to lay an egg in a corner and then to slip off unnoticed. This offering was not found till the next day. The ass discovered it: he had never seen so large and so tough an egg before and thought it was a miracle. But Joseph knew better: he made it into an omelet.

The fish, who could not appear themselves, on account of their distressing inability to breathe out of water, sent a sea gull to represent them.

Other birds flew by, leaving their songs behind them; the monkey brought his playfulness; the cat the mystery of her gaze; the dove the softness of its breast.

Unknown creatures tried to come: fossils which were still waiting to be discovered under the earth, or in the deepest oceans where they know neither moon nor stars in their darkness, nor any change of season.

The spirits of those who had not been able to reach Bethlehem, or who knew they would get there too late, could be felt beating the air. Some of them from the uttermost parts of the earth had actually set out on their microscopic feet which could not carry them for much more than a yard in an hour; although their lives were so short that they must die before they had traversed half that distance even.

There were some miracles: the tortoise hurried; the iguana moderated its pace; the hippopotamus made graceful genuflexions; the parrakeets were silent.

Just before sunset an incident upset everybody. Joseph, tired out with supervising the procession all day long without having had a bite of food, trod absentmindedly on a poisonous spider. The good man had forgotten that even this creature was there to do homage to the child. His unhappy face distressed everyone for quite a long time.

Certain animals from whom more tact might have been expected lingered on: the ox had to turn out the weasel, the squirrel and the badger; they simply would not go.

The Ox and the Ass at the Manger

A few moths, taking advantage of their dim colors, passed the night among the beams over the manger. But the first rays of the sun showed them up next morning and Joseph, who was all against favoritism, chased them out as soon as he saw them.

The flies, who had been told to go, let it be understood that they had always been there and meant to stay and Joseph could find no answer to that.

The ox was now often short of breath, so deep was his wonder at the miraculous beings who moved around the place where he lived. He had formed the habit of holding his breath, like an Asiatic fakir and, like a fakir, he also saw visions. Although he was less happy in exaltation than in humility he knew real ecstasy. But he was too honest to let himself dream of imagining saints and angels. He only saw such apparitions when they actually appeared in and around the stable.

"Deary me," thought the ox, overcome by these apparitions of which he now began to be suspicious. "I think I am only a beast of the field—but suppose I were actually a devil? Why have I horns like the Devil when I've never hurt a living soul? Or—perhaps—I am a necromancer."

Joseph began to notice that the ox seemed unhappy: also, the animal was growing visibly thinner.

"Go out and graze," he said. "You lie here all day under our feet. You'll be nothing but skin and bones if you're not careful."

The ox and the ass went out together.

"It's quite true: you *are* thin," said the ass. "Your joints are sticking out all over you. You'll be having horns everywhere if you're not careful."

"Stop talking about horns."

The ox thought that the ass was right. He had to try to live. Why couldn't he crop the fine tuft of grass in front of him? Did he think it was poisonous? It wasn't that. It was that he just wasn't hungry. He began to tell himself how beautiful the child was.

"To think," he said, "of those great figures which pass in and

33

out of the stable breathing through the feathers of the wings on which they fly. All this heavenly company which moves unsullied through our poor stable! Come, come—eat, can't you—forget the angels for a moment. And don't let yourself be roused by the joy which comes and pulls your ears in the middle of the night. Don't stop on one knee by the crib until you ache all over. Your hide is quite raw over the kneecap. It won't be long before the flies get at it."

A night came when the constellation of Taurus moved across the sky to take its turn at watching above the stable. The red eye of Aldebaran glowed, magnificent and fiery, quite near to earth. The taurine flanks and horns shone with enormous stars. The ox was proud to see the child so guarded. Jesus and Mary and Joseph slept peacefully. So did the ass, its ears lowered and trustful. But the ox, in spite of the knowledge of being under the guardianship of his own great and friendly constellation, was troubled. He felt weak and useless: he thought of what he had tried to do for the child; of his unnecessary vigils; his foolish defense of the crib.

"Does Taurus know about me?" he wondered. "Does that huge red eye shining so alarmingly, see me down here? These stars, they are so far away it's hard to tell in what direction they are looking."

Suddenly Joseph, who had been restless for some minutes, sat up and raised his arms to heaven. He who was usually so quiet in his speech and gestures shouted till he woke them all, even Jesus.

"The angel of the Lord came to me in my dream. We must go away at once, because of Herod. He is jealous of the child."

The Virgin took her son out of the manger and held him as if the King of the Jews were already at the door with a butcher's knife in his hand.

The ass rose to its feet.

"And him?" asked Joseph, looking at the ox.

"He seems too weak to come with us," said Mary.

The ox tried to show that he was nothing of the sort. He made a great effort to get on his legs but he had never felt so rooted to the ground. He looked up to the constellation of Taurus, praying for strength to stand up. He could not count on anything but the stars for aid. The heavenly steer did not make a sign. It shone in the night, its flaring eye fixed on a point far away from the ox in the stable.

"He's eaten nothing for days," said the Virgin to Joseph.

The ox thought:

"I know quite well that they mean to leave me behind them. It was too good to last. Still, I should only have been old bones and a hindrance to them on their way. My ribs are tired of my hide and ask no better than to turn into a skeleton under the winds of heaven."

The ass came up to the ox and they rubbed muzzles together. The ass was thus able to convey to the ox that the Virgin had asked a neighbor to see that he was properly looked after when they had gone. But the ox lay with half-closed eyes and seemed worn out.

The Virgin stroked him and said:

"We are not going on a real journey. We are only playing a game with you."

"Of course not—we shall be coming back in no time," said Joseph. "No one goes for long journeys in the middle of the night."

"It's a beautiful night," the Virgin went on. "We are taking advantage of it to give the boy an airing. He's been looking a little pale lately."

"Quite so, quite so," said the good man.

That's what is called a white lie. The ox understood perfectly and, not wishing to hinder them in their packing, he pretended to fall asleep. That was how he lied back to them.

"He's gone off," said the Virgin. "We'll leave the straw from the crib for him to eat as soon as he wakes up. And the flute," she added in a low voice. "He likes to blow into it when he thinks he is alone."

They were ready to start. The stable door creaked on its hinges.

"I ought to have oiled them," thought Joseph. He was afraid he might have roused the ox: but the ox still pretended to sleep on.

Joseph closed the door very carefully.

While the ass of the manger was, step by step, becoming the donkey of the Flight into Egypt, the ox lay with his eyes fixed on the straw on which the child Jesus had lain an hour ago.

He knew quite well that he would not touch it—or the flute.

The constellation of Taurus leapt up the sky and, thrusting one horn into the zenith, fixed itself to the firmament in the place it has never left since then.

When the neighbors came in, soon after dawn, the ox had ceased to ruminate for good.

Christmas at the Bachs'

A. E. BRACHVOGEL

I T WAS the morning of Christmas Eve. The days are then
astonishingly short. One can hardly get down to a job before
it's dark again, and yet father and son need the daylight so
badly for their work! In the living room Friedemann and Sebastian are sitting at a table, which has been pulled up in front of
the window. Each has a shining copperplate in front of him,
set upon an old windowseat cushion for pad, upon which the
copperplate rotates while the gleaming metal stylus etches deep,
restlessly moving back and forth, and digging out measures, intervals and cadenzas on the already marked staves of the original
MSS. Sebastian Bach, too poor to have the work done by an
engraver, too little a follower of the modern trend in music
fashion to find a publisher—this same Sebastian Bach painfully
engraves the whole *Art of the Fugue* with his son, so that his
life's masterpiece shall not be lost.

The old man's mouth is twisted bitterly. Yes, yes, he is no
Hasse, no Rameau, no Couperin or Chiabran. He does not
write operas or dear little Canzonettas! Who the devil would
buy church music today, or even listen to it? Gradually, the
century prepares to erase the Lord God from His universe, so
who would have a taste for His hymns?

The old man is wearing green glasses. Can't you see how
rheumy his eyes are? The blinding brightness of the copper
burns them, and he may go blind before he has succeeded in
casting the ephemeral tones he creates into permanence for
posterity. Quiet Anna Magdalena decorates the Christmas tree
in the schoolroom, Friedrich and Christian are still at school,
and David is sitting on the floor, playing with scraps of paper

37

which he throws high up into the air. He is making "pigeons fly."

"I wonder how Old Nicolas and Fredericka are faring in Naumburg?" says the father, who had to interrupt his work to sharpen his instrument and wipe his glasses. "They haven't written for quite some time. I thought perhaps they would have come to Leipzig for Christmas."

"How can they be anything but well?" replies Friedemann without looking up. "They have their own home, a good job— oh, indeed, everything must go well with them."

His father looks at Friedemann, and then the conversation was already at an end. Every time their talk got onto any subject other than their work, the evil spirits of envy and anguish, which raged within the son, closed his father's lips. Even the most innocent banter was thus poisoned. Finally, the father put down his stylus with an authoritative air.

"Friedemann," he said, "it's just no good. Your misfortunes make you wicked and envious. You cling far too stubbornly to your melancholy, and you will isolate yourself more and more from your fellow men. If you were truly religious, you would know that in the end God works everything out well, and that faith would give you the strength to lift yourself above your sorrow, and hope, in its turn, would give you the strength to work cheerfully."

"But, dear father, am I not doing all I possibly can? What else is there I can do?"

"Just making such an effort, Friedemann, will not help you. You are only torturing yourself by trying to force yourself. That's why you don't succeed. Without joy, without hope, any work of art is stillborn. It becomes more and more clear to me that you don't have the basic essentials of religious faith. You are lacking in the spirit of service, which finds creative strength in its very humility. Today our Lord is born, the Saviour of our poor human race. Oh, if only God would give me the joy of knowing that a Saviour was born in you, too, who would set you

German, 17th century. At the Organ

free from yourself, and would give you new heart, new courage! For then, my dear son, everything would work out, believe me. All of us, and you yourself, would together find our happiness in you."

In spite of himself he had begun to cry, and he silently embraced his son. It was a last cry wrung from his paternal heart. Friedemann could hardly bear it. Gently he pushed his father aside. "Wait just one moment, dear Father, I'll be right back." He rushed out of the room in order to hide his emotion. Sebastian was left to his sad thoughts, while David played quietly at his feet. The old man put his hands together as though in a despairing prayer, and turned his burning eyes toward the window, and out, up to the gray sky full of swirling snowflakes.

Shortly after Friedemann entered the room quietly. He was very pale, and in his hand he was holding a sheet with music on it.

"Here, father, I have made one last attempt. I was going to give it to you tonight, but since you and I are so sad I thought perhaps that this is the best moment."

Sebastian pressed his hand. He was trembling as he took the composition and spread it out suspiciously. Dear God, how the fear of false hope showed in his face! His son watched him closely, as though his father were about to pass a sentence of death upon him. Sebastian's face was flushed a deep red. He looked now at Friedemann, now at the paper, as though he were in a dream.

"Oh, father, it is bad, isn't it?"

"Bad? Are you crazy? No, my dearest, it's good, so good and so beautiful, that if you will forgive me for saying so, I can't really quite believe that it is yours." As he spoke a blissful joy, all his old pride in his Friedemann, came back into Sebastian's heart with heady jubilation. Sobbing and laughing at the same time, like a child, he embraced his son and rushed out to the boy's mother, waving the music high in the air in front of him.

Friedemann felt reborn. The sun of his old self-confidence began to warm his sick heart, and rosy hope softly opened the doors of its temple, through which his trembling soul advanced furtively. He followed his father. There, in the schoolroom, the old man was already at the piano, and he played the introduction, while Mother Magdalena in her dear voice was singing the hymn which rose up to our Lord like a prayer.

> On earth grows no small blade,
> But heaven has dew besprint
> Each small flower in the shade.
> Still the sun's gold does glint,
> And when your self finds you
> Alone in forest night,
> Your dew and sunshine, too,
> Will pour upon you bright.
> Then shoots shall blossom green
> From out your deepest heart,
> For no live thing is seen
> But flowering is its part.

His mother was beside herself with joy. She laughed and cried, and the father played and hummed the hymn again and again, and could not get his fill of it. Finally he jumped up. "Tell me, dear son, wherever in all the world did you find the beautiful poem? And how glorious the music is!"

"I wrote the poem, too, father."

"Oh, you see, mother, how the old strength is still in him! This came straight from his very soul, it is part of his very self, and that is why it is so magnificent and mighty! Take courage, dearest Friedemann, and don't be moody any more, because the old Lord is still alive, and today he has sent you the genuine, most beautiful Christ child, Who is your own Saviour, and without Whom we cannot exist in this our life."

And that is how it was. Friedemann smiled again, and the old blessed spirit of love, rosy self-confidence with its shy smile, dwelt with him again. Today is the Christ feast, and it was caroled throughout the house as of old. Familiar voices called "Christ's feast," and there, standing on the threshold, was dear Fredericka holding two blond children and there was cheerful Old Nicolas.

"Come in, come in," said Sebastian happily, "that my house may be filled." And greetings and kisses and joy and tears were all mixed up, because once again it was like in the old days. The days of sorrow were forgotten, or melted away into the hours of joy, into the hope of happy days. And once again the door opened, and in came Mietzler, with a deputation from the society of the musical sciences, and presented Sebastian with an honorary membership in the name of all the musicians.

"You know, Mother, when heaven sends you joy, it does so thoroughly, and I must thank God and praise this day, when I can be truly happy, from the bottom of my heart, after the long days of sorrow. And Friedemann, you, too, must help me. Come, put your thinking cap on! We will write a Christmas song, and the society shall have it right away, so that they may learn what kind of new member they are getting. Come, dear boy."

Evening came. The Christmas tree shone in fairy splendor, the lovely legend of the Love that descended from heaven for the salvation of freedom and brotherhood of the divided world wove its golden web once more around the mourning hearts of a sorrowful mankind. There, at the instrument, in the magical twinkling light of the Christmas tree, sat the old bard, in a frenzy of enthusiasm, with his wife, his child, and his child's child. And all were singing the Christmas song:

> Be not afraid; look ye,
> for I bring unto you joyful tidings
> which shall be to all people.
> For unto you there is born this day
> in the city of David a Saviour which is
> Christ the Lord.

Christmas at the Bachs'

The old carol singer has long been sleeping in the kingdom of peace, but his immortal song still clarions forth in our hearts, and they become young and new, when the organ plays on Christmas night:

For I bring unto you joyful tidings.

FROM *Friedemann Bach*
TRANSLATED BY ANNE FREMANTLE

St. Bride of the Isles*

FIONA MACLEOD

I

BEFORE ever St. Colum came across the Moyle to the island of Iona, that was then by strangers called Innis-nan-Dhruidhneach, the Isle of the Druids, and by the natives Ioua, there lived upon the south-east slope of Dun-I a poor herdsman named Dùvach. Poor he was, for sure, though it was not for this reason that he could not win back to Ireland, green Banba, as he called it: but because he was an exile thence, and might never again smell the heather blowing over Sliabh-Gorm in what of old was the realm of Aoimag.

He was a prince in his own land, though none on Iona save the Arch-Druid knew what his name was. The high priest, however, knew that Dùvach was the royal Dùghall, called Dùghall Donn, the son of Hugh the King, the son of Art, the son of Conn. In his youth he had been accused of having done a wrong against a noble maiden of the blood. When her child was born he was made to swear across her dead body that he would be true to the daughter for whom she had given up her life, that he would rear her in a holy place, but away from Eiré, and that he would never set foot within that land again. This was a bitter thing for Dùghall Donn to do: the more so as, before the

---

* This legendary romance is based upon the ancient and still current (though often contradictory) legends concerning Brighid, or Bride, commonly known as "Muime Chriosd"—i.e., the Foster-Mother of Christ. From the universal honor and reverence in which she was and is held—second only in this respect to the Virgin herself—she is also called "Mary of the Gael." Another name, frequent in the West, is "Brighde-nam-Brat"—i.e., St. Bride of the Mantle, a name explained in the course of my legendary story. Brighid the Christian saint should not, however, be confused with a much earlier and remoter Brighid, the ancient Celtic Muse of Song.—Author's note

King, and the priests, and the people, he swore by the Wind, and by the Moon, and by the Sun, that he was guiltless of the thing of which he was accused. There were many there who believed him because of that sacred oath: others, too, forasmuch as that Morna the Princess had herself sworn to the same effect. Moreover, there was Aodh of the Golden Hair, a poet and seer, who avowed that Morna had given birth to an immortal, whose name would one day be as a moon among the stars for glory. But the King would not be appeased, though he spared the life of his youngest son. So it was that, by the advice of Aodh of the Druids, Dùghall Donn went northwards through the realm of Clanadon and so to the sea-loch that was then called Loc Feobal. There he took boat with some wayfarers bound for Alba. But in the Moyle a tempest arose, and the frail galley was driven northward, and at sunrise was cast like a fish, spent and dead, upon the south end of Ioua, that is now Iona. Only two of the mariners survived: Dùghall Donn and the little child. This was at the place where, on a day of the days in a year that was not yet come, St Colum landed in his coracle, and gave thanks on his bended knees.

When, warmed by the sun, they rose, they found themselves in a waste place. Ill was Dùghall in his mind because of the portents, and now to his fear and amaze the child Bridget knelt on the stones, and, with claspt hands, small and pink as the sea-shells round about her, sang a song of words which were unknown to him. This was the more marvellous, as she was yet but an infant, and could say no word even of Erse, the only tongue she had heard.

At this portent, he knew that Aodh had spoken seeingly. Truly this child was not of human parentage. So he, too, kneeled, and, bowing before her, asked if she were of the race of the Tuatha de Danann, or of the older gods, and what her will was, that he might be her servant. Then it was that the kneeling babe looked at him, and sang in a low sweet voice in Erse:

45

I am but a little child,
Dùghall, son of Hugh, son of Art,
But my garment shall be laid
On the lord of the world,
Yea, surely it shall be that He
The King of the Elements Himself
Shall lean against my bosom,
And I will give him peace,
And peace will I give to all who ask
Because of this mighty Prince,
And because of his Mother that is the Daughter of Peace.

And while Dùghall Donn was still marvelling at this thing, the Arch-Druid of Iona approached, with his white-robed priests. A grave welcome was given to the stranger. While the youngest of the servants of God was entrusted with the child, the Arch-Druid took Dùghall aside and questioned him. It was not till the third day that the old man gave his decision. Dùghall Donn was to abide on Iona if he so willed: but the child was to stay. His life would be spared, nor would he be a bondager of any kind, and a little land to till would be given him, and all that he might need. But of his past he was to say no word. His name was to become as nought, and he was to be known simply as Dùvach. The child, too, was to be named Bride, for that was the way the name Bridget was called in the Erse of the Isles.

To the question of Dùghall, that was thenceforth Dùvach, as to why he laid so great stress on the child that was a girl, and the reputed offspring of shame at that, Cathal the Arch-Druid replied thus: "My kinsman Aodh of the Golden Hair who sent you here, was wiser than Hugh the King and all the Druids of Aoimag. Truly, this child is an Immortal. There is an ancient prophecy concerning her: surely of her who is now here, and no other. There shall be, it says, a spotless maid born of a virgin of the ancient immemorial race in Innisfail. And when for the seventh time the sacred year has come, she will hold Eternity in

46

her lap as a white flower. Her maiden breasts shall swell with milk for the Prince of the World. She shall give suck to the King of the Elements. So I say unto you, Dùvach, go in peace. Take unto thyself a wife, and live upon the place I will give thee on the east side of Ioua. Treat Bride as though she were thy spirit, but leave her much alone, and let her learn of the sun and the wind. In the fulness of time the prophecy shall be fulfilled."

So was it, from that day of the days. Dùvach took a wife unto himself, who weaned the little Bride, who grew in beauty and grace, so that all men marvelled. Year by year for seven years the wife of Dùvach bore him a son, and these grew apace in strength, so that by the beginning of the third year of the seventh cycle of Bride's life there were three stalwart youths to brother her, and three comely and strong lads, and one young boy fair to see. Nor did anyone, not even Bride herself, saving Cathal the Arch-Druid, know that Dùvach the herdsman was Dùghall Donn, of a princely race in Innisfail.

In the end, too, Dùvach came to think that he had dreamed, or at the least that Cathal had not interpreted the prophecy aright. For though Bride was of exceeding beauty, and of a strange piety that made the young Druids bow before her as though she were a bàndia, yet the world went on as before, and the days brought no change. Often, while she was still a child, he had questioned her about the words she had said as a babe, but she had no memory of them. Once, in her ninth year, he came upon her on the hillside of Dun-I singing these self-same words. Her eyes dreamed far away. He bowed his head, and, praying to the Giver of Light, hurried to Cathal. The old man bade him speak no more to the child concerning the mysteries.

Bride lived the hours of her days upon the slopes of Dun-I, herding the sheep, or in following the kye upon the green hillocks and grassy dunes of what then as now was called the Machar. The beauty of the world was her daily food. The spirit within her was like sunlight behind a white flower. The birdeens in the green bushes sang for joy when they saw her blue eyes.

The tender prayers that were in her heart for all the beasts and birds, for helpless children, and tired women, and for all who were old, were often seen flying above her head in the form of white doves of sunshine.

But when the middle of the year came that was, though Dùvach had forgotten it, the year of the prophecy, his eldest son, Conn, who was now a man, murmured against the virginity of Bride, because of her beauty and because a chieftain of the mainland was eager to wed her. "I shall wed Bride or raid Ioua," was the message he had sent.

So one day, before the great fire of the summer-festival, Conn and his brothers reproached Bride.

"Idle are these pure eyes, O Bride, not to be as lamps at thy marriage-bed."

"Truly, it is not by the eyes that we live," replied the maiden gently, while to their fear and amazement she passed her hand before her face and let them see that the sockets were empty.

Trembling with awe at this portent, Dùvach intervened.

"By the Sun I swear it, O Bride, that thou shalt marry whomsoever thou wilt and none other, and when thou willest, or not at all if such be thy will."

And when he had spoken, Bride smiled, and passed her hand before her face again, and all there were abashed because of the blue light as of morning that was in her shining eyes.

I I

The still weather had come, and all the isles lay in beauty. Far south, beyond vision, ranged the coasts of Eiré: westward, leagues of quiet ocean dreamed into unsailed wastes whose waves at last laved the shores of Tirná'n-Og, the Land of Eternal Youth: northward, the spell-bound waters sparkled in the sunlight, broken here and there by purple shadows, that were the isles of Staffa and Ulva, Lunga and the isles of the columns, misty Coll, and Tiree that is the land beneath the wave; with, pale blue in the heat-haze, the mountains of Rûm called

Haleval, Haskeval, and Oreval, and the sheer Scuir-na-Gillian and the peaks of the Cuchullins in remote Skye.

All the sweet loveliness of a late spring remained, to give a freshness to the glory of summer. The birds had song to them still.

It was while the dew was yet wet on the grass that Bride came out of her father's house, and went up the steep slope of Dun-I. The crying of the ewes and lambs at the pastures came plaintively against the dawn. The lowing of the kye arose from the sandy hollows by the shore, or from the meadows on the lower slopes. Through the whole island went a rapid trickling sound, most sweet to hear: the myriad voices of twittering birds, from the dotterel in the seaweed to the larks climbing the blue spirals of heaven.

This was the morning of her birth, and she was clad in white. About her waist was a girdle of the sacred rowan, the feathery green leaves of it flickering dusky shadows upon her robe as she moved. The light upon her yellow hair was as when morning wakes, laughing low with joy amid the tall corn. As she went she sang, soft as the crooning of a dove. If any had been there to hear he would have been abashed, for the words were not in Erse, and the eyes of the beautiful girl were as those of one in a vision.

When, at last, a brief while before sunrise, she reached the summit of the Scuir, that is so small a hill and yet seems so big in Iona where it is the sole peak, she found three young Druids there, ready to tend the sacred fire the moment the sun-rays should kindle it. Each was clad in a white robe, with fillets of oak leaves; and each had a golden armlet. They made a quiet obeisance as she approached. One stepped forward, with a flush in his face because of her beauty, that was as a sea-wave for grace, and a flower for purity, and sunlight for joy, and moonlight for peace, and the wind for fragance.

"Thou mayst draw near if thou wilt, Bride, daughter of Dùvach," he said, with something of reverence as well as of grave courtesy in his voice: "for the holy Cathal hath said that the Breath of the Source of All is upon thee. It is not lawful for women to be here at this moment, but thou hast the law shining upon thy face and in thine eyes. Hast thou come to pray?"

But at that moment a low cry came from one of his companions. He turned, and rejoined his fellows. Then all three sank upon their knees, and with outstretched arms hailed the rising of God.

As the sun rose, a solemn chant swelled from their lips, ascending as incense through the silent air. The glory of the new day came soundlessly. Peace was in the blue heaven, on the blue-green sea, on the green land. There was no wind, even where the currents of the deep moved in shadowy purple. The sea itself was silent, making no more than a sighing slumber-breath round the white sands of the isle, or a hushed whisper where the tide lifted the long weed that clung to the rocks.

In what strange, mysterious way, Bride did not see; but as the three Druids held their hands before the sacred fire there was a faint crackling, then three thin spirals of blue smoke rose, and soon dusky red and wan yellow tongues of flame moved to and fro. The sacrifice of God was made. Out of the immeasurable heaven He had come, in His golden chariot. Now, in the wonder and mystery of His love, He was re-born upon the world, re-born a little fugitive flame upon a low hill in a remote isle. Great must be His love that He could die thus daily in a thousand places: so great His love that He could give up His own body to daily death, and suffer the holy flame that was in the embers He illumined to be lighted and revered and then scattered to the four quarters of the world.

Bride could bear no longer the mystery of this great love. It moved her to an ecstasy. What tenderness of divine love that could thus redeem the world daily: what long-suffering for all the evil and cruelty done hourly upon the weeping earth: what patience with the bitterness of the blind fates! The beauty of the worship of Be'al was upon her as a golden glory. Her heart

Italian, 15th century. Angel with Staff

leaped to a song that could not be sung. The inexhaustible love and pity in her soul chanted a hymn that was heard of no Druid or mortal anywhere, but was known of the white spirits of Life.

Bowing her head, so that the glad tears fell warm as thunder-rain upon her hands, she rose and moved away.

Not far from the summit of Dun-I is a hidden pool, to this day called the Fountain of Youth. Hitherward she went, as was her wont when upon the hill at the break of day, at noon, or at sundown. Close by the huge boulder, which hides it from above, she heard a pitiful bleating, and soon the healing of her eyes was upon a lamb which had become fixed in a crevice in the rock. On a crag above it stood a falcon, with savage cries, lusting for warm blood. With swift step Bride drew near. There was no hurt to the lambkin as she lifted it in her arms. Soft and warm was it there, as a young babe against the bosom that mothers it. Then with quiet eyes she looked at the falcon, who hooded his cruel gaze.

"There is no wrong in thee, Seobhag," she said gently; "but the law of blood shall not prevail for ever. Let there be peace this morn."

And when she had spoken this word, the wild hawk of the hills flew down upon her shoulder, nor did the heart of the lambkin beat the quicker, while with drowsy eyes it nestled as against its dam. When she stood by the pool she laid the little woolly creature among the fern. Already the bleating of it was sweet against the forlorn heart of a ewe. The falcon rose, circled above her head, and with swift flight sped through the blue air. For a time Bride watched its travelling shadow: when it was itself no more than a speck in the golden haze, she turned, and stooped above the Fountain of Youth.

Beyond it stood then, though for ages past there has been no sign of either, two quicken-trees. Now they were gold-green in the morning light, and the brown-green berries that had not yet reddened were still small. Fair to see was the flickering of the long finger-shadows upon the granite rocks and boulders.

St. Bride of the Isles

Often had Bride dreamed through their foliage; but now she stared in amaze. She had put her lips to the water, and had started back because she had seen, beyond her own image, that of a woman so beautiful that her soul was troubled within her, and had cried its inaudible cry, worshipping. When, trembling, she had glanced again, there was none beside herself. Yet what had happened? For, as she stared at the quicken-trees, she saw that their boughs had interlaced, and that they now became a green arch. What was stranger still was that the rowan-clusters hung in blood-red masses, although the late heats were yet a long way off.

Bride rose, her body quivering because of the cool sweet draught of the Fountain of Youth, so that almost she imagined the water was for her that day what it could be once in each year to every person who came to it, a breath of new life and the strength and joy of youth. With slow steps she advanced towards the arch of the quickens. Her heart beat as she saw that the branches at the summit had formed themselves into the shape of a wreath or crown, and that the scarlet berries dropped therefrom a steady rain of red drops as of blood. A sigh of joy breathed from her lips when, deep among the red and green, she saw the white merle of which the ancient poets sang, and heard the exceeding wonder of its rapture, which was now the pain of joy and now the joy of pain.

The song of the mystic bird grew wilder and more sweet as she drew near. For a brief while she hesitated. Then, as a white dove drifted slow before her under and through the quicken-boughs, a dove white as snow but radiant with sunfire, she moved forward to follow, with a dream-smile upon her face and her eyes full of the sheen of wonder and mystery, as shadowy waters flooded with moonshine.

And this was the passing of Bride, who was not seen again of Dùvach or her foster-brothers for the space of a year and a day. Only Cathal, the aged Arch-Druid, who died seven days thence, had a vision of her, and wept for joy.

III

When the strain of the white merle ceased, though it had seemed to her scarce longer than the vanishing song of the swallow on the wing, Bride saw that the evening was come. Through the violet glooms of dusk she moved soundlessly, save for the crispling of her feet among the hot sands. Far as she could see to right or left there were hollows and ridges of sand; where, here and there, trees or shrubs grew out of the parched soil, they were strange to her. She had heard the Druids speak of the sunlands in a remote, nigh unreachable East, where there were trees called palms, trees in a perpetual sunflood yet that perished not, also tall dark cypresses, black-green as the holy yew. These were the trees she now saw. Did she dream, she wondered? Far down in her mind was some memory, some floating vision only, mayhap, of a small green isle far among the northern seas. Voices, words, faces, familiar yet unfamiliar when she strove to bring them near, haunted her.

The heat brooded upon the land. The sigh of the parched earth was "Water, water."

As she moved onward through the gloaming she descried white walls beyond her: white walls and square white buildings, looming ghostly through the dark, yet home-sweet as the bells of the cows on the sea-pastures, because of the yellow lights every here and there agleam.

A tall figure moved towards her, clad in white, even as those figures which haunted her unremembering memory. When he drew near she gave a low cry of joy. The face of her father was sweet to her.

"Where will be the pitcher, Brighid?" he said, though the words were not the words that were near her when she was alone. Nevertheless she knew them, and the same manner of words was upon her lips.

"My pitcher, father?"

"Ah, dreamer, when will you be taking heed! It is leaving your

54

pitcher you will be, and by the Well of the Camels, no doubt: though little matter will that be, since there is now no water, and the drought is heavy upon the land. But . . . Brighid . . ."

"Yes, my father?"

"Sure now, it is not safe for you to be on the desert at night. Wild beasts come out of the darkness, and there are robbers and wild men who lurk in the shadow. Brighid . . . Brighid . . . is it dreaming you are still?"

"I was dreaming of a cool green isle in northern seas, where . . ."

"Where you have never been, foolish lass, and are never like to be. Sure, if any wayfarer were to come upon us you would scarce be able to tell him that yonder village is Bethlehem, and that I am Dùghall Donn the inn-keeper, Dùghall, the son of Hugh, son of Art, son of Conn. Well, well, I am growing old, and they say that the old see wonders. But I do not wish to see this wonder, that my daughter Brighid forgets her own town, and the good inn that is there, and the strong sweet ale that is cool against the thirst of the weary. Sure, if the day of my days is near it is near. "Green be the place of my rest," I cry, even as Oisìn the son of Fionn of the hero-line of Trenmor cried in his old age; though if Oisìn and the Fiànn were here not a green place would they find now, for the land is burned dry as the heather after a hill-fire. But now, Brighid, let us go back into Bethlehem, for I have that for the saying which must be said at once."

In silence the twain walked through the gloaming that was already the mirk, till they came to the white gate, where the asses and camels breathed wearily in the sultry darkness, with dry tongues moving round parched mouths. Thence they fared through narrow streets, where a few white-robed Hebrews and sons of the desert moved silently, or sat in niches. Finally, they came to a great yard, where more than a score of camels lay huddled and growling in their sleep. Beyond this was the inn, which was known to all the patrons and friends of Dùghall

Donn as the "Rest and Be Thankful," though formerly as the Rest of Clan-Ailpean, for was he not himself through his mother MacAlpine of the Isles, as well as blood-kin to the great Cormac the Ard-Righ, to whom his father, Hugh, was feudatory prince?

As Dùghall and Bride walked along the stone flags of a passage leading to the inner rooms, he stopped and drew her attention to the water-tanks.

"Look, you, my lass," he said sorrowfully, "of these tanks and barrels nearly all are empty. Soon there will be no water whatever, which is an evil thing though I whisper it in peace, to the Stones be it said. Now, already the folk who come here murmur. No man can drink ale all day long, and those wayfarers who want to wash the dust of their journey from their feet and hands complain bitterly. And . . . what is that you will be saying? The kye? Ay, sure, there is the kye; but the poor beasts are o'ercome with the heat, and there's not a Cailliach on the hills who could win a drop more of milk from them than we squeeze out of their udders now, and that only with rune after rune till all the throats of the milking lassies are as dry as the salt grass by the sea.

"Well, what I am saying is this: 'tis months now since any rain will be falling, and every crock of water has been for the treasuring as though it had been the honey of Moy-Mell itself. The moon has been full twice since we had the good water brought from the mountain-springs; and now they are for drying up too. The seers say that the drought will last. If that is a true word, and there be no rain till the winter comes, there will be no inn in Bethlehem called 'The Rest and Be Thankful'; for already there is not enough good water to give peace even to your little thirst, my birdeen. As for the ale, it is poor drink now for man or maid, and as for the camels and asses, poor beasts, they don't understand the drinking of it."

"That is true, father; but what is to be done?"

"That's what I will be telling you, my lintie. Now, I have been told by an oganach out of Jerusalem, that lives in another place

56

close by the great town, that there is a quenchless well of pure water, cold as the sea with a north wind in it, on a hill there called the Mount of Olives. Now, it is to that hill I will be going. I am for taking all the camels and all the horses, and all the asses, and will lade each with a burthen of water-skins, and come back home again with water enough to last us till the drought breaks."

That was all that was said that night. But at the dawn the inn was busy, and all the folk in Bethlehem were up to see the going abroad of Dùghall Donn and Ronald McIan, his shepherd, and some Macleans and Maccallums that were then in that place. It was a fair sight to see as they went forth through the white gate that is called the Gate of Nazareth. A piper walked first, playing the Gathering of the Swords: then came Dùghall Donn on a camel, and McIan on a horse, and the herdsmen on asses, and then there were the collies barking for joy.

Before he had gone, Dùghall took Bride out of the hearing of the others. There was only a little stagnant water, he said; and as for the ale, there was no more than a flagon left of what was good. This flagon and the one jar of pure water he left with her. On no account was she to give a drop to any wayfarer, no matter how urgent he might be; for he, Dùghall, could not say when he would get back, and he did not want to find a dead daughter to greet him on his return, let alone there being no maid of the inn to attend to customers. Over and above that, he made her take an oath that she would give no one, no, not even a stranger, accommodation at the inn, during his absence.

Afternoon and night came, and dawn and night again, and yet again. It was on the afternoon of the third day, when even the crickets were dying of thirst, that Bride heard a clanging at the door of the inn.

When she went to the door she saw a weary grey-haired man, dusty and tired. By his side was an ass with drooping head, and on the ass was a woman, young, and of a beauty that was as the cool shadow of green leaves and the cold ripple of running waters. But beautiful as she was it was not this that made Bride start: no, nor the heavy womb that showed the woman was with child. For she remembered her of a dream—it was a dream, sure —when she had looked into a pool on a mountain-side, and seen, beyond her own image, just this fair and beautiful face, the most beautiful that ever man saw since Nais, of the Sons of Usna, beheld Deirdrê in the forest—ay, and lovelier far even than she, the peerless among women.

"Gu'm beannaicheadh Dia an tigh," said the grey-haired man in a weary voice, "the blessing of God on this house."

"Soraidh leat," replied Bride gently, "and upon you likewise."

"Can you give us food and drink, and, after that, good rest at this inn? Sure it is grateful we will be. This is my wife, Mary, upon whom is a mystery: and I am Joseph, a carpenter in Arimathea."

"Welcome, and to you, too, Mary: and peace. But there is neither food nor drink here, and my father has bidden me give shelter to none who comes here against his return."

The carpenter sighed, but the fair woman on the ass turned her shadowy eyes upon Bride, so that the maiden trembled with joy and fear.

"And is it forgetting me you will be, Brighid-Alona," she murmured, in the good sweet Gaelic of the Isles; and the voice of her was like the rustle of leaves when a soft rain is falling in a wood.

"Sure, I remember," Bride whispered, filled with deep awe. Then without a word she turned, and beckoned them to follow: which, having left the ass by the doorway, they did.

"Here is all the ale that I have," she said, as she gave the flagon to Joseph: "and here, Mary, is all the water that there is. Little there is, but it is you that are welcome to it."

Then, when they had quenched their thirst she brought out oatcakes and scones and brown bread, and would fain have added milk, but there was none.

"Go to the byre, Brighid," said Mary, "and the first of the kye shall give milk."

So Bride went, but returned saying that the creature would not give milk without a sian or song, and that her throat was too dry to sing.

"Say this sian," said Mary:

> Give up thy milk to her who calls
> Across the low green hills of Heaven
> And stream-cool meads of Paradise!

And sure enough, when Bride did this, the milk came: and she soothed her thirst, and went back to her guests rejoicing. It was sorrow to her not to let them stay where they were, but she could not, because of her oath.

The man Joseph was weary, and said he was too tired to seek far that night, and asked if there was no empty byre or stable where he and Mary could sleep till morning. At that, Bride was glad: for she knew there was a clean cool stable close to the byre where her kye were: and thereto she led them, and returned with peace at her heart.

When she was in the inn again, she was afraid once more: for lo, though Mary and Joseph had drunken deep of the jar and the flagon, each was now full as it had been. Of the food, too, none seemed to have been taken, though she had herself seen them break the scones and the oatcakes.

It was dusk when her reverie was broken by the sound of the pipes. Soon thereafter Dùghall Donn and his following rode up to the inn, and all were glad because of the cool water, and the grapes, and the green fruits of the earth, that they brought with them.

While her father was eating and drinking, merry because of the ale that was still in the flagon, Bride told him of the wayfarers. Even as she spoke, he made a sign of silence, because of a strange, unwonted sound that he heard.

"What will that be meaning?" he asked, in a low, hushed voice.

"Sure it is the rain at last, father. That is a glad thing. The earth will be green again. The beasts will not perish. Hark, I hear the noise of it coming down from the hills as well." But Dùghall sat brooding.

"Ay," he said at last, "is it not foretold that the Prince of the World is to be born in this land, during a heavy falling of rain, after a long drought? And who is for knowing that Bethlehem is not the place, and that this is not the night of the day of the days? Brighid, Brighid, the woman Mary must be the mother of the Prince, who is to save all mankind out of evil and pain and death!"

And with that he rose and beckoned to her to follow. They took a lantern, and made their way through the drowsing camels and asses and horses, and past the byres where the kye lowed gently, and so to the stable.

"Sure that is a bright light they are having," Dùghall muttered uneasily; for, truly, it was as though the shed were a shell filled with the fires of sunrise.

Lightly they pushed back the door. When they saw what they saw they fell upon their knees. Mary sat with her heavenly beauty upon her like sunshine on a dusk land: in her lap, a Babe, laughing sweet and low.

Never had they seen a Child so fair. He was as though wrought of light.

"Who is it?" murmured Dùghall Donn, of Joseph, who stood near, with rapt eyes.

"It is the Prince of Peace."

And with that Mary smiled, and the Child slept.

"Brighid, my sister dear"—and, as she whispered this, Mary held the little one to Bride.

The fair girl took the Babe in her arms, and covered it with her mantle. Therefore it is that she is known to this day as Brighde-nam-Brat, St. Bride of the Mantle.

60

It was on this night that, far away in Iona, the Arch-Druid Cathal died. But before the breath went from him he had his vision of joy, and his last words were:

Bridget Bride upon her knee,
The King of the Elements asleep on her breast!

At the coming of dawn Mary awoke, and took the Child. She kissed Bride upon the brows, and said this thing to her: "Brighid, my sister dear, thou shalt be known unto all time as Muime Chriosd."

IV

No sooner had Mary spoken than Bride fell into a deep sleep. So profound was this slumber that when Dùghall Donn came to see to the wayfarers, and to tell them that the milk and the porridge were ready for the breaking of their fast, he could get no word of her at all. She lay in the clean, yellow straw beneath the manger, where Mary had laid the Child. Dùghall stared in amaze. There was no sign of the mother, nor of the Babe that was the Prince of Peace, nor of the douce, quiet man that was Joseph the carpenter. As for Bride, she not only slept so sound that no word of his fell against her ears, but she gave him awe. For as he looked at her he saw that she was surrounded by a glowing light. Something in his heart shaped itself into a prayer, and he knelt beside her, sobbing low. When he rose, it was in peace. Mayhap an angel had comforted his soul in its dark shadowy haunt of his body.

It was late when Bride awoke, though she did not open her eyes, but lay dreaming. For long she thought she was in Tir-Tairngire, the Land of Promise, or wandering on the honey-sweet plain of Magh-Mell; for the wind of dreamland brought exqisite odours to her, and in her ears was a most marvellous sweet singing.

With that, Bride remembered all, and opened her eyes.

61

Nought strange was there to see, save that she lay in the stable. Then as she noted that the gloaming had come, she wondered at the soft light that prevailed in the shed, though no lamp or candle burned there. In her ears, too, still lingered a wild and beautiful music.

It was strange. Was it all a dream, she pondered. But even as she thought thus, she saw half of her mantle lying upon the straw in the manger. Much she marvelled at this, but when she took the garment in her hand she wondered more. For though it was no more than a half of the poor mantle wherewith she had wrapped the Babe, it was all wrought with mystic gold lines and with precious stones more glorious than ever Arch-Druid or Island Prince had seen. The marvel gave her awe at last, when, as she placed the garment upon her shoulder, it covered her completely.

She knew now that she had not dreamed, and that a miracle was done. So with gladness she went out of the stable, and into the inn. Dùghall Donn was amazed when he saw her, and then rejoiced exceedingly.

"Why are you so merry, my father," she asked.

"Sure it is glad that I am. For now the folk will be laughing the wrong way. This very morning I was so pleased with the pleasure, that while the pot was boiling on the peats I went out and told every one I met that the Prince of Peace was come, and had just been born in the stable behind the 'Rest and Be Thankful.' Well, that saying was just like a weasel among the rabbits, only it was an old toothless weasel: for all Bethlehem mocked me, some with jeers, some with hard words, and some with threats. Sure, I cursed them right and left. No, not for all my cursing—and by the blood of my fathers, I spared no man among them, wishing them sword and fire, the black plague and the grey death—would they believe. So back it was that I came, and going through the inn I am come to the stable. 'Sorrow is on me like a grey mist,' said Oisìn, mourning for Oscur, and sure it was a grey mist that was on me when not a sign of man, woman, or child was to be seen, and you so sound asleep that a March gale in the Moyle wouldn't have roused you. Well, I went back, and told this thing, and all the people in Bethlehem mocked at me. And the Elders of the People came at last, and put a fine upon me: and condemned me to pay three barrels of good ale, and a sack of meal, and three thin chains of gold, each three yards long: and this for causing a false rumour, and still more for making a laughing-stock of the good folk of Bethlehem. There was a man called Murdoch-Dhu, who is the chief smith in Nazareth, and it's him I'm thinking will have laughed the Elders into doing this hard thing."

It was then that Bride was aware of a marvel upon her, for she blew an incantation off the palm of her hand, and by that frith she knew where the dues were to be found.

"By what I see in the air that is blown off the palm of my hand, father, I bid you go into the cellar of the inn. There you will find three barrels full of good ale, and beside them a sack of meal, and the sack is tied with three chains of gold, each three yards long."

But while Dùghall Donn went away rejoicing, and found that which Bride had foretold, she passed out into the street. None saw her in the gloaming, or as she went towards the Gate of the East. When she passed by the Lazar-house she took her mantle off her back and laid it in the place of offerings. All the jewels and fine gold passed into invisible birds with healing wings: and these birds flew about the heads of the sick all night, so that at dawn every one arose, with no ill upon him, and went on his way rejoicing. As each went out of Bethlehem that morning of the mornings he found a clean white robe and new sandals at the first mile; and, at the second, food and cool water; and, at the third, a gold piece and a staff.

The guard that was at the Eastern Gate did not hail Bride. All the gaze of him was upon a company of strange men, shepherd-kings, who said they had come out of the East led by a star. They carried rare gifts with them when they first came to

Bethlehem: but no man knew whence they came, what they wanted, or whither they went.

For a time Bride walked along the road that leads to Nazareth. There was fear in her gentle heart when she heard the howling of hyenas down in the dark hollows, and she was glad when the moon came out and shone quietly upon her.

In the moonlight she saw that there were steps in the dew before her. She could see the black print of feet in the silver sheen on the wet grass, for it was on a grassy hill that she now walked, though a day ago every leaf and sheath there had lain brown and withered. The footprints she followed were those of a woman and of a child.

All night through she tracked those wandering feet in the dew. They were always fresh before her, and led her away from the villages, and also where no wild beasts prowled through the gloom. There was no weariness upon her, though often she wondered when she should see the fair wondrous face she sought. Behind her also were footsteps in the dew, though she knew nothing of them. They were those of the Following Love. And this was the Lorgadh-Brighde of which men speak to this day: the Quest of the holy St Bride.

All night she walked; now upon the high slopes of a hill. Never once did she have a glimpse of any figure in the moonlight, though the steps in the dew before her were newly made, and none lay in the glisten a short way ahead.

Suddenly she stopped. There were no more footprints. Eagerly she looked before her. On a hill beyond the valley beneath her she saw the gleaming of yellow stars. These were the lights of a city. "Behold, it is Jerusalem," she murmured, awe-struck, for she had never seen the great town.

Sweet was the breath of the wind that stirred among the olives on the mount where she stood. It had the smell of heather, and she could hear the rustle of it among the bracken on a hill close by.

"Truly, this must be the Mount of Olives," she whispered,

"The Mount of which I have heard my father speak, and that must be the hill called Calvary."

But even as she gazed marvelling, she sighed with new wonder; for now she saw that the yellow stars were as the twinkling of the fires of the sun along the crest of a hill that is set in the east. There was a living joy in the dawntide. In her ears was a sweet sound of the bleating of ewes and lambs. From the hollows in the shadows came the swift singing rush of the flowing tide. Faint cries of the herring gulls filled the air; from the weedy boulders by the sea the skuas called wailingly.

Bewildered, she stood intent. If only she could see the footprints again, she thought. Whither should she turn, whither go? At her feet was a yellow flower. She stooped and plucked it.

"Tell me, O little sun-flower, which way shall I be going?" and as she spoke a small golden bee flew up from the heart of it, and up the hill to the left of her. So it is that from that day the dandelion is called am-Bèarnàn-Bhrighde.

Still she hesitated. Then a sea-bird flew by her with a loud whistling cry.

"Tell me, O eisireùn," she called, "which way shall I be going?"

And at this the eisireùn swerved in its flight, and followed the golden bee, crying, "This way, O Bride, Bride, Bride, Bride, Bri-i-i-ide!"

So it is that from that day the oyster-catcher has been called the Gille-Bhrighde, the Servant of St. Bridget.

And she saw before her two quicken-trees, of which the boughs were inter-wrought so that they made an arch. Deep in the green foliage was a white merle that sang a wondrous sweet song. Above it the small branches were twisted into the shape of a wreath or crown, lovely with the sunlit rowan-clusters, from whose scarlet berries red drops as of blood fell.

Before her flew a white dove, all aglow as with golden light. She followed, and passed beneath the quicken arch.

Sweet was the song of the merle, that was then no more;

65

sweet the green shadow of the rowans, that now grew straight as young pines. Sweet the far song in the sky, where the white dove flew against the sun.

Bride looked, and her eyes were glad. Bonnie the blooming of the heather on the slopes of Dun-I. Iona lay green and gold, isled in her blue waters. From the sheiling of Dùvach, her father, rose a thin column of pale blue smoke. The collies, seeing her, barked loudly with welcoming joy.

The bleating of the sheep, the lowing of the kye, the breath of the salt wind from the open sea beyond, the song of the flowing tide in the Sound beneath: dear the homing.

With a strange light in her eyes she moved down through the heather and among the green bracken: white, wonderful, fair to see.

The Christmas Silence

JESSICA POWERS

Here in the cloister they who seek discover
A wandered fragment of the Christmas silence
That hid itself from the disquieted earth:
The silence of the Virgin bending over
The little Uncreated Innocence
Upon the bed of a most hidden birth,
The silence that was Joseph's sacrament
Through years that were a threshold to this hour
And which was seed and stem to the white flower
That blossomed on his rod,
The speechlessness of the unlettered shepherds
Who stood amazed before the Lamb of God.
The angels sang at Christmas, but their music
Was like a stillness to the inner ear,
And soft as petals from a shaken bough.

They who go walking in the Christmas silence
Through any season of the changing year
Come to a Man with peace upon his brow
And see the Mother and the Infant near.
This house, as once the Saint of Alcantara
Said of Teresa's, is the little hospice
Of Bethlehem.
Cloister or cave—its solitudes shall be
The dwelling of a human trinity
And they who enter learn a wordless language
And the Divine Untold addresses them.

Geoffrey Tory. The Nativity

The Little Old Woman

OTTO BRUDER

THE FOLLOWING tale was told to us by a refugee who, after many hardships, managed to escape from his persecutors. During those years when particularly harsh and cruel measures were being taken to put a stop to the worship of God and an effort was being made to eradicate by force the old pious customs in the hearts of the people, a strict watch was kept to see that no one took it into his head to celebrate the Christian festivals. These were considered particularly dangerous because in them old custom was deeply connected with child-like faith.

The authorities kept a sharp eye out for Christmas celebrations also, perhaps because they had a presentiment that their power (like that of King Herod) might be mortally menaced by the Child to whom has been promised the dominion of the world.

In any event, they forbade on pain of heavy punishment any celebration of the birth of the Saviour. At that time many people could be seen along the border who had secretly stolen away by night to hear the Christmas bells ringing from across the frontier and to take comfort in the sound. On these pilgrimages, many met death from the bullets of the frontier guards.

But on Christmas Eve patrols were sent out into the villages to nip in the bud any trace of the hated Christmas joy.

And so horsemen came riding into the village of K. to find out whether the command of the authorities was being obeyed. First they rode to the church, eager to rouse up a pious congregation in the midst of its worship. But the house of God was deserted and the clank of their spurs on the stone floor echoed back from the vaulted ceiling.

69

In their annoyance, they ripped the pictures from the walls, smashed the many-colored windowpanes and set off to subject the village to a thorough search. But there too, except for the miserable cattle, there was not a soul to be found. Then rage overcame them and they went from house to house, beating down the doors, falling over the provisions, flinging open chests and trunks, looting what was to be looted and battering furniture and china to bits with their rifles. Finally they all gathered together and were on the point of riding on when one of the soldiers came running up shouting that he had seen a light shining from a barn outside the village. At once they sprang on their horses and galloped down the street yelling and shouting. At the barn they shattered the door with their sabres and the butts of their guns, and after forcing their way in they found the entire village assembled. In the light of a stable lantern, men, women, old people and children were sitting about in a circle on the straw, gazing calmly and quietly at the intruders. Only the children began to cry softly and clung for protection to the garments of their elders.

The commander stepped forward and ordered the villagers to explain themselves. No one answered him. He then ordered his men to ransack the barn. The peasants rose to their feet and offered no resistance. The soldiers rummaged about in the straw, tearing it apart and poking it with their sabres, and searched the villagers thoroughly. But they found nothing, no cross, no consecrated vessel; nor was there any priest to be seen among them. The tormentors then tried to compel the peasants with blows and kicks to give an explanation. The leader, a thick-set, powerful man, went about with a pointed pistol from one to the other. But, except for the soft moans of the old people and the whimpering of the children, not a sound could be extracted from the silent group, not one could be prevailed upon to tell what the occasion of the gathering might be.

Such obduracy had to be punished and still more cruel methods were about to be employed on the villagers. Glowering, the commander called his men together. Then, in a moment of dreadful stillness, a little old woman stepped into the circle. She must have borne all of eighty years on her back for she was very much hunched over, her pale face furrowed with wrinkles and her hair as gray as ashes. She shuffled up, bowed low before the commander and there was such an air of dignity and poise about the little old woman that the brutal commander, as though compelled by some higher power, lowered his pistol, bowed his head and, with lips compressed, stared at the floor. But a ripple of emotion passed over the soldiers. It was as if these men, all sons of peasants, had heard a voice to which they were not yet wholly deaf calling from the depths of their hearts. They too bowed their flaxen heads and fingered their weapons in embarrassment.

The little old woman then turned to face the village people, drew herself up as straight as her gaunt old body would allow, looked at one villager after the other, a deep, kindly expression in her eyes, raised her hand and blessed them all with the sign of the cross. Then she spoke, and her fine, thin voice rang like a tiny silver bell: "Beloved, unto us this day is born a Saviour!"

A flicker of joy passed over the faces of the villagers. There was the sound of sobbing and tears could be seen pouring down their cheeks. Everyone, as if with one voice, repeated the greeting: Unto us this day is born a Saviour.

Lightning flashed above the head of the commander. He tossed back his head and gripped his pistol tightly. But now the little old woman had turned to him. She took a few steps forward and stood still right in front of him, so close that he could not avoid her eyes.

Again she raised her hand and again made the sign of the cross over him and his soldiers, and again she spoke in the same bright and joyous voice: "Go to your mothers, beloved, go home. For unto you too, my dears, unto you too is born this day a Saviour." The commander's eyes opened wide and he looked past the old woman into the dusk of the room. It was as if everyone were holding his breath. The soldiers' heads were bowed. A few had edged back toward the door, as if trying to get away as quickly as possible in order to hide their emotion. The silence lasted for several seconds, then the lips of the commander moved and he whispered, so that it was audible only to the old woman: "Mother—Mother!" But suddenly he pulled himself together and firing a shot at the ceiling which terrified everyone but hit no one, he bellowed to his soldiers in a bulllike voice: "Out!" and again: "Out!" And at once the room was empty of soldiers. The villagers could hear the steps outside, could hear the men leaping on their horses. They heard them rushing, at a gallop, down the village street, and then the hoofbeats faded away into the distance.

TRANSLATED BY JANE BANNARD GREENE

The Golden Crucifix

GRAZIA DELEDDA

I WAS LIVING in Sardegna at the time and I wanted to unearth some Christmas story about the island. I used to know an old peasant who knew many of them—a tenant on one of our small holdings down in the valley.

He used to come to visit us in the summer and fall, hunched over his walking stick, a sack slung around his neck, his wispy grey beard dropping into the open end of the bag. He always came to see us late in the afternoon, when the evening star was smiling at us children through the purple twilight. The old peasant seemed like one of the Three Wise Men who had taken the wrong turn and had lost his companions. But he offered things more precious to us than gold and the Wise Men's crown—fruits and strange tales.

He very seldom came to see us in the winter, and was not so interesting then because he carried only olives, and olives are bitter. Therefore we often went to visit him down in the valley. It was comfortable there, sheltered from the cold wind, with the clouds spreading like a veil over a crib, the water withdrawn and the mountain slopes dry. When the weather was good it seemed like spring. Almond trees were blooming, deceived by the mildness like dreamers, and the olives glistened in the grass like purple pearls.

The old man lived in a tiny hut in the midst of an olive grove that rested on a small plateau protected by harsh grey stones and wild bushes. He had a primitive bee-hive that had long since been abandoned by the bees. The wild cats loved to lie in it, beautiful like little tigresses.

When we came to see him this time, the enclosure was

73

warmed by the sun, the olives were silvery, and the afternoon so limpid that on the slopes of the opposite mountain one could see shining rivulets and the women collecting acorns hidden in the grass.

The little old man had spread the olives on the ground to let them dry and was picking up those that seemed a little spoiled. He didn't feel like talking. His tongue had grown stiff from solitude and silence. However, the servant had brought a good medicine to free the rusty words. So the old man drank deeply and began to complain.

"What kind of a tale do you want me to tell? I am old and speak only to the earth that calls me. If you want stories, you know how to read. Why don't you look for them in the books?"

"Drink some more," said the servant, bending down to select some olives. "Tell us about the time you were going to get married, why don't you?"

"That's a true story, not a legend," he replied. "I'll tell you that one because it happened around this time, on Christmas Eve. I was twenty years old then, and was engaged. Of course, I was very young to get married, but my father had died, and my mother was always ill. She had heart trouble and was God-fearing, so she said to me: 'Get married so that when I die you will not have to carry the cross of life alone, or fall in the clutches of the first woman you meet.'

"But whom to choose? I wasn't rich and I really didn't care about wealth. All I wanted was a wife who would be honest and God-fearing. We thought this over, asking ourselves who she should be.

"There was a very respectable family living near us, father, mother and seven children. They were all good workers and went to church and confession as God decrees. Three of the seven children were girls, beautiful, tall and slim with waists you could span with your two hands. They kept their eyes lowered, the bodices buttoned tightly and their hands under their aprons. Nor did they walk like you modern girls, looking at people as if

74

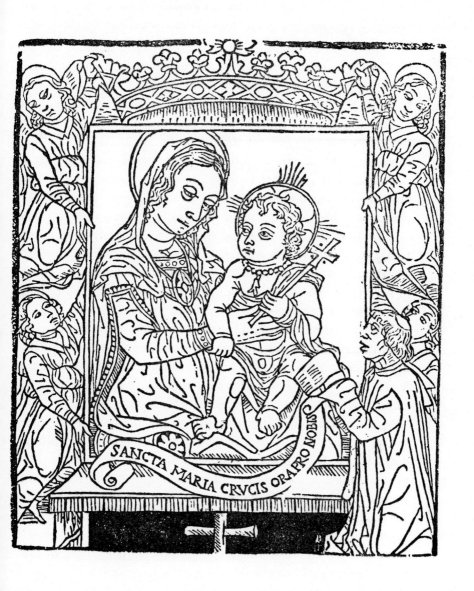

Italian, 16th century. Madonna and Child

you were going to eat them. My mother asked the youngest for me, and I was accepted. When Christmas time came, I had to give her the present with which, as is customary, I engaged myself to marry her. By accepting it she agreed to take me as her husband.

"We thought and thought about that present. Sitting opposite each other near the fire, my mother and I debated as to whether the present should be a gold coin, an embroidered scarf, or a ring. Finally my mother said: 'Listen, son, I have only a few more days to live and every step is a farewell to the things of this earth. Take this golden crucifix and give it to her.'

"She gave me her cross together with the mother of pearl rosary to which it was attached. But her eyes were glistening with tears, and her lips were parted with emotion and the aching of her heart. I was so troubled that I tried to give it back to her; but unable to speak she merely pushed my hand back.

"I wrapped the rosary and the cross in a handkerchief, wrapped the little bundle in yet another handkerchief, and carried it in my pocket for three days like a relic. From time to time I touched it for fear of losing it and felt, I don't know why, a strange anxiety, although my heart swelled with love.

"On Christmas Eve I went to call on my intended. Two other young men were there too, to whom her sisters were betrothed. The kitchen, with so many people in it, looked very festive. But everybody was serious because of the presence of the in-laws with their serene but rather somber miens. We felt the same respect for them that one has for the saints over the altar, and the girls came and went with lowered eyes, offering wine and cookies to their young men, answering the compliments paid them in low voices and without smiling.

"I felt at home in such surroundings because I was a serious boy, an orphan accustomed to look upon life seriously. It made me happy to steal an occasional glance at my future wife and when ever she raised her eyes and looked at me, as often as her back was turned to her father and mother, it was as though the

76

sky had opened. The kitchen with the old people, the young men and their betrothed, and the four brothers who were busy skinning a couple of goats for dinner, was like a Holy Court in the presence of God, the saints and the angels. How happy I was that evening! I have never been so happy since. I was anxiously waiting for the moment when we would return from mass, and I could present my gift to the girl and so be bound to her.

"Suddenly somebody knocked at the door. One of the brothers went to open it and came back with a stranger, a tall man with a sack over his shoulders, a twisted walking stick in his hand. I looked him over carefully as he advanced silently on soft shoes like those worn by the people of Oliano. At first glance he seemed very old, with a short white beard and light colored eyes; but then I realized that he was young, fair-haired and tired as though he had come from very far away.

"None of us knew him, and the women stared at him curiously. Everyone thought he was a friend of the father who received him with dignified cordiality.

" 'Take a seat,' he said. 'Where do you come from?'

"The stranger sat among us without removing his sack, the stick on his knees, his legs stretched out toward the fire. He looked at us, one after the other, smiling as if we were old acquaintances.

" 'I come from very far and am just passing through the village,' he said in a voice even calmer than that of my future father-in-law. 'I thought I'd step in, because I see you are having a celebration.'

" 'Yes, indeed, we are celebrating, as you can see,' my father-in-law-to-be replied. 'Our girls are engaged, and here are the young men, strong and handsome as young lions. We are in want of nothing.'

" 'Of nothing, indeed,' cried the young men, nudging each other with their elbows and laughing. The girls, after so much gravity, also burst into laughter and could not stop. I laughed, too, and so did father and mother. It was like an infectious di-

77

sease. The only one who remained quiet was the stranger, looking at us like a child, neither surprised nor displeased. Then, when everybody had become serious again, he turned to the women and said:

" 'Many years ago I passed through this same village and happened, as tonight, to come to a house where there was a young engaged couple. And everybody was happy and gay as you are now. But the bride stared at me intently, and when I was about to leave she followed me to the door and said: "You are my true love. I have been waiting for you. Stay here and give me the present." I gave her the gift, and although I went away and she married another, I was her true husband. Her son will give to you young brides the gift I gave her, and you in turn will pass it on to your sons for their brides.'

"We looked at each other and weren't laughing and smiling any longer. The man seemed odd to us, almost mad. And after our merriment we almost began to fear him.

"My mother-in-law said: "Tell us, what was thy present?'

" 'A golden crucifix.'

"At that I felt shivers run down my back. The son of the stranger's true love could only be I. I was the only one who had brought my mother's golden cross as a gift for my bride. I couldn't open my mouth. My head was whirling. I saw everything confusedly. My ears were buzzing and I couldn't hear the words exchanged between the stranger and the others. I felt a terrible pain in my heart, and a weight, a weight was breaking my back, just as if the crucifix in my pocket had suddenly become tremendously heavy and were pulling down my shoulders.

"Having warmed his feet at the fire, the stranger rose quietly. Tall and silent, his stick in his hand and the sack on his back, he opened the door and went out into the darkness.

" 'Who was he?' asked my mother-in-law.

" 'And who would know that?' answered my father-in-law. 'I never met the man, though his face seems familiar. Probably I saw him years ago when he came calling on his true love.'

"I remained silent, and once more all of us were as we had been before, serious and grave. The girls went swiftly to and fro preparing dinner; but my betrothed was pale and kept her eyes averted. No longer did she look at me. My heart was beating rapidly, and through the haze that still shrouded my head it seemed to me that the eyes of all those in the room stared at me with distrust. And thus it remained until the time came for us to go to mass. We arose, but I felt heavy and unsteady and moved as though I had drunk too much. We walked in single file, the women in front and then the men.

"When we arrived at the church the others mixed with the crowd, but I stood apart. Slowly I moved back, back to the basin with the holy water, back to the door and down the steps. At the entrance I turned my back on God's house and ran, ran as if chased by demons. I wandered among the fields like a madman until the sun rose. Then I returned to my house.

"Mother was already up. She was lighting the fire and she looked tranquil, but pale as though she hadn't slept all night. Seeing me in my dishevelled state, she thought I had been drinking and spread my straw pallet on the floor for me to lie on. Her only words were: 'A fine figure you're cutting, son!'

"I threw myself on the floor, beating my fists against the pallet. Then I got to my knees, took the crucifix out of my pocket and twisted it. The rosary snapped, and the beads scattered over the floor. It seemed they, too, were afraid of me. My mother gasped. A great lump of pity rose in my throat, and I told her everything. 'What else could I do?' I moaned. 'You were the stranger's true love. You were that woman. But how could I give your crucifix to my bride? They all looked at me as if they had guessed. I ran away from shame.'

"My mother remained silent. She gathered up the beads in her apron and began to thread them, one by one, on the rosary. She waited until I had calmed down. Then she said:

" 'Why couldn't the two other young men have been the sons of the stranger's beloved?' "

79

" 'Because they had gold coins to give to their brides, and not golden crucifixes,' I replied.

" 'The gold coins also have crosses on them,' she replied. 'Listen to me. That stranger comes to the house of each bride, giving her a cross to bear. Do you think that last night the three young girls did not go out after him? Yes, and he gave each one of them a cross, and their sons will be his sons. How simple you are! Don't you believe in God? Yes, you do believe in God and in Jesus, and you know that Jesus is not dead. He is alive. He is in this world with us, and he enters the homes of those who are charitable, to bless and multiply their loaves of bread. He blesses and turns into sweet wine the water for those of good heart. And to all brides he gives a crucifix, a golden one, but always a cross. He was that stranger and, you simpleton, you didn't recognize him.'

"So," the old man said, finishing his story, "the crucifix remained my own."

Signor Santa

JO PAGANO

I

THE WHOLE blame says my mother, lies on my father's *stubborn insistence* that he play Santa Claus. If he had taken her advice in the first place and minded his own business everything would have turned out differently; as it was . . .

"But what was I to do?" cries my father. "*Corpo di Bacco!* Why lay all the blame on me? It was not my idea in the beginning. Gianpaolo himself suggested it. With my stomach, said he, I would make an admirable Santa Claus—and I thought, for the sake of the occasion . . . "

And so on and so forth. Nevertheless, in all fairness, I do not think it just to lay the whole blame for what happened on my father. Certainly he acted from the best of motives—that much cannot be denied; but can the same be said of Signor Simone? In this there are those of us who are inclined to take my father's view of the matter; indeed, we are inclined to feel that if ever the last detail of all that bewildering tangle of cross-purposes which went to make up that fateful Christmas Eve were finally unearthed and laid fair and square before an impartial jury, Signor Simone would not have a leg left to stand on. On the other hand, there is also, without doubt, a certain amount of reasonableness in the position taken by my mother—that is, that my father would have been much better off if, in the first place, he had gracefully withdrawn and let Signor Simone go ahead and *be* Santa Claus, since his heart seemed so set on it; still, can one exactly blame my father? After all, why *should* he have given in? Who did Signor Simone think he was anyway? Simply because he was Gianpaolo's wife's second cousin.

81

But let us not anticipate. To begin at the beginning:

It was a couple of weeks before Christmas that we first learned of the great gathering which our *paesanos*, the Maccaluccis, were planning on having that Christmas Eve. (May God help us forget it, as my mother wailed afterwards.) The celebration was to have a dual function, for not only were we to gather in humble memory of the Holy One, we were also to give honor to Erminio, the Maccaluccis' second son, who was returning for his Christmas vacation from the seminary where he was studying to become a priest. They were going to have a great celebration—cards, music, dancing, as well as the traditional Christmas Eve supper, and they had invited all of their friends.

Gianpaolo grew very excited as he told us about it. Like all peasant-Italians, he had a devout respect for holidays and formal occasions of any description, especially those of a churchly origin, and if necessary he would have mortgaged his house in order to celebrate this Christmas in a fitting manner—but fortunately such a drastic measure was not necessary. As usual, it was my father who provided the necessary finances—fifty dollars, to be exact. ("He must think you really *are* Santa Claus," said my mother.) But to proceed:—

All, no doubt, would have gone without mishap, had it not been for the unexpected arrival, some ten days or so before Christmas, of Mrs. Maccalucci's second cousin, Silvestro Simone. (Accursed be his name!) He was an imposing individual, matching, in fleshly bulk, the two hundred odd pounds with which Heaven (and my mother's spaghetti) had adorned my father; he had a face like a beefsteak, a voice like a steam roller, and a huge belly which seemed almost too much for the rest of him to carry around. This man, this contemptible, loathsome scoundrel, had worked alongside my father and Gianpaolo in the Colorado coal mines of their youth, but it had been nearly thirty years since he and my father had seen each other. ("Could he not have made it thirty more?" wailed my mother.) During this time, much water, as the old saw has it, had flowed under many bridges; the passing years had carried my father and Gianpaolo many miles from those dark tunnels beneath the earth in which they had spent their first years in this country. These same years had carried Signor Simone many miles from the coal mines also, but in a different direction; for, while Gianpaolo and my father, imitating the course of the sun, had traveled westward, arriving, by successive stages, in California, Simone had journeyed east. He had been married (as we were to hear a dozen times from his own lips) three times; he had had six children by his first wife, four by his second, and eight by his last. ("By God, Luigi, I bet you can't beat *that* record!" he roared to my father.) During these years he had been in one business after another—saloon keeper, restaurant owner, hotel proprietor; and he had wound up in Boston (where he had spent the past six years) as the proprietor of a fancy Italian grocery.

I I

So much for a few brief facts about this reprehensible individual. Would any of us have resented him on the basis, so to speak, of himself? In all fairness, I must say *I do not think so.* We did not begrudge him his money, the diamond-studded elk's tooth that dangled like a glittering eye from his stomach, the fancy Italian grocery (which from his description must have put to shame the Grand Central Terminal); certainly he could have had a dozen wives and fifty children for all we cared about it. What then? Just this—*we did not like his manner.* As my father so succinctly put it, who did Simone think he was anyway? He moved in on Gianpaolo, accompanied by his wife and the four youngest of their eight children, without warning, without apology, seeming to think that the mere fact of his presence was sufficient to put the Maccaluccis in a very ecstasy of appreciation; he ate their food, drank their wine, slept like a king in the paternal bed (which, for want of another, Mr. and Mrs. Maccalucci had had to give up to the Simones, themselves sleeping on a mattress in the attic); and he did not offer to buy even an ice-cream cone for the children! And there is something more, too. In the morning, when the children were waiting in line, so to speak, to get to the bathroom, he—but let us not go into that; enough is enough; suffice it to say that never, in all of our collective experience, had we run across anyone with such a positive genius for making himself offensive.

Does this not make understandable, then, my father's attitude in the matter? Had it been anyone but Simone (as my father himself will vehemently tell you), he would have withdrawn courteously at the first indication of a misunderstanding as to who was to play Santa Claus. But for nearly a week—that is to say, ever since the Simones had popped in from Boston for their 'visit'—we had been hearing reports, from Gianpaolo and Mrs. Maccalucci, about his patronizing behavior; and therefore when, at dinner the Sunday before Christmas (to which the Maccaluccis had invited us in order to meet their house guests), Simone gave indication that he himself had intentions of playing Santa Claus at the celebration, we were more than prepared to resent his presumptuousness.

Long before he proclaimed his intention, however, my father had had more than enough of Signor Simone. He had never liked him, even back in the old days (as he later confessed), but in spite of this dislike, which he had almost forgotten, and which had been revived by the reports Gianpaolo had been relaying to us regarding his guest's behavior, he had looked forward to seeing Simone again, to reminisce about the days of their youth, to discuss old names, old friends, old experiences which they had had in common—this was the spirit in which, accompanied by my mother and me, he had gone to the Maccaluccis' for dinner, prepared, that is to say, to ignore all the ancient dislike and to meet Simone as an old friend, found again after many years of parting, with whom he could drink a glass or two of cordial wine for the sake of the old times. And did Simone make such an agreeable reunion possible? Did he, indeed? *I will*

84

present only the simple facts. Would you like to know the first remark he made to my father as we entered the house?

"Luigi Altieri!" he roared, pumping my father's hand and nearly knocking him down with a terrific blow in the small of his back. "You alive after all these years? By God, I thought you'd be dead long before now!"

This, the greeting he gave to my father; and to my mother?

"Rosa, Rosa!" said he, as though reproachfully. "You still? But how have you been able to endure each other?" And then he laughed, and threw his massive arms about her. "But how fat you've become!" he cried. "*Per Dio,* I should never have known you!"

My father, trying to recover his breath, which had been knocked out of his lungs by the pounding Simone had given him, coughed, sputtered, wheezed; my mother extended one cheek for the kiss which Simone straightaway implanted on it through his mustache.

"And this young man?" said Simone, fixing a curious eye upon me. "Your son, no doubt?"

"This is Robert, my youngest," said my mother coldly. "He is an artist."

"But no!" he said, his features expanding; and suddenly he clasped my hand in a grip that made my toes quiver. "An artist! Well, don't worry, I won't tell anyone!" he cried, and opening his mouth he let loose an extraordinary sound that seemed to begin somewhere in the innermost depths of that remarkable stomach and thence to billow up through his lungs and out of his throat like the mounting roar of a flood-burst; he laughed, chortled, groaned; the walls rocked, the diamond elk's tooth quivered; tears came to his eyes, and he slapped his stomach with his hands.

Was it then so humorous? We all stared; my mother coughed discreetly behind her handkerchief; I drew myself up, and—

But no matter.

III

Such was our introduction to this monster, but unfortunately our acquaintance did not end there; we had come to the Maccaluccis' for dinner, and to dinner we stayed. Meanwhile, we met Mrs. Simone, a pale, ferret-eyed wisp of a woman, and the Simone children, two boys, two girls, the oldest ten, the youngest five; Mr. and Mrs. Maccalucci hovered around us anxiously, took our hats and coats, pulled out chairs, poured some wine; and at last we sat down to dinner.

In the meantime, Simone plied my father with questions: how had he fared during all these years?

"One thing is sure, you haven't starved!" he said, glancing jocularly at my father's stomach. "Do you have so many friends, then?"

My father laughed politely and muttered something behind his moustache; and at that moment the spaghetti arrived.

"Ah!" said Simone, tucking his napkin into his collar contentedly; and forthwith proceeded to heap a good half of the platter onto his own plate.

Midway through the meal the talk turned to the forthcoming Christmas celebration, and then it was that Simone made the remark which, like a lighted match tossed carelessly into a haystack, started everything.

"I have been told," said he to my father in Italian, "that you are planning to play Santa Claus for the children?" And, before my father could answer, "That will have to be changed," said he (precisely, as my father remarked afterward, as though he *owned* the place). "For the past five years I have played Santa Claus for my children, and," said he (waving his fork in the air), "they would not know you, they would think you were an impostor—"

"But, my good friend," began my father courteously, glancing timidly toward Gianpaolo, whose face had turned blood-red . . .

"And besides," Simone continued obliviously, "you have not got the figure for it. Look!" he cried, pounding his stomach. "You should see what a Santa Claus I make—ain't that so?" he added in sudden English to his wife.

At this point Gianpaolo, who had been making an ill-concealed attempt to disguise his mounting anger, exploded into action.

"Eet'sa too late!" he said, so excited that he too lapsed into English, which language, for some reason, he invariably used when he wished to be emphatic. "Eet'sa too late!" he repeated, and then, finding he could not go on without resorting to his native tongue, he let forth a torrent of voluble Italian. The plans had all been made, he explained heatedly. It was impossible to change them now!

But why? Simone demanded. What difference did it make? It made lots of difference! said Gianpaolo. The plans had been made, and and made they must stay. *It was too late to change them!* At this point a gleam came into Simone's eyes. And what of his children? he demanded. How would they feel to see an unfamiliar Santa Claus? That could not be helped, said Gianpaolo, his own eyes glinting; Simone's were not the only children who would be present; *did Simone by any chance think the celebration was given for his special benefit?*

"*Sangue de la Madonna!*" bellowed Simone, crashing his fist against the table. "What do you mean by that?"

87

Gianpaolo leaped up from his chair, quivering with fury. Simone rose like a great shaggy bear to meet him.

"Stop!" cried my father, getting between them. What nonsense! he added. He would gladly withdraw in favor of Simone—

Not for one moment, said Gianpaolo, looking venomously at Simone. *The plans had been made, and made they must stay!*

Simone shrugged and sat down again; finally Gianpaolo resumed his seat, and we went on with the dinner as though nothing had happened.

The question of who was to play Santa Claus at the celebration was not mentioned again, but once or twice I caught Simone giving furtive glances both to Gianaoplo and to my father. Ah, had we but known what lay behind those glances!

But we did not know. The following afternoon my father (despite the warnings of my mother that he had better mind his own business) went downtown, as per arrangement, and rented himself a resplendent Santa Claus outfit; and so the great day arrived.

I V

It was not yet five o'clock when we approached the Maccaluccis' that fateful Christmas Eve, but already darkness had fallen. It had been drizzling all afternoon, and the streets were filled with puddles; long before we got to the house itself we heard the sounds of the gathering; the windows were ablaze with light, and we could hear singing and laughter, the lilting strains of an accordion, the strum of guitars. They had put holly wreaths and silver crosses in the windows, and through the panes we could see the shadowy forms of people moving about.

My father hid the box containing his Santa Claus outfit in the back of the car, and we went up the steps and into the house. There, in the small living room, dining room, and kitchen, upwards of fifty people were gathered. There was a huge fire roar-

ing in the living-room fireplace, and underneath the Christmas
tree stood a miniature manger, complete with the infant Christ,
the Virgin Mother, and the Three Wise Men of Bethlehem, all
in tiny figures of wax; the walls and ceiling were festooned with
ribbons of colored paper and the tip of the tree was crowned
with a gleaming star. As Gianpaolo proudly told us, no expense
had been spared to make the celebration a magnificent one; he
had invited all his friends and their children and the tables
groaned beneath the pitchers of wine, and the house was filled
with the tantalizing odors of the feast which the women were
preparing.

In the midst of all this sat, in lordly fashion, Simone, en-
sconced in the most comfortable chair in the house, a goblet of
wine in one huge hand; he nodded to us coolly as we entered,
and I thought I saw a peculiar gleam, as though of calculation,
come into his eyes as we went past him into the bedroom to
dispose of our hats and coats.

Our arrival had interrupted the music and singing, but as
soon as we had greeted the assembled guests and paid our re-
spects to Erminio, who, since he was one day to be a priest, was
treated with considerable awe by the rest, we found places and
joined in the festivities. The accordionist and guitar players
formed as it were a hub, from which all the other activity radi-
ated; almost all joined in in the singing, and we heard again and
again the familiar melodies of the land from which we had
stemmed,—O Sole Mio, Ciribiribin, Santa Lucia—folksongs,
too, the songs of the field and the plough, deep in the memories
of the oldest present; my father beamed and swayed and shouted;
my mother nodded her head with a far-away look in her eyes. . . .

As it neared time to eat, the gathering became increasingly
exuberant; the wine flowed more and more freely, faces became
flushed, voices grew louder; the musicians perspired and struggled with their instruments and the house rocked to the sound
of stamping feet and clapping hands. In the midst of all this, it

was announced that the feast was ready, and in a few moments more great steaming platters were brought in and laid upon the tables set in the living and dining rooms.

In obedience to the Catholic custom, there was no meat. The main courses were of spaghetti with a savory sauce composed of olive oil flavored with garlic, parsley, and ground hot peppers; a dozen different kinds of fish, fried peppers in oil, olives, three or four kinds of salads, roasted chestnuts, a dozen varieties of Italian pastry drenched in honey, dates, dried figs, fresh grapes and apples and oranges. . . . For upwards of two hours we sat and gorged ourselves, while the flickering candles grew shorter and shorter, and the wind lashed the rain against the windows, and the logs crackled in the fireplace. Gallon after gallon of wine had been consumed, and by the time the feast was over there was not an adult present, at least among the men, who remained sober.

And what of Simone, during all this? He ate and drank as much as any four people present, making slanderous remarks, all the while, regarding the food: the spaghetti had not been salted enough, the fish was undercooked, the olives were dry. . . . Several times it looked as though Gianpaolo, who was seated opposite him across the table, were on the point of throwing some of the cutlery in his direction; but nothing, fortunately, happened, and the meal was concluded without mishap.

As soon as we had finished, the tables were cleared of everything save the fresh fruit, the nuts, and the wine, and the festivities recommenced. In obedience to the Italian custom, the plans were to eat, drink, and make merry all the night long, then go in a troop to early-morning Mass, then return for the Christmas Day dinner. Those who wished could catch an hour or two's sleep in the meantime, but usually there were few, aside from some of the oldest, who slept; the festivities by tradition usually continued without let-up from the afternoon of Christmas Eve on through Christmas Day.

Signor Santa

V

It was now approaching ten o'clock, but the exuberance had not abated. At the tables the men played cards, shouting and slapping their hands on the table as they brought the cards down; the women busied themselves washing the dishes and cleaning up the kitchen; some of the younger couples danced. And through all this the children ran about playing games, shouting, crying, throwing candies and cookies at each other . . . frantic mothers scurried about, trying to control their off-spring . . . an argument or two developed amongst the card players . . . someone spilled a pitcher of wine on the floor . . . yes, everything was progressing beautifully.

And then the fateful hour of midnight approached.

The plans, which my father and his *paesano* had gone over carefully a hundred times, were as follows: a few minutes before midnight my father was to take his Santa Claus outfit and go out in the back to the garage. Here a great sack had been hidden, filled with presents for the children. In the house, meanwhile, the children were to be herded into the living room, around the Christmas tree. Promptly at the stroke of midnight my father was to appear, dressed as Santa Claus, the sack of presents slung over his shoulder.

These, the plans; and what happened?

Fifteen minutes or so before midnight, my father and his *paesano* exchanged a knowing glance. My father coughed, glanced at the children blandly, then, motioning to me to follow him, he got up from the table and went out the front door. We got the box with the Santa Claus suit from the car, then went around the house and to the back, where Gianpaolo was waiting for us in the garage. In a few minutes we had helped my father change into the Santa Claus suit, with its red coat and pantaloons; he stood up proudly and stroked the white whiskers which enveloped his ruddy face like a cloud.

"Well, how do I look?" he demanded.

But he looked magnificent! Gianpaolo reassured him, in a very ecstasy of enthusiasm; he straightened the coat, patted my father's stomach, tucked one sagging corner of the trousers into the boots. Magnificent, magnificent! he repeated. And now for the presents, he added, turning to a canvas which had been laid over some jugs in one corner of the garage, where the sack of presents had been hidden. He lifted the canvas—and then it was that we gained our first inkling that all was not to happen, this fateful eve, as planned. *The sack with the presents had disappeared.*

"*Sangue de la Madonna!*" Gianpaolo ejaculated, wrinkling his forehead in agony, and staring at the blank space beneath the canvas. He tore the canvas off frantically and began to search among the jugs, throwing them this way and that wildly.

But what was the matter? asked my father courteously.

Matter! said Gianpaolo. The presents—*someone had stolen them!*

What? said my father. But that was impossible!

At that moment, from the direction of the house, we heard a familiar voice calling our *paesano's* name.

"Gianpaolo, Gianpaolo!"

We rushed out into the yard. Mrs. Maccalucci was running toward us, her hair flying wildly in the drizzling rain.

"What's-a-matter?" cried her husband.

"Simone!" she gasped, then began to wail some more and wring her hands. Gianpaolo grabbed her by the shoulders and shook her.

"*What's-a-matter?*" he repeated.

Simone had stolen the presents and, dressed in a Santa Claus suit of his own, was even now preparing to give them out to the children!

"*Corpo di Bacco!*" bellowed Gianpaolo, and, pushing her aside, he ran toward the house, followed by my father and me.

We rushed up the back steps, through the kitchen, through

the dining room, into the living room—and sure enough, there he was, surrounded by the awe-struck children, dressed in a resplendent red Santa Claus suit, complete with whiskers and all.

"*Simone!*" screamed Gianpaolo.

And do you know what Simone did? *He turned and looked at us blandly!*

"*Che fai,* what are you doing?" stuttered Gianpaolo, so beside himself he could hardly talk.

"But can you not see?" retorted Simone suavely. "I am giving the children their presents!"

"You? You?" cried Gianpaolo; then, "Monster!" he cried, and, leaping forward on his short bandy legs, he swung his fist against Simone's jaw. Simone ducked, and with a push of one huge paw knocked Gianpaolo to the floor. My father stared at his undersized friend, where he lay on the floor, then turned to Simone.

"So!" he said; and without another word he leaped upon his friend's assailant. The women screamed, the children whimpered and wailed, the other male guests began milling around excitedly; and in the middle of all this my father and Simone groaned, flailed, tugged. Suddenly my father dealt Simone a resounding smack that knocked him into the fireplace. He bellowed and struggled to regain his feet; suddenly the flames leaped over him and his whiskers caught fire.

"*Mamma mia!*" he screamed. "Help, help!"

From victorious antagonist my father turned abruptly to the rôle of rescuer; he reached forward and pulled Simone upright, slapping at the whiskers to put the fire out. Simone, however, apparently mistook these friendly blows as the signal of a new attack; he hit back; they began to wrestle; suddenly my father's own whiskers caught fire.

They released each other and began dancing around, pulling at their smouldering whiskers. Someone threw a pitcher of wine over them; then all at once there was a scream:—

"Fire! Fire!"

The paper festoons had caught flame; in a moment more the fire had swept to the curtains and the ceiling; pandemonium broke loose. Hysterical mothers grabbed for their children; the men rushed back and forth from the kitchen frantically, bearing buckets and pans of water; someone put in a call for the fire wagon.

From this point on so many things happened at once it is impossible to relate them with any pretense of order; the fire wagons arrived with much clanging of bells and screaming of sirens, and a great crowd of people collected in the street. We had already put out the fire, however, and presently the engines departed. Meanwhile a couple of police patrol cars arrived on the scene, and to these worthy guardians of the public morale much explanation had to be given before they could be persuaded not to herd "the whole damn bunch of us" down to the station. Simone, upon orders of his erstwhile host, packed his clothes (still maintaining stubbornly that it was all a misunderstanding, that his intentions had been the most honorable), and, accompanied by his wife and children, departed in a huff for a hotel; then the guests, one by one, began to leave. At the last, none were left save the Maccaluccis and their own children, my mother and father, and me. My mother and Mrs. Maccalucci were weeping; we sat desolately amidst, as it were, the ruins, and surveyed the charred walls and ceiling, the water-drenched furniture, the sorry remains of the magnificent Christmas tree.

"*Per l'amore di Dio!*" wailed Gianpaolo. "Cousin or no cousin—if I ever see him again I'll kill him!"

At that moment there was the sound of someone coming up the front steps, then entering the house.

"But who can that be?" muttered Gianpaolo, and, mumbling to himself, he started to rise.

At that moment—yes!—we saw the countenance and figure

of Simone (carrying an umbrella archly) appear in the doorway.

He stood and looked at us all haughtily.

"Excuse me," he said coldly. "I forgot my shaving brush."

Gianpaolo stared at him; then suddenly he let out a scream, and, picking up a long knife from the table, he started after Simone. Simone stared at the knife, paled, dropped the umbrella, then, whirling around, started pellmell down the steps, with Gianpaolo hard after him.

VI

These, then, are the simple facts of the case. In conclusion it may be added that Gianpaolo received thirty days for attempted assault with a deadly weapon; Simone, on the other hand, went scot-free, and even now, no doubt, is back in that magnificent Italian grocery in Boston, safely barricaded behind his salami and cheese. Is this, then, justice? On top of all that, my father had to foot the bill for the damages—one hundred and six dollars and eighty cents, to be exact. It is such things that make my mother bitter. If my father had not been so *stubbornly insistent* in the first place, says she, all might have turned out differently; as it was—But enough of all that; we shall leave it for the reader to judge.

The Three Wise Men of Totenleben

ALEXANDER LERNET-HOLENIA

IN THE MONTH of November of the year 1647, the commander-in-chief of the French forces during the Thirty Years
War, Marshal Turenne, set out on a long journey on horseback. He wished to inspect, in person, certain advance positions
of his army, at that occupying the Palatinate. On that occasion,
his horsemen picked up two young people who were traveling
through the country poorly clad and on foot. One was a young
man, the other a blonde young woman; both looked miserable.
The woman was pregnant, perhaps already in her seventh or
eighth month. Questioned, they replied they were husband and
wife, who had been forced to leave the place where they had
hitherto been living, with the wife's parents, where the husband
had plied his trade, because everything had been put to the
torch by the soldiers. They were now on their way to the husband's home—a village called Totenleben on the lower Main
River, where they hoped to find living quarters and perhaps
some means of livelihood as well, for they possessed nothing
but the clothes on their backs, and their hopes for the child
about to be born.

Marshal Turenne, whose mind had been otherwise occupied
during this recital, took in only a few snatches of this cross-
examination, conducted as it was in German. Nevertheless he
noted the odd name of the village* which was the goal of the
two young people. He dismissed them, and then reached a
strange decision.

One night of this same extraordinarily severe winter, he sud-

* Totenleben, or roughly "Where the Dead Live."

96

denly appeared, accompanied by a troop of horsemen, in the region of the lower Main.

Both he and his men were armed to the teeth and wrapped in warm coats and furs. The moon glistened on their helmets. All the land around was devastated. Preceding the troop by some hundred paces, two horsemen with rifles in their hands stopped now and again in front of a clump of snow-covered bushes or at the ruins of a burned farm and cried out: "Who goes there?" But there was no one to answer. The whole region lay still as in death, only a few savage dogs fled across the snowy fields, continuing their howling from the distance. As they passed by a place of execution, the remains of a corpse dangled from the gallows. As the calvacade pressed steadily forward, silver hoarfrost spun its web in the icy ruts.

The riders stopped at the edge of a wood. Turenne dismounted from his steed and two henchmen, apparently according to orders previously given, approached him and removed his fur coat and hat. The moonlight gleamed on his cuirass and on the gold chain he wore around his neck.

Meanwhile, several of his officers had gotten off their horses and approached him while the serving men pulled a very strange garment over his armor. It was a white robe, bespangled with golden stars. They covered his face with a black veil. The whole was the costume for the eve of Twelfth Night, such as waits or carol singers wear.

And now the servants took the pistols from his saddlebag, and placed them in his hands.

"I am going now," he said to his officers. "Do you, my lords, wait for me here. If I have not returned by three o'clock in the morning, then have the village searched for me."

"Yes, your excellency," was the officers' reply. The Marshal departed alone, trudging over the field of snow.

He had walked several hundred paces when the silhouette of a village suddenly appeared before him. At its northern boundary a light was shining. Toward this he made his way. The beam

97

came from a peculiar lantern made out of oiled paper in the shape of a star, and attached to a pole some eight feet high.

Two men, one of whom carried the pole, stood by the light. They, too, wore the costume of waits, though the veils they wore were white.

Turenne raised his pistols and stepped up to them as he gave his own name. The two answered, giving their names: "Wrangel," and "Melander." They were, respectively, the commander-in-chief of the Swedes, newly appointed after Torstenson's retirement, and the Supreme Chief of the Imperial Armies, Count Melander of Holzapfel.

All three of them now raised their veils and looked into one another's eyes, then let the veils fall once more over their faces. Turenne hid his pistols under the silk sash that he wore under his robe, and said: "I have asked you gentlemen to come here in this disguise so that we may be able to discuss the matters that concern us, undisturbed and in secret. This is the eve of Twelfth Night and we shall be taken for waits. We would do best to proceed to the village now, to find quarters where we can begin our deliberations."

"There is no longer any village," said Melander. "It has been burned to the ground. Your own troops, Count, may have set fire to it."

"It may have been done by your troops, Count," replied Turenne.

"Be that as it may," said Wrangel, "we ought to see to it that we find some shelter somewhere. Surely we do not want to stand about here in the cold."

Accordingly they began to move on with their star. Along the village street there were only heaps of rubble where once there had been houses. But near the burned out church they managed to find a house passably preserved, with its windows boarded up. A faint light shone from between the boards.

They went up to the door and knocked. They had to do this

98

German, 15th century. The Three Kings

repeatedly before a voice from within inquired what they wanted.

"Open the door," they called, whereupon the door, which no longer had any hinges, was pulled back a bit with a creak. A man stuck his head out.

"What's your business?" he asked.

"We are waits," said Melander, "Let us in."

"Waits?" the man asked. "So early?"

"Yes," said Melander, "Let us in."

And with these words, he crossed the threshold, followed by the two others, after they had put aside the pole with the lantern.

"But look here," said the man, after closing the door behind them, "today is only Christmas Eve."

"No, indeed," said Wrangel, "it's Twelfth Night. Do you people here still go by the old calendar? We've already got a new one."

"What sort of a new one?" the man asked.

"The pope has changed the calendar," said Melander. "It was already fourteen days behind, and no longer agreed with the position of the stars. Don't you know that? Didn't your priest tell you that?"

"Our priest has been dead for a long time," said the man. "The Swedes killed him; the village is in ruins; the whole countryside is desolate. How should we know whether the pope has changed the calendar or not? We are celebrating Christmas Eve today, if you can still call it celebrating."

"Well," said Wrangel, "never mind. We would like to stay here for a while. Bring us something to eat and a couple of glasses of wine. We'll pay you in good honest coin."

"I used to be the innkeeper here," said the man, "and my business prospered. But now I have scarcely bread enough for my own family, and if we are thirsty, we have to drink melted snow, for our wells are all stopped up. Sit down, for a seat is all I have to offer. What manner of men are you to believe that

100

you can get alms by singing as waits? Where do you come from? Here, in this village, we are the only ones left alive; and there is not a grain of wheat or a single beast left in the whole region. Everything has been destroyed by the war. They say that in the Henneberg district people have even eaten the corpses of the dead. How much longer will this war go on?"

The three commanders shrugged their shoulders and looked about them. All they saw was a hearth on which a fire cast its flickering light, and a table with a few benches around it. Smoke filled the room. The innkeeper's wife and a half-grown boy— both of them alarmingly emaciated—were watching the strangers. In addition, there were two other people in the room—a young man and his young, blonde wife. Turenne recognized them as the same two whom he had encountered on his reconnaissance trip.

"Who are they?" he asked in faulty German.

"They are poor people," said the innkeeper, "who came to this place but who could find no shelter anywhere. The man was originally from here; he moved away and got married. But he had to come back, and now I've given them a lodging in the stable. The wife is expecting a child."

"You don't say!" said Turenne. The three strangers sat down at the table.

In the meantime, the others busied themselves near the hearth setting up a Christmas crèche of moss and small wooden figures. The innkeeper still had the figures, since the marauding soldiers had not thought them worth taking. They were brightly colored and represented the Holy Family, the angels, the adoring Magi, the shepherds, the ox and the ass.

For a while the three generals looked on; then they began their talk. They spoke in French.

"The peace talks that started at Muenster last year," said Turenne, "are not being conducted in the interest of the armies. If peace were really to come, there would be no need to have armed forces. But the soldier has grown accustomed to making

101

his living by soldiering, and we, his leaders, have the responsibility for his livelihood. And to speak frankly, war has become a trade like any other. I do not know what you gentlemen may think about this, but I, for my part, will leave nothing undone to prevent the war from ending in such a way as to cause us and our men to lose our predominant role, and run the risk of being driven away at a moment's notice. To discuss together what measures should be taken against the conclusion of an overhasty peace is the purpose of my invitation. For even though we are enemies, we are all in the same boat; however you look at it, what's good for one is good for all three of us."

When those who were setting up the crèche heard the talk in a foreign language, they looked over at the three in surprise. For a time the innkeeper listened anxiously, then he approached the table:

"Who are you?" he asked. "You are no ordinary waits. You are foreigners and perhaps soldiers as well. What is your business here? Haven't you convinced yourself by this time that this country, this village, this house are in ruins and that there's nothing more for you to carry off? What do you want from us? Are you freebooters or spies? Have you been sent by those who want to take our very lives? That is the only thing you can still take from us."

"Be still," said Melander, "we are the Three Wise Men, and that's all. Don't disturb us, we have to discuss something here." And he threw him a golden coin.

The innkeeper looked at the shining gold piece, for he had not seen its like for many a long year. He took it quickly and tested it with his fingers. At the same time, his bearing changed completely. He wanted to look into the faces of the three, yet his glance could not penetrate their veils. Only now did he notice the boots and spurs visible below their robes, and the metal ends of their leather sword-sheaths.

"Your pardon, My Lords!" he said, bowing obsequiously, "I would not for the world—I did not know—"

"Very well, very well," said Melander, "leave us alone."

"May we at least," said the innkeeper, "sing the Christmas song for the gentlemen? It will not disturb you?"

"Sing it, for all I care," said Melander, "but do it quietly. Don't make a hullaballoo!"

Retreating backwards and continuing to bow very low, the innkeeper withdrew. He whispered to his people, showing them the gold piece. The others looked over at the three, then the innkeeper's wife advanced and kissed Melander's hand to thank him. "Never mind, never mind," said Melander, and took no notice whatever of her. Meanwhile the talk in French went on. After some time, those around the crèche began to sing the Christmas song. They sang it softly in moving, tender tones.

Towards the end of the song, the young wife stopped singing; she tottered, and clung to her husband. Her pains had begun.

Had it not been for the strangers, the innkeeper would have allowed her to remain in the room and have her baby there. But in the presence of the others he did not dare to do this. The woman was led into the stable where she lay on a pile of moss and dead leaves.

The generals had not noticed when the song was interrupted nor when the woman was led out of the room. They were in the habit of disregarding others as so much chaff. They went on with their talk; the French sentences were interrupted by the names *Torstenson, Jan of Werth, Max Emanuel.* For some unknown reason, suddenly the generals appeared to be at odds now, and their voices rose in excitement. It was Melander who pronounced himself most emphatically as against continuation of the war. He said that surely the country was sufficiently desolate, it was plain to see how poverty-stricken the people had become here as well as elsewhere; there was undoubtedly some truth in the innkeeper's story of cannibalism. For some time reports had been coming in that after certain battles people had appeared at night on the battlefields to dismember the dead bodies, and roast and consume them.

And so the three went on quarreling until a cry and then another was heard coming from the stable. Then they looked up.

"What's the matter?" asked Wrangel. But now all was quiet. "Wherever are those fellows?" he asked. He rose from the table, went to the door leading to the stable, and beat on it with the butt of his pistol.

Some little time passed before the innkeeper appeared.

"Who screamed out there?" asked Wrangel. "What is going on out there?"

"Oh, Sir!" said the innkeeper. "Oh, Sir!" and a very strange expression came over his face.

"What is it?" Wrangel cried, "What's the matter?"

"Just imagine, Sir," said the innkeeper, "while you were sitting there, something happened. It's been such a long time since anything like that has happened here. There were always strange soldiers who murdered, struck down and burned and then there were always fewer and fewer people here. But now another soul has been added, once more. The young wife gave birth to a child, a boy. Perhaps, after all, peace will come soon. Don't you want to come and look at the child, gentlemen?"

The three looked at one another. At first they perhaps intended asking the innkeeper if he had lost his mind, bothering them like this, and telling him to go to the devil. But then perhaps one or the other of them recalled the time when a child was born in his own family and what rejoicing there had been. Or perhaps they thought of the day when they themselves had been children. And Turenne may have been thinking for a moment of the woman's blonde hair.

For a long time they had not heard anyone speak in tones such as the innkeeper used. The child was the child of strangers, it was no concern of his, and yet he was as moved as if it had indeed been his own. For here, in this destroyed countryside, resembling an icy waste covered with the corpses of the dead, a child had begun to live—bringing a breath of spring. In the midst of the triumph of death, which was the daily business of the generals, a child had been born, and it seemed as if it had been born also unto them.

The first to step through the threshhold of the stable door was Melander. He was followed by Wrangel, and then Turenne. There lay the woman on her bed of straw, her face was white as snow, in the light of the pine torch her hair shone like spun gold. The others knelt around her as they wrapped the baby in a few odds and ends of old rags and laid the child in her arms.

The generals stood there in silence and gazed upon the mother and child for a long time. Then Turenne removed the golden chain which he wore under his Twelfth Night robe, and placed it near the child. Melander pulled off his glove and took a ruby ring from his finger, and Wrangel laid a pouch full of money down on the bed of straw.

To those who received the gifts it seemed as if a miracle had happened. The young man wanted to express his faltering thanks, but was not able to utter a single word. For the generals suddenly declined such thanks almost disdainfully. Altogether they appeared to be somewhat embarrassed by what they had just done. They found an excuse for themselves in looking upon it as a mere whim, such as highborn gentlemen sometimes indulge in. They soon departed, leaving behind them their strange lantern, and ordered the innkeeper, who was chattering and laughing and who continued to wipe his eyes, to stay behind when he wanted to accompany them.

At the outskirts of the village, they saluted one another curtly and each one went on his way, their talk unfinished.

But in their hearts was peace.

TRANSLATED BY JUDITH BERNAYS HELLER

Christmas with the Goblins

ZACHRIS TOPELIUS

O N Christmas Eve the pretty little house yonder at the corner of the street was brilliantly lighted. A large Christmas tree stood upon the table, its shining boughs covered with fine stars, sweets, and apples. The children within doors found it impossible to keep still whenever any one knocked or made a noise without. They had not to wait long, however, before the Yule Goat[1] arrived, and asked as usual whether the children had been good? With one voice they all answered "Yes."

"Very well," said the Yule Goat; "but I must tell you that this year I bring only half as many Christmas boxes as usual; still, if you have been good you shall all be boxed."

"Why have you only half as many this year?" asked the children.

"I will tell you why," said the Yule Goat. "I come far from the north, and on my road here I have peeped in at the door of so many poor cottages, and seen so many little children who have not even a piece of bread for Christmas Eve this year,[2] that, I have given half my Christmas boxes to them. Was I right in doing so?"

"Yes, yes, that was right, that was kindly done," cried the children. But Fredrik and Lotta held their tongues, for Fredrik used generally to get twenty Christmas boxes, and Lotta thirty, and it seemed to them very unfair that they should only get half as many this time.

---

[1] A person dressed up as a goat, who brings Christmas presents to the children.
[2] A year when there was a great famine in Finland.

"Was not I right in doing so?" asked the Yule Goat for the second time.

Fredrik turned on his heel, and answered sulkily, "What a shabby Christmas this is! I am sure the very goblins have a better one than you have brought us this year."

Then Lotta began to pout in her turn, and said, "Shan't I get more than fifteen Christmas boxes? I am sure the goblins will have a far better Christmas tonight."

"Very well," said the Yule Goat, "if you think so, I can take you to the goblins at once," and saying this, he seized Fredrik and Lotta one by each hand, and carried them away in spite of their struggles to get loose.

On and on they went, quick as lightning through the air. Before the children had time to speak they found themselves in the middle of a large forest, surrounded by snow. It was frightfully cold; the snow whirled round them so fast that they could scarcely see the lofty fir trees which stood in the darkness about them, and close by they heard the wolves howl. Then the Yule Goat left them at once; he had no time to wait, for he had many children still to visit that evening who deserved his coming far more than Fredrik and Lotta.

Both the children began to scream and cry, but the more they shouted the nearer the wolves howled.

"Come, Lotta," said Fredrik; "we must try to find some cottage in the forest."

"I think I see a light over there amongst the trees," said Lotta; "let us go to it."

"No, I am sure it isn't a light," said Fredrik; "it is only icicles that glitter in the darkness upon the trees."

"I think I see a great mountain before us," said Lotta. "Can it be Rastekaïs, the trolls' mountain, you know, where Sampo Lappelill rode on the wolf of the mountain king?"

"What nonsense you talk!" answered Fredrik; "Rastekaïs is at least 450 miles from our home. But come on, we will go up the mountain, we can see better from there."

No sooner said than done. They scrambled through huge snowdrifts, and climbed over bushes and fallen trees, and after a time they arrived at the mountain. There was a little door in the mountain, and through this a faint light shone out. Fredrik and Lotta followed this light, and soon discovered to their great amazement that it was Rastekaïs after all, and that now they were actually with the goblins. But it was too late to turn back, and besides that the wolves were so close behind them that they almost peeped in through the door.

Full of fear and amazement, Fredrik and Lotta stopped close within the door, and saw before them a large hall, in which trolls and goblins were keeping Christmas. There were many thousands of them assembled, all very short, hardly two feet in height, dressed in grey, with wrinkled faces, moving quickly about, just as they are described in the story of Sampo Lappelill. They were not afraid of the dark, for instead of candles they had frozen glow-worms and rotten tree-twigs, which shone like phosphorus in the dark. But when they wanted to make a grand illumination they stroked a large black cat on the back till it sparkled, and then many amongst them shrieked, "Stop, stop! it is far too light; no one can stand such a glare."

It is a peculiarity of all trolls and goblins in the world that they hate light, and feel wretched when anybody happens to see them. For this reason they were holding a feast at Christmastide; having observed that the days were becoming shorter and shorter as the end of the year approached, and the nights longer and longer. And they thought, as they think every Christmas—(for one is apt to believe what one wishes to take place)—that at last there would be no more day, only one long night; and this idea made them so wildly happy that they danced in the mountain, and kept a merry Christmas after their own fashion, for they were all heathens, and did not know of any better way of celebrating the festival.

It was easy to see that the trolls did not suffer from the cold. They offered each other lollipops of ice during the cold winter night, and blew upon them to cool them, lest they should be too warm. They also handed round a dainty dish, made of fern and spiders' legs; and they had a Christmas tree of ice crystals, and a little goblin to act as Yule Goat.

This year the gigantic cruel mountain king was not with the goblins. Ever since he exploded in a snowstorm at Enare parsonage no one knows what has become of him; many think that he has gone to Spitzbergen to reign in a heathen kingdom, and be as far away from Christian people as possible. He left his realm here in the north to the king of sin and darkness, whose name was Mundus, and who was now sitting in the midst of the hall. By his side sat the troll queen, her name was Caro (which is rather like a dog's name), and they both had long beards. They gave each other Christmas boxes just as other people do. King Mundus gave Queen Caro a pair of stilts, and when she mounted on them she thought herself the tallest and grandest lady in the whole world. Queen Caro gave King Mundus such an enormous pair of snuffers that he could snuff all the candles in the world with them, and as he snuffed them, he put them out. Many children would like to get a pair of snuffers like those as a Christmas box from the goblins.

King Mundus now rose from his throne, and made a very grand speech to the assembled trolls, in which he informed them that light would soon be at an end, and that shadows of darkness would spread forever over the world, which henceforth would

be governed by trolls. All the goblins and trolls shouted "Hurrah! Long live our great King Mundus and his beautiful Queen Carol Hurrah! Sin and darkness for ever! Hip, hip, hurrah!"

The King said, "Where is my chief watchman, whom I sent up to the top of the mountain to see whether any light still remains in the world?"

The watchman came and said, "Sir King, your power is great: all is darkness!"

After a while the King said again, "Where is my watchman?" and the watchman came.

"Sir King," he said, "far down on the horizon I see a small light, just like a twinkling star, coming out of a black cloud."

The King said, "Go back to the top of the mountain."

After a time the King said again, "Where is my watchman?" and the watchman came.

"Sir King," he said, "the sky is black with heavy snowclouds; I no longer see the little star."

The King said, "Go back to the top of the mountain."

After a time the King said, "Where is my watchman?" and the watchman came.

But now the King saw that the watchman trembled, and was quite blind.

The King asked, "My faithful watchman, why do you tremble, and how is it you have become blind?"

The watchman answered: "Sir King, the clouds have dispersed, and a star, larger and brighter than any other star, beams on the firmament: the sight of it struck me with blindness, and made me tremble."

The King said, "What does this betoken? Has not Light perished, and does not Darkness reign for ever?"

All the trolls and goblins round about stood dumb and awestruck; at last one amongst them said,

"Sir King, here by the door stand two children of men. Let us ask them, perhaps they know more than we."

"Bring the children here," said the King.

In an instant Fredrik and Lotta were dragged before the throne, and it is easy to imagine how frightened they felt.

The Queen noticed their great alarm, and said to one of the female goblins who stood near the throne, "Give those poor children some dragon-blood and some blackbeetle-shells to refresh themselves with, the poor things can't open their mouths."

"Eat and drink! eat and drink!" said the female goblin, but the children did not feel inclined to do that.

The King now said to the children, "You are in my power, and if I like I can change you into crows or spiders; but I will give you a riddle instead, and if you can guess its meaning I shall have you safely conducted back to your home. Do you agree to this?"

"Yes," said the children.

"Very well," said the King. "Why is it that a light rises in the darkest night of the year, when darkness and trolldom reign over the world, and all light seems to be gone? Far in the east shines a star, beaming with a lustre far more beautiful than all other stars, and threatening my power with destruction. Tell me, children, what does that star betoken?"

Lotta said, "It is the star that rises on Christmas night over Bethlehem in Judæa, giving light to the whole world."

The King asked, "Why does it shine thus?"

Fredrik answered, "Because this night our Saviour is born, and He is the Light that lightens up the whole world. From this night the light increases and the days become longer."

The King began to tremble violently on his throne, and asked again,

"What is the name of this Master and King of Light who is born tonight, and who comes to save the world from sin and darkness?"

Both the children answered, "Jesus Christ, the Son of God."

Hardly had they pronounced these words, when the mountain began to shake and tremble and fall together, and a storm-wind, rushing through the large hall, overturned the King's throne, and the star shone into the darkest dens and clifts. All the trolls and goblins disappeared like shadows and smoke, till there was nothing left but the Christmas tree of ice, which began to glitter and melt; and high above in the air the voices of angels were heard like sounds of harps. The children covered their faces with their hands, not daring to look up, and a sleepiness fell over them as if they were very tired, and they knew nothing more of what happened in the mountain.

When they woke up they were both in their beds, the fire burnt merrily, and old nurse Kajea, who always used to waken them, stood near the little beds and cried, "Make haste, and get up to go to church!"

Fredrik and Lotta sat up and looked with astonishment at Kajea, wondering if she could possibly be only two foot high and wear a beard, and want to give them dragon-blood and blackbeetle shells. But they soon saw the breakfast table standing ready, covered with Christmas cakes; and on this day all the children had coffee, which they did not get every day. In the streets they heard the clinking of sledge-bells, for people were driving past to church for the early morning service. Lights were burning in every window, but they shone brightest of all in the church windows.

Fredrik and Lotta looked at each other, but they did not dare to tell Kajea that they had been present at the goblins' Christmas. Perhaps she would not have believed them, but would have laughed, and told them that they had been sleeping in their own beds all through the night. You don't know, and I don't know, and in fact nobody exactly knows how it was. But if you know, and if I know, then we will pretend not to know; and if nobody knows, then nobody knows whether you know or I know; and now you know what I know (who know nothing), and it would be funny to know what you know, and whether you know more than I know.

One thing I know, and that is that sooner or later ungrateful children always come to the goblins. There they get icicle lolli-

pops, dragon-blood, and blackbeetles, instead of the nice presents they despise at home. For the king of sin and darkness lays
hold of them before they are aware of it. It is well for them,
then, if they can see a clear star rising above the darkness of the
world, and can name a Name before which all that is wicked in
the world falls down and perishes.

Fredrik and Lotta never forgot the goblins' Christmas. They
not only missed all their Christmas boxes, but they were also
ashamed of themselves. Yes, they were so much ashamed that
they did not dare to look up in church on Christmas morning.
All was bright and beautiful there; the Star of Bethlehem had
come down and brought light and radiance into all good children's glad eyes. Fredrik and Lotta saw this very clearly, but
they dared not look up themselves; they resolved that they
would become good children also. Have they kept their resolu-
tion? I don't know, but I hope they have. When you see them
you can ask them.

The Peace Egg

J. H. EWING

EVERY one ought to be happy at Christmas. But there are many things which ought to be, and yet are not; and people are sometimes sad even in the Christmas holidays.

The Captain and his wife were sad, though it was Christmas Eve. Sad, though they were in the prime of life, blessed with good health, devoted to each other and to their children, with competent means, a comfortable house on a little freehold property of their own, and, one might say, everything that the heart could desire. Sad, though they were good people, whose peace of mind had a firmer foundation than on their earthly goods alone; contented people, too, with plenty of occupation for mind and body. Sad—and in the nursery this was held to be past all reason—though the children were performing that ancient and most entertaining play or Christmas mystery of good St. George of England, known as *The Peace Egg*, for their benefit and behoof alone.

The play was none the worse that most of the actors were too young to learn parts, so that there was very little of the rather tedious dialogue, only plenty of dress and ribbons, and of fighting with the wooden swords. But though St. George looked bonny enough to warm any father's heart, as he marched up and down with an air learned from many a parade in barrack-square and drill-ground, and though the valiant Slasher did not cry in spite of falling hard and the Doctor treading accidentally on his little finger in picking him up, still the Captain and his wife sighed nearly as often as they smiled, and the mother dropped tears as well as pennies into the cap which the King of Egypt brought round after the performance.

114

The Peace Egg

Many years back, the Captain's wife had been a child herself, and had laughed to see the village mummers act the Peace Egg, and had been quite happy on Christmas Eve. Happy, though she had no mother. Happy, though her father was a stern man, very fond of his only child, but with an obstinate will that not even she dare thwart. She had lived to thwart it, and he had never forgiven her. It was when she married the Captain. The old man had a prejudice against soldiers, which was quite reason enough, in his opinion, for his daughter to sacrifice the happiness of her future life by giving up the soldier she loved. At last he gave her her choice between the Captain and his own favour and money. She chose the Captain, and was disowned and disinherited.

The Captain bore a high character, and was a good and clever officer, but that went for nothing against the old man's whim. He made a very good husband too, but even this did not move his father-in-law, who never held any intercourse with him or his wife since the day of their marriage, and who had never seen his own grandchildren. Though not so bitterly prejudiced as the old father, the Captain's wife's friends had their doubts about the marriage. The place was not a military station, and they were quiet country folk who knew very little about soldiers, whilst what they imagined was not altogether favorable to "red-coats," as they called them. Soldiers are well-looking generally, it is true (and the Captain was more than well-looking—he was handsome); brave, of course, it is their business (and the Captain had V. C. after his name, and several bits of ribbon on his patrol jacket). But then, thought the good people, they are here today and gone tomorrow, you "never know where you have them;" they are probably in debt, possibly married to several women in several foreign countries, and, though they are very courteous in society, who knows how they treat their wives when they drag them off from their natural friends and protectors to distant lands where no one can call them to account?

115

"Ah, poor thing!" said Mrs. John Bull, Jun., as she took off her husband's coat on his return from business, a week after the Captain's wedding, "I wonder how she feels? There's no doubt the old man behaved disgracefully, but it's a great risk marrying a soldier. It stands to reason military men aren't domestic; and I wish—Lucy Jane, fetch your papa's slippers quick!—she'd had the sense to settle down comfortably among her friends with a man that would have taken care of her."

"Officers are a wild set, I expect," said Mr. Bull, complacently, as he stretched his limbs in his own particular armchair, into which no member of his family ever intruded. "But the red-coats carry the day with plenty of girls who ought to know better. You women are always caught by a bit of finery. However, there's no use our bothering *our* heads about it. As she has brewed she must drink."

The Captain's wife's drinking was lighter and more palatable than her friends believed. The Captain (who took off his own coat when he came home, and never wore slippers but in his dressing-room) was domestic enough. A selfish companion must, doubtless, be a great trial amid the hardships of military life, but when a soldier is kind-hearted he is often a much more helpful and thoughtful and handy husband than an equally well-meaning civilian. Amid the ups and downs of their wanderings, the discomforts of shipboard, and of stations in the colonies, bad servants and unwonted sicknesses, the Captain's tenderness never failed. If the life was rough, the Captain was ready. He had been, by turns, in one strait or another, sick nurse, doctor, carpenter, nursemaid, and cook to his family, and had, moreover, an idea that nobody filled these offices quite so well as himself. Withal, his very profession kept him neat, well-dressed, and active. In the roughest of their ever-changing quarters he was a smarter man, more like the lover of his wife's young days, than Mr. Bull amid his stationary comforts. Then if the Captain's wife was—as her friends said—"never settled," she was also forever entertained by new scenes; and domestic mischances do not weigh very heavily on people whose possessions are few and their intellectual interests many. It is true that there were ladies in the Captain's regiment who passed by sea and land from one quarter of the globe to another, amid strange climates and customs, strange trees and flowers, beasts, and birds; from the glittering snows of North America to the orchids of the Cape, from beautiful Pera to the lily-covered hills of Japan, and who in no place rose above the fret of domestic worries, and had little to tell on their return but of the universal misconduct of servants, from Irish "helps" in the colonies, to *compradors* and China-boys at Shanghai. But it was not so with the Captain's wife. Moreover, she became accustomed to her fate, and she moved her whole establishment from the Curragh to Corfu with less anxiety than that felt by Mrs. Bull over a port-wine stain on the best table-cloth.

And yet, as years went and children came, the Captain and his wife grew tired of travelling. New scenes were small comfort when they heard of the death of old friends. One foot of murky English sky was dearer, after all, than miles of the unclouded heavens of the south. The grey hills and over-grown lanes of her old home haunted the Captain's wife by night and day, and home-sickness (that weariest of all sicknesses) began to take the light out of her eyes before their time. It preyed upon the Captain too. Now and then he would say, fretfully, "I *should* like an English resting-place, however small, before *every*body is dead! But the children's prospects have to be considered." The continued estrangement from the old man was an abiding sorrow also, and they had hopes that, if only they could get to England, he might be persuaded to peace and charity this time.

At last they were sent home. But the hard old father still would not relent. He returned their letters unopened. This bitter disappointment made the Captain's wife so ill that she almost died, and in one month the Captain's hair became iron grey. He reproached himself for having ever taken the daughter from her father, "to kill her at last," as he said. And (thinking of his own

117

children) he even reproached himself for having robbed the old widower of his only child. After two years at home his regiment was ordered to India. He failed to effect an exchange, and they prepared to move once more—from Chatham to Calcutta. Never before had the packing to which she was so well accustomed been so bitter a task to the Captain's wife.

It was at the darkest hour of this gloomy time that the Captain came in, waving above his head a letter which changed all their plans.

Close by the old home of the Captain's wife there had lived a man, much older than herself, who yet had loved her with a devotion as great as that of the young Captain. She never knew it, for when he saw that she had given her heart to his younger rival, he kept a generous silence, and never asked for what he knew he might have had—the old man's influence and authority in his favor. So generous was the affection which he could never conquer, that he constantly tried to reconcile the father to his children whilst he lived, and, when he died, he bequeathed his house and small estate to the woman he had loved.

"It will be a legacy of peace," he thought, on his deathbed. "The old man cannot hold out when she and her children are constantly in sight. And it may please God that I shall know of the reunion I have not been permitted to see with my eyes."

And thus it came about that the Captain's regiment went to India without him, and that the Captain's wife and her father lived on opposite sides of the same road.

MASTER ROBERT

The eldest of the Captain's children was a boy. He was named Robert, after his grandfather, and seemed to have inherited a good deal of the old gentleman's character, mixed with gentler traits. He was a fair, fine boy, tall and stout for his age, with the Captain's regular features, and (he flattered himself) the Captain's firm step and martial bearing. He was apt—like his grandfather—to hold his own will to be other people's law, and

German, 15th century. Angel Appearing to the Shepherds

(happily for the peace of the nursery) this opinion was devoutly shared by his brother Nicholas. Though the Captain had sold his commission, Robin (or Robert) continued to command an irregular force of Volunteers in the nursery, and never was colonel more despotic. His brother and sister were by turns infantry, cavalry, engineers and artillery, according to his whim, and when his affections finally settled upon the Highlanders of "The Black Watch," no female power could induce him to keep his stockings above his knees, or his knickerbockers below them.

The Captain alone was a match for his strong-willed son.

"If you please, sir," said Sarah, one morning, flouncing in upon the Captain, just as he was about to start for the neighboring town—"If you please, sir, I wish you'd speak to Master Robert. He's past my powers."

"I've no doubt of it," thought the Captain, but he only said, "Well, what's the matter?"

"Night after night do I put him to bed," said Sarah, " and night after night does he get up as soon as I'm out of the room, and says he's orderly officer for the evening, and goes about in his night-shirt, and his feet as bare as boards."

The Captain fingered his heavy moustache to hide a smile, but he listened patiently to Sarah's complaints.

"It ain't so much *him* I should mind, sir," she continued, "but he goes round the beds and wakes up the other young gentlemen and Miss Dora, one after another, and when I speak to him, he gives me all the sauce he can lay his tongue to, and says he's going round the guards. The other night I tried to put him back into his bed, but he got away and ran all over the house, me hunting him everywhere, and not a sign of him, till he jumps out on me from the garret-stairs, and nearly knocks me down. "I've visited the outposts, Sarah," says he; "all's well." And off he goes to bed as bold as brass."

"Have you spoken to your mistress?" asked the Captain.

"Yes, sir," said Sarah. "And missis spoke to him, and he promised not to go round the guards again."

120

"Has he broken his promise?" asked the Captain, with a look of anger, and also of surprise.

"When I opened the door last night, sir," continued Sarah, in her shrill treble, "what should I see in the dark but Master Robert a-walking up and down with the carpet-brush stuck in his arm. "Who goes there?" says he. "You owdacious boy!" says I. "Didn't you promise your Ma you'd leave off them tricks?" "I'm not going round the guards," says he; "I promised not. But I'm for sentry duty tonight." And say what I would to him, all he had for me was, "You mustn't speak to a sentry on duty." So I says, "As sure as I live till morning, I'll go to your Pa," for he pays no more attention to his Ma than to me, nor to any one else."

"Please to see that the chair-bed in my dressing-room is moved into your mistress's bedroom," said the Captain. "I will see to Master Robert."

With this Sarah had to content herself, and she went back to the nursery. Robert was nowhere to be seen, and made no reply to her summons. On this the unwary nursemaid flounced into the bedroom to look for him, when Robert, who was hidden beneath a table, darted forth, and promptly locked her in.

"You're under arrest," he shouted, through the keyhole.

"Let me out!" shrieked Sarah.

"I'll send a file of the guard to fetch you to the orderly-room, by-and-by," said Robert, "for preferring frivolous complaints." And he departed to the farmyard to look at the ducks.

That night, when Robert went up to bed, the Captain quietly locked him into his dressing-room, from which the bed had been removed.

"You're for sentry duty, to-night," said the Captain. "The carpet-brush is in the corner. Good-evening."

As his father anticipated, Robert was soon tired of the sentry game in these new circumstances, and long before the night had half worn away he wished himself safely undressed and in his own comfortable bed. At half-past twelve o'clock he felt as if

121

J. H. Ewing

he could bear it no longer, and knocked at the Captain's door.

"Who goes there?" said the Captain.

"Mayn't I go to bed, please?" whined poor Robert.

"Certainly not," said the Captain. "You're on duty."

And on duty poor Robert had to remain, for the Captain had a will as well as his son. So he rolled himself up in his father's railway rug, and slept on the floor.

The next night he was very glad to go quietly to bed, and remain there.

IN THE NURSERY

The Captain's children sat at breakfast in a large, bright nursery. It was the room where the old bachelor had died, and now *her* children made it merry. This was just what he would have wished.

They all sat round the table, for it was breakfast time. There were five of them, and five bowls of boiled bread and milk smoked before them. Sarah (a foolish, gossiping girl, who acted as nurse till better could be found) was waiting on them, and by the table sat Darkie, the black retriever, his long, curly back swaying slightly from the difficulty of holding himself up, and his solemn hazel eyes fixed very intently on each and all of the breakfast bowls. He was as silent and sagacious as Sarah was talkative and empty-headed. The expression of his face was that of King Charles I. as painted by Vandyke. Though large, he was unassuming. Pax, the pug, on the contrary, who came up to the first joint of Darkie's leg, stood defiantly on his dignity (and his short stumps). He always placed himself in front of the bigger dog, and made a point of hustling him in doorways and going first downstairs. He strutted like a beadle, and carried his tail more tightly curled than a bishop's crook. He looked as one may imagine the Frog in the Fable would have looked had he been able to swell himself rather nearer to the size of the ox. This was partly due to his very prominent eyes, and partly to an obesity, favoured by habits of lying inside the fender, and

122

of eating meals more proportioned to his consequence than to his hunger. They were both favourites of two years' standing, and had very nearly been given away, when the good news came of an English home for the family, dogs and all.

Robert's tongue was seldom idle, even at meals. "Are you a Yorkshirewoman, Sarah?" he asked, pausing, with his spoon full in his hand.

"No, Master Robert," said Sarah.

"But you understand Yorkshire, don't you? I can't, very often; But Mamma can, and can speak it, too. Papa says Mamma always talks Yorkshire to servants and poor people. She used to talk Yorkshire to Themistocles, Papa said, and he said it was no good; for though Themistocles knew a lot of languages, he didn't know that. And Mamma laughed, and said she didn't know she did. Themistocles was our man-servant in Corfu," Robin added, in explanation. "He stole lots of things, Themistocles did; but Papa found him out."

Robin now made a rapid attack on his bread and milk, after which he broke out again.

"Sarah, who is that tall old gentleman at church, in the seat near the pulpit? He wears a cloak like what the Blues wear, only all blue, and is tall enough for a lifeguardsman. He stood when we were kneeling down, and said, *Almighty and most merciful Father* louder than anybody."

Sarah knew who the old gentleman was, and knew also that the children did not know, and that their parents did not see fit to tell them as yet. But she had a passion for telling and hearing news, and would rather gossip with a child than not gossip at all. "Never you mind, Master Robin," she said, nodding sagaciously. "Little boys aren't to know everything."

"Ah, then, I know you don't know," replied Robert; "if you did, you'd tell. Nicholas, give some of your bread to Darkie and Pax. I've done mine. *For what we have received the Lord make us truly thankful.* Say your grace, and put your chair away, and come along. I want to hold a court-martial." And seizing his

123

own chair by the seat, Robin carried it swiftly to its corner. As he passed Sarah he observed tauntingly," You pretend to know, but you don't."

"I do," said Sarah.

"Your ma's forbid you to contradict, Master Robin," said Sarah; "and if you do, I shall tell her. I know well enough who the old gentleman is, and perhaps I might tell you, only you'd go straight off and tell again."

"No, no, I wouldn't!" shouted Robin. "I can keep a secret indeed I can! Pinch my little finger, and try. Do, do tell me, Sarah, there's a dear Sarah, and then I shall know you know." And he danced round her, catching at her skirts.

To keep a secret was beyond Sarah's powers.

"Do let my dress be, Master Robin," she said, "you're ripping out all the gathers, and listen while I whisper. As sure as you're a living boy, that gentleman's your own grandpapa."

Robin lost his hold on Sarah's dress; his arms fell by his side, and he stood with his brows knit for some minutes, thinking. Then he said, emphatically, "What lies you do tell, Sarah!"

"Oh, Robin!" cried Nicholas, who had drawn near, his thick curls standing stark with curiosity, "Mamma said lies wasn't a proper word, and you promised not to say it again."

"I forgot," said Robin. "I didn't mean to break my promise. But she does tell—ahem!—*you know what.*"

"You wicked boy!" cried the enraged Sarah; "how dare you to say such a thing, and everybody in the place knows he's your ma's own pa."

"I'll go and ask her," said Robin, and he was at the door in a moment; but Sarah, alarmed by the thought of getting into a scrape herself, caught him by the arm.

"Don't you go, love; it'll only make your ma angry. There; it was all my nonsense."

"Then it's not true?" said Robin, indignantly. "What did you tell me so for?"

"It was all my jokes and nonsense," said the unscrupulous

Sarah. "But your ma wouldn't like to know I've said such a thing. And Master Robert wouldn't be so mean as to tell tales, would he, love?"

"I'm not mean," said Robin, stoutly; "and I don't tell tales; but you do, and you tell *you know what*, besides. However, I won't go this time; but I'll tell you what—if you tell tales of me to Papa any more, I'll tell him what you said about the old gentleman in the blue cloak." With which parting threat, Robin strode off to join his brothers and sister.

Sarah's tale had put the court-martial out of his head, and he leaned against the tall fender, gazing at his little sister, who was tenderly nursing a well-worn doll. Robin sighed.

"What a long time that doll takes to wear out, Dora!" said he. "When will it be done?"

"Oh, not yet, not yet!" cried Dora, clasping the doll to her, and turning away. "She's quite good, yet."

"How miserly you are," said her brother; "and selfish, too; for you know I can't have a military funeral till you'll let me bury that old thing."

Dora began to cry.

"There you go, crying!" said Robin, impatiently. "Look here: I won't take it till you get the new one on your birthday. You can't be so mean as not to let me have it then?"

But Dora's tears still fell. "I love this one so much," she sobbed. "I love her better than the new one."

"You want both; that's it," said Robin, angrily. "Dora, you're the meanest girl I ever knew!"

At which unjust and painful accusation Dora threw herself and the doll upon their faces, and wept bitterly. The eyes of soft-hearted Nicholas began to fill with tears, and he squatted down before her, looking most dismal. He had a fellow-feeling for her attachment to an old toy, and yet Robin's will was law to him.

"Couldn't we make a coffin, and pretend the body was inside?" he suggested.

125

"No, we couldn't," said Robin. "I wouldn't play the Dead March after an empty candle-box. It's a great shame—and I promised she should be chaplain in one of my night-gowns, too."

"Perhaps you'll get just as fond of the new one," said Nicholas, turning to Dora.

But Dora only cried, "No, no! he shall have the new one to bury, and I'll keep my poor, dear, darling Betsy." And she clasped Betsy tighter than before.

"That's the meanest thing you've said yet," retorted Robin; "for you know Mamma wouldn't let me bury the new one." And with an air of great disgust, he quitted the nursery.

"A MUMMING WE WILL GO"

Nicholas had sore work to console his little sister, and Betsy's prospects were in a very unfavourable state, when a diversion was caused in her favour, by a new whim that put the military funeral out of Robin's head.

After he left the nursery he strolled out of doors, and, peeping through the gate at the end of the drive, he saw a party of boys going through what looked like a military exercise with sticks and a good deal of stamping; but, instead of mere words of command, they all spoke by turns, as in a play. In spite of their strong Yorkshire accent, Robin overheard a good deal, and it sounded very fine. Not being at all shy, he joined them, and asked so many questions that he soon got to know all about it. They were practising a Christmas mumming-play, called "The Peace Egg." Why it was called thus they could not tell him, as there was nothing whatever about eggs in it, and so far from being a play of peace, it was made up of a series of battles between certain valiant knights and princes, of whom St. George of England was the chief and conqueror. The rehearsal being over, Robin went with the boys to the sexton's house (he was father to the "King of Egypt"), where they showed him the dresses they were to wear. These were made of gay-coloured materials, and covered with ribbons, except that of the "Black

Prince of Paradine," which was black, as became his title. The boys also showed him the book from which they learned their parts, and which was to be bought for one penny at the post-office shop.

"Then are you the mummers who come round at Christmas, and act in people's kitchens, and people give them money, that Mamma used to tell us about?" said Robin.

St. George of England looked at his companions as if for counsel as to how far they might commit themselves, and then replied, with Yorkshire caution, "Well, I suppose we are."

"And do you go out in the snow from one house to another at night; and oh, don't you enjoy it?" cried Robin.

"We like it well enough," St. George admitted.

Robin bought a copy of "The Peace Egg." He was resolved to have a nursery performance, and to act the part of St. George himself. The others were willing for what he wished, but there were difficulties. In the first place, there are eight characters in the play, and there were only five children. They decided among themselves to leave out "the Fool," and Mamma said that another character was not to be acted by any of them, or indeed mentioned; "the little one who comes in at the end," Robin explained. Mamma had her reasons, and these were always good. She had not been altogether pleased that Robin had bought the play. It was a very old thing, she said, and very queer; not adapted for a child's play. If Mamma thought the parts not quite fit for the children to learn, they found them much too long; so in the end she picked out some bits for each, which they learned easily, and which, with a good deal of fighting, made quite as good a story of it as if they had done the whole. What may have been wanting otherwise was made up for by the dresses, which were charming.

Robin was St. George, Nicholas the Valiant Slasher, Dora the Doctor, and the other two Hector and the King of Egypt. "And now we've no Black Prince!" cried Robin, in dismay.

"Let Darkie be the Black Prince," said Nicholas. "When you

wave your stick he'll jump for it, and then you can pretend to fight with him."

"It's not a stick, it's a sword," said Robin. "However, Darkie may be the Black Prince."

"And what's Pax to be?" asked Dora; "for you know he will come if Darkie does, and he'll run in before everybody else too."

"Then he must be the Fool," said Robin, "and it will do very well, for the Fool comes in before the rest, and Pax can have his red coat on, and the collar with the little bells."

CHRISTMAS EVE

Robin thought that Christmas would never come. To the Captain and his wife it seemed to come too fast. They had hoped it might bring reconciliation with the old man, but they had hoped in vain.

There were times now when the Captain almost regretted the old bachelor's bequest. The familiar scenes of her old home sharpened his wife's grief. To see her father every Sunday in church, with marks of age and infirmity upon him, but with not a look of tenderness for his only child, this tried her sorely.

"She felt it less abroad," thought the Captain. "An English home in which she frets herself to death is, after all, no great boon."

Christmas Eve came.

"I'm sure it's quite Christmas enough now," said Robin. "We'll have 'The Peace Egg' to-night."

So as the Captain and his wife sat sadly over their fire, the door opened, and Pax ran in shaking his bells, and followed by the nursery mummers. The performance was most successful. It was by no means pathetic, and yet, as has been said, the Captain's wife shed tears.

"What is the matter, Mamma?" said St. George, abruptly dropping his sword and running up to her.

"Don't tease Mamma with questions," said the Captain, "she is not very well, and rather sad. We must all be very kind and good to poor dear Mamma;" and the Captain raised his wife's hand to his lips as he spoke. Robin seized the other hand and kissed it tenderly. He was very fond of his mother. At this moment Pax took a little run, and jumped on to Mamma's lap, where, sitting facing the company, he opened his black mouth and yawned, with a ludicrous inappropriateness worthy of any clown. It made everybody laugh.

"And now we'll go and act in the kitchen," said Nicholas.

"Supper at nine o'clock, remember," shouted the Captain. "And we are going to have real furmety and Yule cakes, such as Mamma used to tell us of when we were abroad."

"Hurray!" shouted the mummers, and they ran off, Pax leaping from his seat just in time to hustle the Black Prince in the doorway. When the dining-room door was shut St. George raised his hand, and said "Hush!"

The mummers pricked their ears, but there was only a distant harsh and scraping sound, as of stones rubbed together.

"They're cleaning the passages," St. George went on, "and Sarah told me they meant to finish the mistletoe, and have everything cleaned up by supper-time. They don't want us, I know. Look here, we'll go *real mumming* instead. That *will* be fun!"

The Valiant Slasher grinned with delight.

"But will mamma let us?" he inquired.

"Oh, it will be all right if we're back by supper-time," said St. George, hastily. "Only of course we must take care not to catch cold. Come and help me to get some wraps."

The old oak chest in which spare shawls, rugs, and coats were kept was soon ransacked, and the mummers' gay dresses hidden by motley wrappers. But no sooner did Darkie and Pax behold the coats, &c., than they at once began to leap and bark, as it was their custom to do when they saw any one dressing to go out. Robin was sorely afraid that this would betray them; but though the Captain and his wife heard the barking they did not guess the cause.

So the front door being very gently opened and closed, the nursery mummers stole away.

THE NURSERY MUMMERS AND THE OLD MAN

It was a very fine night. The snow was well-trodden on the drive, so that it did not wet their feet, but on the trees and shrubs it hung soft and white.

"It's much jollier being out at night than in the daytime," said Robin.

"Much," responded Nicholas, with intense feeling.

"We'll go a wassailing next week," said Robin. "I know all about it, and perhaps we shall get a good lot of money, and then we'll buy tin swords with scabbards for next year. I don't like these sticks. Oh, dear! I wish it wasn't so long between one Christmas and another."

"Where shall we go first?" asked Nicholas, as they turned into the high road. But before Robin could reply, Dora clung to Nicholas, crying, "Oh, look at those men!"

The boys looked up the road, down which three men were coming in a very unsteady fashion, and shouting as they rolled from side to side.

"They're drunk," said Nicholas, "and they're shouting at us."

"Oh, run, run!" cried Dora; and down the road they ran, the men shouting and following them. They had not run far, when Hector caught his foot in the Captain's great-coat, which he was wearing, and came down headlong in the road. They were close by a gate, and when Nicholas had set Hector upon his legs, St. George hastily opened it.

"This is the first house," he said. "We'll act here;" and all, even the Valiant Slasher, pressed in as quickly as possible. Once safe within the grounds, they shouldered their sticks, and resumed their composure.

"You're going to the front door," said Nicholas. "Mummers ought to go to the back."

"We don't know where it is," said Robin, and he rang the front door bell. There was a pause. Then lights shone, steps were heard, and at last a sound of much unbarring, unbolting, and unlocking. It might have been a prison. Then the door was opened by an elderly, timid-looking woman, who held a tallow candle above her head.

"Who's there?" she said, "at this time of night?"

"We're Christmas mummers," said Robin, stoutly; "we didn't know the way to the back door, but——"

"And don't you know better than to come here?" said the woman. "Be off with you, as fast as you can."

"You're only the servant," said Robin. "Go and ask your master and mistress if they wouldn't like to see us act. We do it very well."

"You impudent boy, be off with you!" repeated the woman. "Master 'd no more let you nor any other such rubbish set foot in this house——"

"Woman!" shouted a voice close behind her, which made her start as if she had been shot, "who authorizes you to say what your master will or will not do, before you've asked him? The boy is right. You *are* the servant, and it is not your business to choose for me whom I shall or shall not see."

"I meant no harm, sir, I'm sure," said the housekeeper; "but I thought you'd never——"

"My good woman," said her master, "if I had wanted somebody to think for me, you're the last person I should have employed. I hire you to obey orders, not to think."

"I'm sure, sir," said the housekeeper, whose only form of argument was reiteration, "I never thought you would have seen them——"

"Then you were wrong," shouted her master. "I will see them. Bring them in."

He was a tall, gaunt old man, and Robin stared at him for some minutes, wondering where he could have seen somebody very like him. At last he remembered. It was the old gentleman of the blue cloak.

The children threw off their wraps, the housekeeper helping them, and chattering ceaselessly, from sheer nervousness.

"Well, to be sure," said she, "their dresses are pretty, too. And they seem quite a better sort of children, they talk quite genteel. I might ha' knowed they weren't like common mummers, but I was so flusterated, hearing the bell go so late, and——"

"Are they ready?" said the old man, who had stood like a ghost in the dim light of the flaring tallow candle, grimly watching the procedings.

"Yes, sir. Shall I take them to the kitchen, sir?"

"——for you and the other idle hussies to gape and grin at? No. Bring them to the library," he snapped, and then stalked off, leading the way.

The housekeeper accordingly led them to the library, and then withdrew, nearly falling on her face as she left the room by stumbling over Darkie, who slipped in last like a black shadow.

The old man was seated in an old carved chair by the fire.

"I never said the dogs were to come in," he said.

"But we can't do without them, please," said Robin, boldly. "You see there are eight people in 'The Peace Egg,' and there are only five of us; and so Darkie has to be the Black Prince, and Pax has to be the Fool, and so we have to have them."

"Five and two make seven," said the old man, with a grim smile; "what do you do for the eighth?'"

"Oh, that's the little one at the end," said Robin, confidentially. "Mamma said we weren't to mention him, but I think that's because we're children. You're grown up you know, so I'll show you the book, and you can see for yourself," he went on, drawing 'The Peace Egg' from his pocket: "there,

132

that's the picture of him, on the last page; black, with horns and a tail."

The old man's stern face relaxed into a broad smile as he examined the grotesque woodcut; but when he turned to the first page the smile vanished in a deep frown, and his eyes shone like hot coals with anger. He had seen Robin's name.

"Who sent you here?" he asked, in a hoarse voice. "Speak, and speak the truth! Did your mother send you here?"

Robin thought the old man was angry with them for playing the truant. He said, slowly, "N—no. She didn't exactly send us; but I don't think she'll mind our having come if we get back in time for supper. Mamma never *forbid* our going mumming, you know."

"I don't suppose she ever thought of it," Nicholas said, candidly, wagging his curly head from side to side.

"She knows we're mummers," said Robin, "for she helped us. When we were abroad, you know, she used to tell us about the mummers acting at Christmas, when she was a little girl; and so we thought we'd be mummers, and so we acted to Papa and Mamma, and so we thought we'd act to the maids, but they were cleaning the passages, and so we thought we'd really go mumming; and we've got several other houses to go to before supper-time; we'd better begin, I think," said Robin; and without more ado he began to march round and round, raising his sword, and shouting—

"I am St. George, who from Old England sprung,

My famous name throughout the world hath rung."
And the performance went off quite as creditably as before.

As the children acted the old man's anger wore off. He watched them with an interest he could not repress. When Nicholas took some hard thwacks from St. George without flinching the old man clapped his hands; and, after the encounter between St. George and the Black Prince, he said he would not have had the dogs excluded on any consideration.

It was just at the end, when they were all marching round and round, holding on by each other's swords "over the shoulder," and singing "A mumming we will go, &c.," that Nicholas suddenly brought the circle to a standstill by stopping dead short, and staring up at the wall before him.

"What *are* you stopping for?" said St. George, indignantly turning round.

"Look there!" cried Nicholas, pointing to a little painting which hung above the old man's head.

Robin looked, and said, abruptly, "It's Dora."

"Which is Dora?" asked the old man, in a strange, sharp tone.

"Here she is," said Robin and Nicholas in one breath, as they dragged her forward.

"She's the Doctor," said Robin; "and you can't see her face for her things. Dor, take off your cap and pull back that hood. There! Oh, it *is* like her!"

It was a portrait of her mother as a child; but of this the nursery mummers knew nothing. The old man looked as the peaked cap and hood fell away from Dora's face and fair curls, and then he uttered a sharp cry, and buried his head upon his hands. The boys stood stupefied, but Dora ran up to him, and, putting her little hands on his arms, said, in childish pitying tones, "Oh, I am so sorry! Have you got a headache? May Robin put the shovel in the fire for you? Mamma has hot shovels for her headaches." And, though the old man did not speak or move, she went on coaxing him, and stroking his head, on which the hair was white. At this moment Pax took one of his unexpected runs, and jumped on to the old man's knee, in his own particular fashion, and then yawned at the company. The old man was startled, and lifted his face suddenly. It was wet with tears.

"Why, you're crying!" exclaimed the children with one breath.

"It's very odd," said Robin, fretfully. "I can't think what's the matter tonight. Mamma was crying too when we were acting, and papa said we weren't to tease her with questions, and he kissed her hand, and I kissed her hand too. And Papa said we must all be very good and kind to poor dear Mamma, and so I mean to be, she's so good. And I think we'd better go home, or perhaps she'll be frightened," Robin added.

"She's so good, is she?" asked the old man. He had put Pax off his knee, and taken Dora on to it.

"Oh, isn't she!" said Nicholas, swaying his curly head from side to side as usual.

"She's always good," said Robin, emphatically; "and so's Papa. But I'm always doing something I oughtn't to," he added, slowly. "But then, you know, I don't pretend to obey Sarah. I don't care a fig for Sarah; and I won't obey any woman but Mamma."

"Who's Sarah?" asked the grandfather.

"She's our nurse," said Robin, "and she tells—I mustn't say what she tells—but it's not the truth. She told one about *you* the other day," he added.

"About me?" said the old man.

"She said you were our grandpapa. So then I knew she was telling *you know what*."

"How did you know it wasn't true?" the old man asked.

"Why, of course," said Robin, "if you were our Mamma's father, you'd know her, and be very fond of her, and come and see her. And then you'd be our grandfather, too, and you'd have us to see you, and perhaps give us Christmas boxes. I wish you were," Robin added with a sigh. "It would be very nice."

"Would *you* like it?" asked the old man of Dora.

And Dora, who was half asleep and very comfortable, put her little arms about his neck as she was wont to put them round the Captain's, and said, "Very much."

He put her down at last, very tenderly, almost unwillingly,

135

and left the children alone. By-and-by he returned, dressed in the blue cloak, and took Dora up again.

"I will see you home," he said.

The children were not missed. The clock had only just struck nine when there came a knock on the door of the dining-room, where the Captain and wife still sat by the Yule log. She said "Come in," wearily, thinking it was the furmety and the Christmas cakes.

But it was her father, with her child in his arms!

PEACE AND GOODWILL

Lucy Jane Bull and her sisters were quite old enough to understand a good deal of grown-up conversation when they overheard it. Thus, when a friend of Mrs. Bull's observed during an afternoon call that she believed that "officers' wives were very dressy," the young ladies were at once resolved to keep a sharp look-out for the Captain's wife's bonnet in church on Christmas Day.

The Bulls had just taken their seats when the Captain's wife came in. They really were going to hide their faces, and look at the bonnet afterwards, but for the startling sight that met the gaze of the congregation. The old grandfather walked into church abreast of the Captain.

"They've met in the porch," whispered Mr. Bull under the shelter of his hat.

"They can't quarrel publicly in a place of worship," said Mrs. Bull, turning pale.

"She's gone into his seat," cried Lucy Jane in a shrill whisper.

"And the children after her," added the other sister, incautiously, aloud.

There was now no doubt about the matter. The old man in his blue cloak stood for a few moments politely disputing the question of precedence with his handsome son-in-law. Then the Captain bowed and passed in, and the old man followed him.

The Peace Egg

By the time that the service was ended everybody knew of the happy peacemaking, and was glad. One old friend after another came up with blessings and good wishes. This was a proper Christmas, indeed, they said. There was a general rejoicing.

But only the grandfather and his children knew that it was owing to "The Peace Egg."

Christmas Carol

MAY PROBYN

Lacking samite and sable,
  Lacking silver and gold,
The Prince Jesus in the poor stable
  Slept, and was three hours old.

As doves by the fair water,
  Mary, not touched of sin,
Sat by Him,—the King's daughter,
  All glorious within.

A lily without one stain, a
  Star where no spot hath room—
Ave, gratia plena—
  Virgo Virginum.

Clad not in pearl-sewn vesture,
  Clad not in cramoisie,
She hath hushed, she hath cradled to rest, her
  God the first time on her knee.

Where is one to adore Him?
  The ox hath dumbly confessed,
With the ass, meek kneeling before Him.
  "Et homo factus est."

Not throned on ivory or cedar,
  Not crowned with a Queen's crown,
At her breast it is Mary shall feed her
  Maker, from Heaven come down.

Italian, 15th century. Flight into Egypt

May Probyn

The trees in Paradise blossom
　Sudden, and its bells chime—
She giveth Him, held to her bosom,
　Her immaculate milk the first time.

The night with wings of angels
　Was alight, and its snow-packed ways
Sweet made (say the Evangels)
　With the noise of their virelays.

Quem vidistis, pastores?
　Why go ye feet unshod?
Wot ye within yon door is
　Mary, the Mother of God?

No smoke of spice is ascending
　There—no roses are piled—
But, choicer than all balms blending,
　There Mary hath kissed her Child.

"Dilectus meus mihi
　Et ego Illi"—Cold
Small cheek against her cheek, He
　Sleepeth three hours old.

The Vision of the Shepherds

W. H. AUDEN

ONE

THE FIRST SHEPHERD

The winter night requires our constant attention,
  Watching that water and good-will,
Warmth and well-being, may still be there in the morning.

THE SECOND SHEPHERD

  For behind the spontaneous joy of life
There is always a mechanism to keep going,

THE THIRD SHEPHERD

  And someone like us is always there.

THE FIRST SHEPHERD

We observe that those who assure us their education
  And money would do us such harm,
How real we are just as we are, and how they envy us,
  For it is the centerless tree
And the uncivilized robin who are the truly happy,
  Have done pretty well for themselves:

THE SECOND SHEPHERD

Nor can we help noticing how those who insist that
  We ought to stand up for our rights,
And how important we are, keep insisting also
  That it doesn't matter a bit
If one of us gets arrested or injured, for
  It is only our numbers that count.

141

W. H. Auden

THE THIRD SHEPHERD

In a way they are right,

THE FIRST SHEPHERD

But to behave like a cogwheel
When one knows one is no such thing,

THE SECOND SHEPHERD

Merely to add to a crowd with one's passionate body,
Is not a virtue.

THE THIRD SHEPHERD

What is real
About us all is that each of us is waiting.

THE FIRST SHEPHERD

That is why we are able to bear
Ready-made clothes, second-hand art and opinions
And being washed and ordered about;

THE SECOND SHEPHERD

That is why you should not take our conversation
Too seriously, nor read too much
Into our songs;

THE THIRD SHEPHERD

Their purpose is mainly to keep us
From watching the clock all the time.

THE FIRST SHEPHERD

For, though we cannot say why, we know that something
Will happen:

THE SECOND SHEPHERD

What we cannot say,

142

THE THIRD SHEPHERD

Except that it will not be a reporter's item
Of unusual human interest;

THE FIRST SHEPHERD

That always means something unpleasant.

THE SECOND SHEPHERD

But one day or
The next we shall hear the Good News.

TWO

THE THREE SHEPHERDS

Levers nudge the aching wrist;
"You are free
Not to be,
Why exist?"
Wheels a thousand times a minute
Mutter, stutter,

"End the self you cannot mend,
Did you, friend, begin it?"
    And the streets
    Sniff at our defeats.
Then who is the Unknown
Who answers for our fear
As if it were His own,
So that we reply
Till the day we die;
"No, I don't know why,
But I'm glad I'm here"?

THREE

CHORUS OF ANGELS

Unto you a Child,
A Son is given.
Praising, proclaiming
The ingression of Love,
Earth's darkness invents
The blaze of Heaven,
And frigid silence
Meditates a song;
For great joy has filled
The narrow and the sad,
While the emphasis
Of the rough and big,
The abiding crag
Is on forgiveness:
And wandering wave,
Sing Glory to God
And good-will to men,
All, all, all of them.
Run to Bethlehem.

The Vision of the Shepherds

Let us run to learn
How to love and run;
Let us run to Love.

CHORUS

Now all things living,
Domestic or wild,
With whom you must share
Light, water, and air,
And suffer and shake
In physical need,
The sullen limpet,
The exuberant weed,
The mischievous cat,
And the timid bird,
Are glad for your sake
As the new-born Word
Declares that the old
Authoritarian
Constraint is replaced
By His Covenant,
And a city based
On love and consent
Suggested to men,
All, all, all of them.
Run to Bethlehem.

SHEPHERDS

Let us run to learn
How to love and run;
Let us run to Love.

W. H. Auden

CHORUS

The primitive dead
Progress in your blood,
And generations
Of the unborn, all
Are leaping for joy
In your reins today
When the Many shall,
Once in your common
Certainty of this
Child's lovableness,
Resemble the One,
That after today
The children of men
May be certain that
The Father Abyss
Is affectionate
To all Its creatures,
All, all, all of them.
Run to Bethlehem.

The Last Christmas

BERNARD RAYMUND

WHEN they came to his grandfather Mackay's house early on Christmas morning the game was always to see who could say *it* first. But from the time he had been old enough to know anything about it he had always lost. Always as they approached the steps and his dad shifted the bundles of presents in his arms so he could put a hand under his mother's elbow, the front door burst open and the whole crowd of them, his grandfather in the lead, rushed to the edge of the porch shouting *Merry Christmas!* It was like one great concerted laughing thunderclap, and, no matter how hard he tried, it always caught him unprepared. And his grandfather would stand, his mouth wide open, his eyes puckered into blue smiling knots, pointing a gnarled forefinger down at him as if to reproach him for not being first. No matter how warm was their greeting he felt reproachful with himself and scarcely heard when grandfather said, "No, don't stop to take off your rubbers! Here Toots, Jim Boy, Mugs (who but his grandfather ever called Russell that?) help Frank get rid of some of these bundles. And Sadie, got a kiss for your old father?"

This year he really would beat. He was bigger for one thing, and he had it all planned. He would not be startled this time, he would not laugh as he always had before—how could he say *it* when he was laughing? He would begin to take a deep breath just as they passed Dr. Carr's yard, where on each concrete post sat an iron dog holding an end of the iron pipe in his mouth. He would get a good breath and he hoped his mother would not say anything to him so he had to let it out before he got there. That way he most certainly would beat—that is if he didn't

147

holler before the door opened. He could just imagine his feeling of triumph when grandfather would say, "Well, what do you know about that? Baber beat us this time. He most certainly did!"

When they had crossed the mounds of frozen slush between the street car and the curb he put his own small load of presents on top of the heap in his father's arms.

"Here, what's this?" his father grunted. "Haven't I got enough to carry? Can't see where I am going as it is."

"I wanta take a slide," he explained. He could not tell the real reason—that would sound silly, and he guessed not even his mother knew how he felt about every Christmas. His mortification had been too deep to tell anybody about it. Along here there was a good place anyhow, where the pavement had sunk a bit, and taking a short run, his overcoat streaming behind him, he made two complete exhilarating turns. Now he would be the first one there, so there would be less likelihood of his mother or dad getting in the way. Without stopping to pat the head of the nearest iron dog, he filled his lungs with crisp cold air. Now he was all ready.

But as he came in sight of his grandfather's house it came over him that something was different, something not as it had always been. And though it was a small thing and one to be met with everywhere, here in the neat snowy quadrangle of lawn that faced the street it seemed so out of place that it made everything different. Different, and kind of wrong, as if they had come to the wrong address and this was not grandfather's house but that of some strangers and not even on grandfather's street. And the thought of all the queer wrongness ran down his neck in a small prickling stream of cold and he had a sense in that instant that anything might happen and none of it good.

It was a wooden sign, leaning sidewise with an accumulation of snow; forgetting all the fine plans he had made he stopped to read it, his hoard of air escaping in a long plume of frozen vapor. "For Sale," the sign read. "This Beautiful Residence

Property." And below, in large red capitals, "See Your Broker!"

He was wondering if the people out in his grandfather's end of town, the people who would be the only ones likely to pass this way and see the sign, kept brokers in the same fashion that they kept Negro chauffeurs, when his mother leaned over him and hissed, "If I hear *one question* out of you, young man, you know what will happen to *you!*" And though he tried to get another breath ready, somehow it hurt, not in his windpipe where cold air naturally ought to hurt, but in the corners of his eyes and across the bridge of his nose.

But there was no need, for this time the door did not burst open, nor did the family rush out to meet them. In fact they were already up the steps and across the icy veranda before the door was opened, this time not by grandfather, but by Russell.

"Merry Christmas!" he crowed, but if Russell answered he did not hear him.

"I beat, that time!" he exulted, though feeling at the same instant foolish and unnecessarily noisy: "I beat, didn't I?"

"Well?" asked Russ so morosely that any further word he might have uttered seemed to congeal in his throat in a hard and distasteful lump.

His grandmother in her apron had come up behind Russell. "Children, for heaven's sake get away from the doorway so Frank and Sadie can come in out of the cold!"

The door closed, they stood in the dark of the hall a moment breathing the heavy warmth. The chill of outdoors departed from him with one last delightful shiver. The smell of his grandmother's Christmas dinner floated tantalizing from the kitchen.

"Where's Papa?" Baber's mother asked brightly, as if this happened every Christmas morning, as if it *could* happen and nothing be different from all the Christmas mornings of the past.

"Oh, your father slept late." His grandmother's attempt at a light tone did not quite come off. "He stays up until one or two over his solitaire and then he don't seem to get properly asleep.

149

Henry!" she called up the stairs, "Come down and see who's here!"

Grandfather was already coming—not, as Baber was used to seeing him Christmas morning, in his maroon smoking jacket with gilt braid, but wrapped in a faded flannel robe, worn mules on his bare feet that slapped on every step.

"Merry Christmas!" he called out from the landing—and when his eyes twinkled down on them, what difference did it make that he wasn't dressed?

He folded Baber's mother in a hug, gigantic for so small a man, and accepted her kiss; while Baber, clinging to the edge of his robe danced about crying, "Grandpa, see what I got for you!"

He took the narrow package, done in white tissue and tied with silver cord.

"Open it! Open it, Grandpa!"

"Wait. Let me guess what it is!" His grandfather closed his eyes, running his fingers over the package. "I would say it is the kind that doesn't have to be tied. Nothing to fuss with, just slip the ends under your collar. Am I right Baber? And the color, let me see." He held it to his nose, his eyes twinkling. "Black? Or is it blue with white polka dots?"

Baber clapped his hand over his mouth to keep from laughing outright at that, while his grandmother flounced her apron exclaiming, "Oh, Henry, don't be foolish! Here, Frank has something for you and you haven't paid the least bit of attention."

"Ah, cigars! How did you guess it, Frank? I was clear out. Just going to send Muggsy out for some."

Baber tried not to notice Russ's air of injured unbelief. It made him want to take a swat at him, again. If grandfather said so, why . . . then and there his grandfather drew out his amber cigar holder from the pocket of his night shirt and lit his first Christmas morning smoke from the match Baber's dad held for him. "You know, Frank," he explained, "I've never attempted to buy a gift for you since that Christmas we both

150

gave each other, remember, Kipling's 'Many Inventions.'" And at the recollection of that, the most ridiculous of Christmases, they guffawed and slapped one another on the back and spilled cigar ashes on grandmother's hall rug.

The bell pealed and his grandfather opened the door with a "Merry Christmas" that almost blew the postman from the veranda and returned with a tightly rolled cylinder.

"Here's your present to your old father, Sadie Mackay!" he cried. "Every week, right on the dot! Now," he slit the cover with his thumbnail, shook out the copy of the *Outlook*, "we'll see what Lyman Abbott's bright young men have to say this time."

"Henry," mother said, "aren't you *ever* going to get dressed?"

But grandfather, having retrieved his spectacles from the mantle had settled deep in his leather rocker and with a sigh of content, had cocked his feet before the fire.

The tree stood in the corner of the parlor as always, no change could touch *that*, giving off the exciting, resinous smell of Christmas, colored electric bulbs shining from its dusky interior in place of the candles that at home had to be lit with so many precautions, and after too brief a display blown out— the lowermost for him, the top ones for his dad's strong lungs. Under it were parcels still unopened, that he knew without telling were for him, and sitting on the floor he opened them hastily. Captain Marryatt's *Japhet in Search of a Father*, and the larger package a marble game with a labyrinth of brass pegs and a bell that counted one thousand if you rang it. It was foolish how grandfather continued to insist that Santa had left them there for him; he seemed really to believe it and Baber had stopped trying to convince him that he was wrong.

While they were at work coupling on the new cars to Russ's electric train, he heard his father stretch himself heavily on grandfather's leather sofa in the sitting room; from the kitchen came the voices of the womenfolk, his mother in an apron many sizes too large for her, grandmother, and Bilikims, who limped about complaining that they were in her way. There was a rustle on the stairs and Toots, a vision in pink with many flounces, descended slowly, calling "Merry Christmas!" and giving them a wide smile over the banisters. Perching on the piano stool, she sleepily looked over the pieces of new sheet music, *her* present evidently, and then swung herself by one toe absently watching their railroad operations.

"Her fella's takin' her sleigh-riding," whispered Russ.

"Gosh!" Baber exclaimed. "Suppose we could ride on the runners?"

His aunt had overheard. "I'll say you can't!" she laughed shortly. "Not much!"

And presently there came a jangle of sleigh-bells outside, hearing which grandfather flung down his magazine, laid his cigar and spectacles aside, and gathering his robe about him clattered to his room.

Mother answered the door while Toots slipped into her fur coat, wound a pink "Alice" veil about her dark head. Her sister looked anxiously round the edge of the dining room door.

"Be back in time for dinner, Toots?"

Toots shook her head. "Don't set a place for me, Bilikims. We're eating at the Neil House." And in a draft of icy air Toots swept grandly away before Baber could even see what the "fella" looked like.

His grandfather composed his features, shut his eyes tight and said the briefest possible grace. As all unfolded their napkins, the big Christmas ones with fringed borders, Russ asked, "I get a drumstick, don't I Papa?"

But seated at grandfather's left, Baber could see that there was no use asking, for it was a roast of beef—and on Christmas! Grandfather carved deftly, without comment, flipping the pieces on the plates, dishing up the mashed potatoes and the scalloped oysters, Baber's mother adding the gravy, the creamed cauliflower, the cranberry jelly. But of course there was no dressing. From her end of the table grandmother circulated the hot biscuit, the butter, the celery hearts and stuffed olives. And when grandfather had served everyone, Bilikims brought him two poached eggs. He looked at them on his plate, and it seemed to Baber that he saw two tears run down grandfather's nose and drop on them. But of course that couldn't be, not on Christmas.

"Henry is so cranky about his eating," grandmother said across the table. "I declare, Sadie, you have no idea the notions . . ."

"He always was cranky; weren't you Papa?" Baber's mother laughed. "Papa do you remember . . ."

"Aw, Sadie!" grandfather howled, his napkin held out in his fist as if he would leave the table if she kept on.

And after that nobody said anything. Only Baber's mother kept putting things on grandfather's plate: first one of the hot biscuits to sop up the egg, and then a bit of scalloped oyster, and pretty soon his grandfather seemed to feel a lot better. But he would not touch his mince pie, but passed it over to Baber when his mother wasn't looking; he never did eat it anyhow. And when he complained that grandmother had put cream in his coffee when she had known all her life he always took it black, everybody knew the worst was over. Even if there was something wrong that no one wanted to talk about, the Christmas dinner was not spoiled after all.

Afterward, when he and Russell were playing the marble game, grandfather came and stood over them to watch, his cigar between his thumb and forefinger and made so many wisecracks that Russ said, "All right, Papa, if you're so smart why don't you play too?"

So grandfather woke up Baber's dad, and got paper and pencil to keep score with; then they both got down on the floor with Russ and Baber and went to it. Between them they thought up a lot of trick rules, such as if you hit the bell with your first marble, it counted a thousand off your score, and if you shot out of turn whatever you made was taken off. And just when they had got to the most exciting part and grandfather and Russ were tied at fifteen thousand, grandmother came with Russ's overcoat and said that if he was going to take his present over to Johnnie Jabo he'd have to go now.

When they got back his grandfather was reading out loud. The words he could not distinguish, the rich, rounded syllables, like spoken music, stopped him in his tracks.

"Boys," grandmother spoke from somewhere, "I set your ice cream in the ice box. Guess you can share Toots's between you; it will be all melted before she gets back."

"Is it N'apolitan?" Russ wanted to know.

They heard grandmother sigh. "If it's Neapolitan you have to have young man, you're going to be disappointed. The almond macaroons are in the dish on the dining table. Please try to leave some for someone else!"

Although Russ bolted for the back hall, Baber could not leave the doorway to the sitting room. Only the reading lamp was lit and all he could see was his grandfather's wisp of fine hair, the red-covered book he held up before him. Baber's mother sat on the edge of her chair, facing grandfather, while in the shadows beyond the fireplace he saw the glint of his dad's spectacles, the glow of his cigar. Oh, why hadn't he stayed so he could hear it all?

For just then grandfather closed the book with a snap. "And that's all!" He rubbed his big nose on the back of his hand, sniffed delightedly. "That's Mark Twain for you, ageless and undimmed!"

"Like you, Papa."

Grandfather shook a warning finger at her. "Enough of that, Sadie!"

"Frank, be sure to write the title down so we can get it sure; I want to read it again. Will they have it at the library do you think?"

"They will not," grandfather smiled maliciously. "I've tried them, just as an experiment. Don't you know, Sadie, that the libraries are afraid of books like that? I'd lend you my copy quick enough," he lowered his voice, peeped around the back of his chair to make sure that grandmother was not within hearing, "only I promised it to Dr. Carpenter."

"Of the First Methodist?" Baber's dad sounded as if he did not believe it. "Aren't you afraid of his orthodoxy?"

Grandfather cleared his throat, smiled mischievously. "Frank, this is what the legal brethren would call a privileged communication."

This time when Baber's mother said they must go, that Aunt Tassie would be expecting them this evening, he did not protest. He did not say, "Aw Mom, do we hafta? This is Christmas, Mom!" No, he was as surprised as his mother how quickly he got his rubbers on and put on his muffler and overcoat—and even remembered to help his dad into his. I want to go now, he said to himself, I want to go before grandmother turns on the overhead lights, so I can remember grandfather sitting there like that, so I can remember how his voice sounded, I want to go before I break down and bawl.

Fleur-de-Blé

CAMILLE LEMONNIER

I

IN Wavre that evening, in a house on the square, special preparations were being made to celebrate the coming of St. Nicholas. It was the home of the baker, Hans Jans. In a room with two windows over the shop, a big fire and a little lamp shone upon the beautiful guest bed with its flowered chintz curtains and shiny, polished oak.

And in the bed was Fleur-de-Blé, the daughter of Jans.

From time to time, Granny Jans would put a log on the fire, taking care to turn over those which were already burned. Then pushing up her glasses onto the brown net which she wore over her white hair, she would tiptoe softly over to the bed.

"Fleur," she would say in a low voice, opening the curtains.

And then the red lamp would shine on Fleur-de-Blé lying buried in the bedclothes so that all that could be seen of her were her tiny little arms and her tiny little face.

Twice since the big clock in the shop had struck seven o'clock, Granny Jans had parted the bed curtains and called to Fleur-de-Blé and the child had not awakened.

She kept hearing the tinkling of the bell which Jans had fastened to the door of the shop and which rang every time a customer came in. That night a great many people were coming into the shop, for Jans had the best sugar-frosted gingerbread men in town.

And each time she heard the bell, Granny Jans would wonder:

"Will he buy one for six sous or one for a franc? The gingerbread men for one franc have white sugar hair and pink sugar cheeks and the ones for six sous are made of plain ginger bread.

156

Hans should have made some for two francs also, because there are always people who are willing to pay two francs if their neighbor has only paid one."

And Madame Jans stood behind the counter, looking out of the corner of her eye at the little boys with red noses and hands in their pockets who kept crowding around the window to look at the big cookie men, while Jans called out from the bakery:

"Come along, boys! Get your cookies quickly! Very soon now I'm going to start making the gingerbread man for Fleur."

And through the window of the little back room, Madame Jans saw Jans, in the firelight, his arms bare, in a white vest and white trousers. He was moving back and forth past his assistants who were bent over the kneading trough.

Jans took the biggest of his molds, buttered it, carefully poured in the dough and quickly thrust it into the oven.

"Ah, Fleur," thought Madame Jans, "what a beautiful *spike-laus* your papa is making for you! No one in Wavre can turn out such fine dough. Being the daughter of a baker myself, I certainly did well to marry Hans."

Then Jans pulled out from among the burning coals a wonderful man, blond and steaming. He loosened it with a quick tap and lifted it onto a board sprinkled with flour. It was a big fellow with long baggy trousers, a miter on his head, a wig down his back, a crosier in his hand and his pockets stuffed with toys. On the banderole running across his buckled shoes was written: Saint Nicholas.

In sheer admiration, the first assistant baker put his hand to his nose and the second slapped his thigh.

Hans, seeing this, reproved them severely:

"Dirty boys! What do you mean by touching your noses and your trousers with the hands that you use for kneading?"

Then Jans daubed pink icing on the cheeks and nose of the saint, scattered a few anise seeds on the wig, poured chocolate on the suit, spread a layer of gooseberry jelly along the waist-

coat, shook gold dust lightly over the cross and miter, and sprinkled white sugar on the hands and stockings. When he had finished he called his wife and showed her his masterpiece:

"Annette, the dough is mixed with bits of lemon and orange and raisins. I wouldn't sell this Saint Nicholas for five francs because, even for ten, I might never be able to make as good a one again."

And Fleur-de-Blé suddenly woke up and said in her tiny voice:

"Granny, that smells good. Has Saint Nicholas come yet?"

Fleur's little voice was like the ringing of a crystal glass when it has been struck with a knife and the sound is just about to die away.

"No, my child," replied Granny Jans putting the child's arms back under the covers, "Saint Nicholas hasn't come yet, but he is going through the town, that's why it smells good."

"Granny, why does Saint Nicholas smell good when he goes through the town?"

"Because Papa Jans is making his cookie men in the oven. There are some for six sous and some for one franc. Would you like a drink of water?"

"Granny," said the child, "I had a dream. I dreamed that Saint Nicholas came to get me in my bed. He had a big beard like the picture of God that Godmother Dictus gave me. And I said, 'Good day, Saint Nicholas, patron saint of good children.' And he answered, 'Fleur-de-Blé, I am indeed your patron saint, for you are a good little girl and I like good little children. Come with me.' And I said, 'Where to, good Saint Nicholas?' And he answered, 'To play in Paradise.' Then mamma and papa and granny gave me a white dress and they told me that they would come later. And when I got to Paradise, there were little girls and little boys playing all in white.

"They put their arms around me and told me that they played like that night and day, all the time, and there were toys that were much more beautiful than the ones papa gave me last New Year's.

"And the little girls had dolls as big as they were that curtsied and said, 'Thank you, Madame.'

"And then Saint Nicholas kissed me and said:

'Have fun, I love you. You will have dolls just like theirs which will also say, 'Thank you, Madame.' And then, Granny, I smelt something good and woke up."

II

"Here is Dr. Trousseau who has come to see you, Fleur-de-Blé!" exclaimed Granny suddenly.

Monsieur Trousseau pushed open the door. He came straight over to the bed.

"It's Papa Trousseau. How are you, my little lady?" he said. "Let's feel your pulse . . . Hum! hum! And the tongue? You have some color in your cheeks, little one. So we've had some excitement! Oh yes, Saint Nicholas!"

Monsieur Trousseau put his hand on the child's heart, then he laid his ear on her chest. Suddenly he rolled his eyes beneath his heavy gray eyebrows like the balls that the players use to knock down the nine pins at the *Coq sans Tête*. At this moment, like shadows, Jans and his wife entered the room on tiptoe, holding their breath. Monsieur began to puff out his cheeks to hide

159

his anxiety. Then he picked up his hat and his umbrella and ran
to the vicarage to notify the vicar. The vicar was very fond of
the Jans'. Sometimes in the summertime he would come in to
eat pie with them on Sundays.

When the clock struck nine, Fleur-de-Blé woke up.

"Granny, hasn't Saint Nicholas come yet?"

"No, Fleur, he hasn't come yet, but he's going through the
square."

"Oh, Granny, let me see Saint Nicholas going through the
square!"

"Fleur, don't worry. Saint Nicholas doesn't give anything to
children who see him."

"Oh, Granny, down in the square I can hear little Paul crying, 'Saint Nicholas is going by behind the house of Butcher
Canu,' and little Marie calling back, 'No, he won't be going by
for an hour.' "

Father Jans, hearing the sound of voices, came up stairs, and
having wrapped Fleur-de-Blé in a wool petticoat, he carried
her over to the window and raised the little white curtain.

Snow had fallen during the afternoon. There were about
three inches on the ground. The houses on the square were
framed in black beneath a white wig. Snowflakes were still
falling from a reddish sky, as fleece falls from sheep in May
under the clipper's shears. Lights were moving and in front of
the shops the lamps outlined the window panes in red on the
white ground. But what Fleu-de-Blé looked at especially were
the big umbrellas of the market women with their wooden shoes
decorated with tufts of wool and their hands under their aprons.
They were sitting in the middle of the square in front of tables
covered with serge cloths with blue and white checks on which
were spread barley sugar lions, flags of Notre Dame de Hal,
dolls with wooden heads, macaroons, Dinant cookies and
spikelaus.

And as the little wads of snow danced about and powdered

the umbrellas and made the wicks of the candles sputter, the
children of the poor people, with snively noses and thumbs in
their mouths, stared speechlessly, first at the knickknacks on
display and then at the marketwomen who were blowing on
their little earthen warming pans so that they sent out showers
of sparks.

From time to time, Fleur-de-Blé would hear the banging of
a door on the street. Occasionally a neighbor would leave his
house to go to the tavern; or another neighbor, in wooden shoes,
a basket in her hand, would carefully lock her door and bustle
over toward the umbrellas. At times she could catch only shreds
of conversation which trailed off into the evening.

But the snow deadened all these sounds and made them seem
as soft as velvet.

"I can see old Lisbeth very plainly," she said. "She is sweeping
the snow in front of her door, and she has a pail of cinders beside her to throw on the sidewalk after she's through sweeping
it. I can see Monsieur Onuzel, the pastryman, too. He is moving his hands about in his pockets while he smokes his fine porcelain pipe. He's looking over at the gingerbread men that Papa
made this morning. But I'm glad I didn't see Saint Nicholas,
and I want to go back to my bed."

Papa Jans put Fleur back in bed and kissed her.

"Sleep well, my Fleur," he said. "Your papa will make the
house very beautiful to receive Saint Nicholas. We'll spread on
the hearth the fine red rug with black flowers that we hang in
the window between two candles when Monsieur le curé goes
by in the procession."

And Grandmother Jans said:

"Dear God, how can one help loving a child who always goes
to bed without crying and who is always nice to her granny!"

Soon there was no sound in the room but the weak breathing
of the child and the noise of the knitting needles which were
clicking in the dry little hands of Grandmother Jans.

I I I

Suddenly the vicar, his tricorne on his head, opened the door of the shop. Papa Jans and Mamma Jans were counting out their money, separating the little sous, the big sous and the francs.

"It's I, my friends," he greeted them. "Good evening, Madame Jans. I've come to see if Fleur-de-Blé has put her little wooden shoe out on the hearth."

"Ah, it's the vicar," said Jans taking his pipe out of his mouth and leading him into the little room behind the shop. "Granny Jans will be very glad to see you."

At that moment the door of the upstairs room opened and Granny Jans cried out breathlessly:

"Jans! Jans!"

"Ah, yes," said Jans. "Fleur-de-Blé keeps calling me all the time to talk about Saint Nicholas. Those angels! Come up, Monsieur le vicaire."

"Dear Heaven!" cried Granny when she saw them. "Fleur-de-Blé has just got up and she wants to go down into the square. Your blessing, Monsieur le vicaire."

Her eyes wide, Fleur-de-Blé was gazing sightlessly at the windows.

"My Fleur!" cried Jans in wild alarm.

And he put the little girl back under the covers.

The vicar looking at Jans saw that he was as white as a sheet and that his hands were trembling.

Fleur-de-Blé gently closed her eyes and went back to sleep. But her hands, as transparent as the porcelain of the little night lamp, continued to move about uncertainly on the quilt.

"Courage, Jans," said the vicar gently, placing his hand on the baker's shoulder. "Think of our Lord and of his Passion."

But Jans, despair in his eyes, was looking at his child and did not hear.

Then Fleur began to move her lips softly as though she were

162

talking very low to someone who was on the other side of the night; and in the end she spoke these words aloud:

"I am Fleur-de-Blé, the daughter of Baker Jans on the square."

She stopped for a moment and then continued:

"Hello. . . . Always playing . . . Dolls . . . Thank you, Madame."

Her voice was like the very soft music of a violin, and as she spoke, a pale little smile played about her mouth like a bright cloud that melts into the evening sky. Jans saw her lovely little arm come out from under the sheets. She slowly waved her hand toward the empty space. It was the same gesture she made when she said, "Good day, Mr. Crow." when she was reciting one of her fables. Then, after a half an hour Fleur-de-Blé woke up again.

"Hasn't Saint Nicholas come yet?" she asked.

"No, Fleur," said Jans. "Saint Nicholas won't come until midnight."

"At, that's a long time," said the little girl. "But he comes from far away and his donkey is tired. Papa will put out an armchair for Saint Nicholas and a chair for his donkey."

"I won't forget," said Jans, "I will put out the fine armchair which stands in the corner and which Aunt Catherine sits in when she comes to see us at Christmas."

Toward eleven o'clock, Jans went down to lay out on plates the Saint Nicholas presents for Fleur-de-Blé. He had bought a big doll with eyes of mother-of-pearl, curly hair the color of butter and a jointed body. He had also bought a cradle lined with blue satin which swung on a half moon. For these he had paid in all fifteen francs.

He put the doll in the cradle and laid in a big box the silk mantilla, the dress of barège and the pink plush hat which made up the doll's wardrobe. Jans smiled to himself as he thought of the joy of his Fleurette. Some of his old gaiety had returned as he handled all these things.

He took off his shoes and mounted the stairs twice in his

stocking feet; the first time to carry up the plates of candy, the second to carry the doll, the cradle and the box of doll's clothes. He placed them all in the closet off the room where Fleur-de-Blé was sleeping.

And Fleur-de-Blé went on sleeping.

"I want to see her joy when she gets her presents. That's why I'm staying," said the vicar to Granny Jans.

But that was not why the vicar was waiting.

He took his prayer book from his pocket and began to read beside the little lamp, his lips moving as he murmured to himself. But from time to time, he would glance over at Fleur-de-Blé and then he would say to himself, closing his book, and sliding in a finger so as not to lose the place:

"Oh Lord, my God, have pity on these poor people!"

IV

When midnight came, Fleur-de-Blé heard a noise in the house, and opening her eyes, she asked if that were the donkey of Saint Nicholas coming down the chimney. And Jans, who knew very well that it was his boys in the bakery, raised his big eyebrows that were covered with flour and replied that he could certainly hear the sound of the donkey's wooden shoes.

And he added:

"I'll go and see in a minute."

He pressed his ear to the door, pretending to listen, his head bent. Then he went downstairs, with an air of great mystery, taking slow, stealthy steps with his big, long legs. And suddenly from down below came shouts of joy.

It was Jans.

"Fleur! My Fleur! He has been here! Open your little hands."

When he reappeared in the room he was holding the arms of the chair that was kept for Aunt Catherine. And in the armchair were spread out the cradle, the doll, the box, the gingerbread man and the plates of candies.

"Thank you, Saint Nicholas, thank you for Fleur," he called out in the direction of the stairs.

And when the child saw the beautiful doll and the cradle, her little mouth curved into a smile of delight, the color of snow and lilies.

Then Jans showed her the dust on the armchair which he had put there himself by scraping his feet on it, and laughing heartily, he said:

"Look, that's from the donkey of your Mr. Saint Nicholas."

Just then, Fleur-de-Blé's little head began to droop; it was like a tree wounded by a stone which has been drained of all its sap. Looking very pale against the whiteness of the big pillow, with her lovely sad smile which didn't know where to go now, she fell asleep again. There was a heavy silence in the hall below. The clock in the shop struck one, and a dog whined softly in the neighboring courtyard.

"Monsieur le vicaire," cried Mother Jans, clasping her hands, "I think something terrible has happened to us."

"Good Mother Jans," replied the vicar raising his hand to heaven, "let us always remember Him to Whom everything is possible."

And there was silence again, a silence which from moment to moment became more grave around the big bed in which was lying the soul of the house. Outside the snow was rustling against the panes like a bird that is trying to get in. And Jans, his teeth chattering like someone with a fever, kept repeating to himself the name of Fleur.

While these things were happening in the Jans house, a bright, gay light filled the rooms of the house of fat Butcher Canu. The table was piled high with dolls and wooden horses, pipes, flags and drums. Suddenly the big man, who was putting on his night cap, looked up at the Jans house and said to his wife:

"Really, Zénobie, it's not natural. I see shadows moving back and forth on the white curtain. If Fleur were as healthy as

Zéphyrine and Annette, there would be no cause for alarm. But she is like a little feather that might be carried away by the first puff of wind."

And in all the city houses and the country houses, the children of the rich and the poor were sleeping at that hour, their heads resting on their arms, dreaming of the candies and toys that they would find when they woke up.

Granny Jans had let her knitting fall onto her lap and was sleeping beside the fire, her glasses on her nose. But neither Papa Jans nor Mamma Jans could think of sleeping. They stayed beside the bed, their hands clasped, not daring to look at one another for fear of showing their tears. And the vicar, his hands clasped like theirs, said to himself:

"Fleur's breathing is like the church clock when the summer wind carries its sound far out into the country and it is just about to stop striking."

Fleur-de-Blé's breathing had become so faint that it could no longer be heard above the sputtering of the oil in the lamp and the snoring of Granny Jans.

When the good old lady awoke, she was astonished at first to find the vicar still there. But when she saw Papa Jans and Mamma Jans on their knees beside Fleur-de-Blé, she pulled out her big checked handkerchief and began to weep into it, sobbing like a little child.

Just then, Fleur-de-Blé awoke and very softly, so softly this time that Granny, who was a little deaf, could not hear her, she murmured:

"Good day, Saint Nicholas."

And still more softly:

" . . . day, Papa, Mamma, Granny."

Fleur-de-Blé slept until dawn. And as the day approached, her life, like a little bird returning to the sunny lands when the cold winds blow, returned to the great light. Quietly the lamp went down. A dreadful sadness came over the old furniture which had been caressed so often by her little hands. The ivory figure of Christ hanging on the wall seemed to droop on the cross.

It was the hour when the cocks crow. The children of Wavre, who had awakened earlier than usual, were listening at the doors to see if anyone were stirring in the house.

A cry resounded in the room.

"Ah, Monsieur le vicaire!" cried Jans, throwing himself into the arms of the priest.

"Jans, Fleur has just gone up to Paradise!" replied the vicar.

And since that time poor Mr. Jans has never made any more gingerbread men for the feast of Saint Nicholas.

TRANSLATED BY JANE BANNARD GREENE

167

Christmas Eve

NICOLAI GOGOL

I

THE LAST day before Christmas had passed. A clear winter night had come; the stars peeped out; the moon rose majestically in the sky to light good people and all the world so that all might enjoy singing *kolyadki* [1] and praising the Lord. It was freezing harder than in the morning; but it was so still that the crunch of the snow under the boot could be heard half a mile away. Not one group of lads had appeared under the cottage windows yet; only the moon peeped in at them stealthily as though calling to the girls who were dressing up in their best to make haste and run out on the crunching snow. At that moment the smoke rose in puffs from a cottage chimney and passed like a cloud over the sky, and a witch, astride a broomstick, rose up in the air together with the smoke.

If the assessor of Sorotchintsy, in his cap edged with lambskin and cut like an Uhlan's, in his dark blue greatcoat lined with black astrakhan, had driven by at that minute with his three hired horses and the fiendishly plaited whip with which it is his habit to urge on his coachman, he would certainly have noticed her, for there is not a witch in the world who could elude the eyes of the Sorotchintsy assessor. He can count on his fingers how many

---

[1] Among us it is the custom to sing under the window on Christmas Eve carols that are called *kolyadki*. The mistress or master or whoever is left in the house always drops into the singer's bag some sausage or bread or a copper or whatever he has plenty of. It is said that once upon a time there was a blockhead called Kolyada who was taken to be a god and that these *kolyadki* came from that. Who knows? It is not for plain folk like us to give our opinion about it. Last year Father Osip was for forbidding them to sing *kolyadki* about the farms, saying that folk were honoring Satan by doing so, though to tell the truth there is not a word about Kolyada in the *kolyadki*. They often sing about the birth of Christ, and at the end wish good health to the master, the mistress, the children and all the household.

little pigs every peasant woman's sow has farrowed and how much linen is lying in her chest and just which of her clothes and household belongings her goodman pawns on Sunday at the tavern. But the Sorotchintsy assessor did not drive by, and, indeed, what business is it of his? He has his own district. Meanwhile, the witch rose so high in the air that she was only a little black patch gleaming up aloft. But wherever that little patch appeared, there the stars one after another vanished. Soon the witch had gathered a whole sleeveful of them. Three or four were still shining. All at once from the opposite side another little patch appeared, grew larger, began to lengthen out and was no longer a little patch. A short-sighted man would never have made out what it was, even if he had put the wheels of the Commissar's chaise on his nose by way of spectacles. At first it looked like a regular German;[2] the narrow little face, continually twisting and turning and sniffing at everything, ended in a little round heel, like our pigs' snouts; the legs were so thin, that if the mayor of Yareskovo had had legs like that, he would certainly have broken them in the first Cossack dance. But behind he was for all the world a district attorney in uniform, for he had a tail as long and pointed as the uniform coattails are nowadays. It was only from the goat-beard under his chin, from the little horns sticking up on his forehead, and from his being no whiter than a chimney sweep, that one could tell that he was not a German or a district attorney, but simply the devil, who had one last night left him to wander about the wide world and teach good folk to sin. On the morrow when the first bells rang for matins, he would run with his tail between his legs straight off to his lair.

Meanwhile the devil stole silently up to the moon and stretched his hand out to seize it, but drew it back quickly as though he were scorched, sucked his fingers and danced about, then ran up from the other side and again skipped away and drew back his hand. But in spite of all his failures the sly devil did not

---

[2] Among us every one is called a German who comes from a foreign country; even if he is a Frenchman, a Hungarian, or a Swede—he is still a German.

give up his tricks. Running up, he suddenly seized the moon with both hands; grimacing and blowing, he kept flinging it from one hand to the other, like a peasant who has picked up an ember for his pipe with bare fingers; at last, he hurriedly put it in his pocket and ran on as though nothing had happened.

No one in Dikanka noticed that the devil had stolen the moon. It is true the district clerk, coming out of the tavern on all fours, saw the moon for no reason whatever dancing in the sky and swore he had to the whole village; but people shook their heads and even made fun of him. But what motive led the devil to this lawless act? Why, this was how it was; he knew that the rich Cossack, Tchub, had been invited by the sacristan to a supper of frumenty at which a kinsman of the sacristan's, who had come from the bishop's choir, wore a dark blue coat and could take the very lowest bass note, the mayor, the Cossack Sverbyguz and some others were to be present, and at which besides the Christmas frumenty there were to be mulled vodka, saffron vodka and good things of all sorts. And meanwhile his daughter, the greatest beauty in the village, was left at home, and there was no doubt that the blacksmith, a very strong and fine young fellow, would pay her a visit, and him the devil hated more than Father Kondrat's sermons. In his spare time the blacksmith had taken up painting and was reckoned the finest artist in the whole countryside. Even the Cossack officer L——ko, who was still strong and hearty in those days, sent for him to Poltava expressly to paint a paling fence round his house. All the bowls from which the Cossacks of Dikanka supped their beetroot soup had been painted by the blacksmith. He was a God-fearing man and often painted ikons of the saints: even now you may find his Luke the Evangelist in the church of T. But the triumph of his art was a picture painted on the church wall in the chapel on the right. In it he depicted St. Peter on the Day of Judgment with the keys in his hand driving the Evil Spirit out of hell; the frightened devil was running in all directions, foreseeing his doom, while the sinners, who had been imprisoned before, were

Russian, 19th century. Our Lady of the Sign

chasing him and striking him with whips, blocks of wood and anything they could get hold of. While the artist was working at this picture and painting it on a big wooden board, the devil did all he could to hinder him; he gave him a nudge on the arm, unseen, blew some ashes from the forge in the smithy and scattered them on the picture; but, in spite of it all, the work was finished, the picture was brought into the church and let into the wall of the side chapel, and from that day the devil has sworn to revenge himself on the blacksmith.

He had only one night left to wander upon earth; but he was looking for some means of venting his wrath on the blacksmith that night. And that was why he made up his mind to steal the moon, reckoning that old Tchub was lazy and slow to move, and the sacristan's cottage a good long step away: the road passed by cross paths beside the mills and the graveyard and went round a ravine. On a moonlight night mulled vodka and saffron vodka might have tempted Tchub; but in such darkness it was doubtful whether any one could drag him from the stove and bring him out of the cottage. And the blacksmith, who had for a long time been on bad terms with him, would on no account have ventured, strong as he was, to visit the daughter when the father was at home.

And so, as soon as the devil had hidden the moon in his pocket, it was at once so dark all over the world that not every one could have found the way to the tavern, let alone to the sacristan's. The witch gave a shriek when she suddenly found herself in darkness. Then the devil running up, all bows and smiles, put his arm around her and began whispering in her ear the sort of thing that is usually whispered to all the female sex. Things are queerly arranged in our world! All who live in it are always trying to outdo and imitate one another. In old days the judge and the police captain were the only ones in Mirgorod who used to wear cloth overcoats lined with sheepskin in the winter, while all the petty officials wore plain sheepskin; but nowadays the assessor and the chamberlain have managed to get themselves new cloth greatcoats lined with astrakhan. The year before last the treasury clerk and the district clerk bought dark blue duck at sixty kopecks the yard. The sexton has got himself nankeen trousers for the summer and a striped waistcoat of camel's hair. In fact every one tries to be somebody! When will folks give up being vain! I am ready to bet that many would be surprised to see the devil carrying on in that way. What is most annoying is that, no doubt, he fancies himself a handsome fellow, though his figure is a shameful sight. With a face, as Foma Grigoryevitch used to say, the abomination of abominations, yet even he plays the gallant! But in the sky and under the sky it was growing so dark that there was no seeing what followed between them.

"So you have not been to see the sacristan in his new cottage, mate?" said the Cossack Tchub coming out at his door to a tall lean peasant in a short sheepskin, whose stubby beard showed that for at least a fortnight it had not been touched by the broken piece of scythe with which for lack of a razor peasants usually shave their beards. "There will be a fine drinking party there tonight!" Tchub went on, grinning as he spoke. "If only we are not late!"

Hereupon Tchub set straight the belt that closely girt his sheepskin, pulled his cap more firmly on his head and gripped his whip, the terror and the menace of tiresome dogs; but glancing upwards, he stopped. "What the devil! Look! look, Panas . . . !"

"What?" articulated his friend, and he too turned his face upwards.

"What, indeed! There is no moon!"

"What a nuisance! There really is no moon."

"That's just it, there isn't!" Tchub brought out with some annoyance at his friend's imperturbable indifference. "You don't care, I'll be bound."

"Some devil," Tchub went on, wiping his moustaches with his sleeve, "must needs go and meddle—may he never have a glass of

vodka to drink in the mornings, the dog! Upon my word, it's as
though to mock us. . . . As I sat indoors I looked out of the
window and the night was lovely! It was light, the snow was
sparkling in the moonlight; you could see everything as though
it were day. And here before I'm out of the door, you can't see
your hand before your face! May he break his teeth on a crust of
buckwheat bread!"

Tchub went on grumbling and scolding for a long while, and
at the same time he was hesitating what to decide. He had a
desperate longing to gossip over all sorts of nonsense at the
sacristan's, where no doubt the mayor was already sitting, as well
as the bass choir singer, and Mikita, the tar-dealer, who used to
come once a fortnight on his way to Poltava, and who cracked
such jokes that all the village worthies held their sides with
laughing. Already in his mind's eye Tchub saw the mulled vodka
on the table. All this was alluring, it is true; but the darkness of
the night recalled the charms of laziness, so dear to every Cossack.
How nice it would be now to lie on the oven step with his legs
tucked under him, quietly smoking his pipe and listening through
a luxurious drowsiness to the songs and carols of the light-hearted
lads and lasses who gathered in groups under the windows! He
would undoubtedly have decided on the latter course had he been
alone; but for the two together, it was not so dreary and terrible
to go through the dark night; besides, he did not care to seem
sluggish and cowardly to others. When he had finished scolding
he turned again to his friend.

"So there is no moon, mate?"

"No!"

"It's strange really! Let me have a pinch of snuff! You have
splendid snuff, mate! Where do you get it?"

"Splendid! Devil a bit of it!" answered the friend, shutting the
birch-bark snuff box with patterns pricked out upon it. "It
wouldn't make an old hen sneeze!"

"I remember," Tchub still went on, "the innkeeper, Zuzulya,
once brought me some snuff from Nyezhin. Ah, that was snuff!

it was good snuff! So how is it to be, mate? It's dark, you know?"

"So maybe we'll stay at home," his friend brought out, taking hold of the door-handle.

If his friend had not said that, Tchub would certainly have made up his mind to stay at home; but now something seemed egging him on to oppose it. "No, mate, let us go! It won't do, we must go!"

Even as he was saying it, he was vexed with himself that he had said it. He very much disliked turning out on such a night, but it was a comfort to him that he was acting on his own decision and not following advice.

His friend looked round and scratched his shoulders with the handle of his whip, without the slightest sign of vexation on his face, like a man to whom it is a matter of complete indifference whether he sits at home or turns out—and the two friends set off on their road.

Now let us see what Tchub's daughter, the beauty, was doing all by herself. Before Oksana was seventeen, people were talking about nothing but her in almost the whole world, both on this side of Dikanka and on the other side of Dikanka. The lads were all at one in declaring that there never had been and never would be a finer girl in the village. Oksana heard and knew all that was said about her and, like a beauty, was full of caprices. If, instead of a checked skirt and an apron, she had been dressed as a lady, she could never have kept a servant. The lads ran after her in crowds, but, losing patience, by degrees forsook the wilful beauty, and turned to others who were not so spoiled. Only the blacksmith was persistent and would not abandon his courtship, although he was treated not a whit better than the rest. When her father went out, Oksana spent a long while yet dressing herself in her best and prinking before a little looking glass in a pewter frame; she could not tear herself away from admiring herself.

"What put it into folks' heads to spread it abroad that I am pretty?" she said, as it were without thinking, simply to talk to herself about something. "Folks lie, I am not pretty at all!"

But the fresh living face reflected in the looking-glass, in its childish youthfulness, with its sparkling black eyes and inexpressibly charming smile that stirred the soul, at once proved the contrary.

"Can my black eyebrows and my eyes," the beauty went on, still holding the mirror, "be so beautiful that there are none like them in the world? What is there pretty in that turned-up nose, and in the cheeks and the lips? Is my black hair pretty? Ough, my curls might frighten one in the evening, they twist and twine round my head like long snakes! I see now that I am not pretty at all!" And, moving the looking glass a little further away, she cried out: "No, I am pretty! Ah, how pretty! Wonderful! What a joy I shall be to the man whose wife I become! How my husband will admire me! He'll be wild with joy. He will kiss me to death!"

"Wonderful girl!" whispered the blacksmith, coming in softly. "And hasn't she a little conceit! She's been standing looking in the mirror for an hour and can't tear herself away, and praising herself aloud, too!"

"Yes, lads, I am a match for you? Just look at me!" the pretty coquette went on: "how gracefully I step: my shift is embroidered with red silk. And the ribbons on my head! You will never see richer braid! My father bought me all this that the finest young man in the world may marry me." And, laughing, she turned round and saw the blacksmith. . . .

She uttered a shriek and stood still, coldly facing him.

The blacksmith's hands dropped helplessly to his sides.

It is hard to describe what the dark face of the lovely girl expressed. There was sternness in it, and through the sternness a sort of defiance of the embarrassed blacksmith, and at the same time a hardly perceptible flush of vexation delicately suffused her face; and all this was so mingled and so indescribably pretty that to give her a million kisses was the best thing that could have been done at the moment.

"Why have you come here?" was how Oksana began. "Do you want me to shove you out of the door with a spade? You are all very clever at coming to see us. You sniff out in a minute when there are no fathers in the house. Oh, I know you! Well, is my chest ready!"

"It will be ready, my little heart, it will be ready after Christmas. If only you knew how I have worked at it; for two nights I didn't leave the smithy. But, there, no priest's wife will have a chest like it. The iron I bound it with is better than what I put on the officer's chariot, when I worked at Poltava. And how it will be painted! You won't find one like it if you wander over the whole neighborhood with your little white feet! Red and blue flowers will be scattered over the whole ground. It will glow like fire. Don't be angry with me! Allow me at least to speak to you, to look at you!"

"Who's forbidding you? Speak and look!"

Hereupon she sat down on the bench, glanced again at the looking glass and began arranging her hair. She looked at her neck, at her new shift, embroidered in red silk, and a subtle feeling of complacency could be read on her lips and fresh cheeks, and was reflected in her eyes.

"Allow me to sit beside you," said the blacksmith.

"Sit down," said Oksana, with the same emotion still perceptible on her lips and in her gratified eyes.

"Wonderful, lovely Oksana, allow me to kiss you!" ventured the blacksmith, growing bolder, and he drew her towards him with the intention of snatching a kiss. But Oksana turned away her cheek, which had been exceedingly close to the blacksmith's lips, and pushed him away.

"What more do you want? When there's honey he must have a spoonful! Go away, your hands are harder than iron. And you smell of smoke. I believe you have smeared me all over with your soot."

Then she picked up the looking glass and began prinking again.

"She does not love me!" the blacksmith thought to himself,

hanging his head. "It's all play to her while I stand before her like a fool and cannot take my eyes off her. And I should like to stand before her always and never to take my eyes off her! Wonderful girl! What would I not give to know what is in her heart, and whom she loves. But no, she cares for nobody. She is admiring herself; she is tormenting poor me, while I am so sad that everything is darkness to me. I love her as no man in the world ever has loved or ever will."

"Is it true that your mother's a witch?" Oksana brought out, and she laughed. And the blacksmith felt that everything within him was laughing. That laugh echoed as it were at once in his heart and in his softly thrilling veins, and for all that his soul was vexed that he had not the right to kiss that sweetly laughing face.

"What care I for mother? You are father and mother to me and all that is precious in the world. If the Tsar summoned me and said: 'Smith Vakula, ask me for all that is best in my kingdom, I will give you anything. I will bid them make you a golden forge and you shall work with silver hammers.' 'I don't care,' I should say to the Tsar, 'for precious stones or a golden forge nor for all your kingdom: give me rather my Oksana.'"

"You see, what a fellow you are! Only my father's no fool either. You'll see that, when he doesn't marry your mother!" Oksana said, smiling slily. "But the girls are not here. . . . What's the meaning of it? We ought to have been singing long ago, I am getting tired of waiting."

"Let them stay away, my beauty!"

"I should hope not! I expect the lads will come with them. And then there will be dances. I can fancy what funny stories they will tell!"

"So you'll be merry with them?"

"Yes, merrier than with you. Ah! some one knocked; I expect it is the girls and the lads."

"What's the use of my staying longer?" the blacksmith said to himself. "She is jeering at me. I am no more to her than an old rusty horseshoe. But if that's so, anyway I won't let another man laugh at me. If only I see for certain that she likes some one better than me, I'll teach him to keep off. . . ."

A knock at the door and a cry of "Open!" ringing out sharply in the frost interrupted his reflections.

"Stay, I'll open the door," said the blacksmith, and he went out intending in his vexation to break the ribs of any one who might be there.

The frost grew sharper, and up aloft it turned so cold that the devil kept hopping from one hoof to the other and blowing into his fists, trying to warm his frozen hands. And indeed it is small wonder that he should be cold, being used day after day to knocking about in hell, where, as we all know, it is not as cold as it is with us in winter, and where, putting on his cap and standing before the hearth, like a real cook, he fries sinners with as much satisfaction as a peasant woman fries a sausage at Christmas.

The witch herself felt that it was cold, although she was warmly clad; and so, throwing her arms upwards, she stood with one foot out, and putting herself into the attitude of a man flying along on skates, without moving a single muscle, she dropped through the air, as though on an ice slope, and straight into her chimney.

The devil set off after her in the same way. But as the creature is nimbler than any dandy in stockings, there is no wonder that he reached the top of the chimney almost on the neck of his mistress, and both found themselves in a roomy oven among the pots.

The witch stealthily moved back the oven door to see whether her son, Vakula, had invited visitors to the cottage; but seeing that there was no one, except the sacks that lay in the middle of the floor, she crept out of the oven, flung off her warm pelisse, set herself to rights, and no one could have told that she had been riding on a broom the minute before.

Vakula's mother was not more than forty years old. She was

neither handsome nor ugly. Indeed, it is hard to be handsome at such an age. However, she was so clever at alluring even the steadiest Cossacks (who, it may not be amiss to observe, do not care much about beauty) that the mayor and the sacristan, Osip Nikiforovitch (if his wife were not at home, of course), and the Cossack, Korny Tchub, and the Cossack, Kassian Sverbyguz, were all dancing attendance on her. And it must be said to her credit that she was very skilful in managing them: not one of them dreamed that he had a rival. If a God-fearing peasant or a gentleman (as the Cossacks call themselves) wearing a cape with a hood went to church on Sunday or, if the weather was bad, to the tavern, how could he fail to look in on Soloha, eat curd dumplings with sour cream, and gossip in the warm cottage with its chatty and agreeable mistress? And the Cossack would purposely go a long way round before reaching the tavern, and would call that "looking in on his way." And when Soloha went to church on a holiday, dressed in a bright-checked *plahta*[3] with a cotton *zapaska*,[3] and above it a dark blue overskirt on the back of which gold flourishes were embroidered, and took up her stand close to the right side of the choir, the sacristan would be sure to begin coughing and unconsciously screw up his eyes in her direction; the mayor would smooth his moustaches, begin twisting the curl behind his ear, and say to the man standing next to him: "Ah, a nice woman, a devil of a woman!" Soloha would bow to each one of them, and each one would think that she was bowing to him alone.

But any one fond of meddling in other people's business would notice at once that Soloha was most gracious to the Cossack Tchub. Tchub was a widower. Eight stacks of corn always stood before his cottage. Two pairs of stalwart oxen poked their heads out of the wattled barn by the roadside and mooed every time they saw their crony, the cow, or their uncle, the stout bull, pass.

---

[3] Russian women sometimes wore a skirt made of two separate pieces of material held together at the waist, the front section being the *zapaska*, the back the *plahta*.

A bearded billy goat used to clamber on to the very roof, from which he would bleat in a harsh voice like the police captain's, taunting the turkeys when they came out into the yard, and turning his back when he saw his enemies, the boys, who used to jeer at his beard. In Tchub's trunks there was plenty of linen and many full coats and old-fashioned over dresses with gold lace on them; his wife had been fond of fine clothes. In his vegetable patch, besides poppies, cabbages and sunflowers, two fields were sown every year with tobacco. All this Soloha thought that it would not be amiss to join to her own farm, and already reckoning in what good order it would be when it passed into her hands, she felt doubly well disposed to old Tchub. And to prevent her son Vakula from courting Tchub's daughter [4] and succeeding in getting possession of it all himself (then he would very likely not let her interfere in anything), she had recourse to the common maneuver of all dames of forty—that is, setting Tchub at loggerheads with the blacksmith as often as she could. Possibly these sly tricks and subtlety were the reason that the old women were beginning here and there, particularly when they had drunk a drop too much at some merry gathering, to say that Soloha was certainly a witch, that the lad Kizyakolupenko had seen a tail on her back no bigger than a peasant woman's distaff; that, no longer ago than the Thursday before last, she had run across the road in the form of a black cat; that on one occasion a sow had run up to the priest's wife, had crowed like a cock, put Father Kondrat's cap on her head and run away again. . . .

It happened that just when the old women were talking about this, a cowherd, Tymish Korostyavy, came up. He did not fail to tell them how in the summer, just before St. Peter's Fast, when he had lain down to sleep in the stable, putting some straw under his head, he saw with his own eyes a witch, with her hair down, in nothing but her shift, begin milking the cows, and he could not stir he was so spellbound, and she had smeared his

---

[4] Had her son married Tchub's daughter, she could not by the rules of the Russian Church have married Tchub—[*Translator's Note*]

lips with something so nasty that he was spitting the whole day afterwards. But all that was somewhat doubtful, for the only one who can see a witch is the assessor of Sorotchintsy. And so all the notable Cossacks waved their hands impatiently when they heard such tales. "They are lying, the bitches!" was their usual answer.

After she had crept out of the stove and set herself to rights, Soloha, like a good housewife, began tidying up and putting everything in its place; but she did not touch the sacks. "Vakula brought those in, let him take them out himself!" she thought. Meanwhile the devil, who had chanced to turn round just as he was flying into the chimney, had caught sight of Tchub arm-in-arm with his neighbor already a long way from home. Instantly he flew out of the chimney, cut across their road and began flinging up heaps of frozen snow in all directions. A blizzard sprang up. All was whiteness in the air. The snow zigzagged like network behind and in front and threatened to plaster up the eyes, the mouth and the ears of the friends. And the devil flew back to the chimney again in the firm conviction that Tchub would go back home with his neighbor, would find the blacksmith there and probably give him such a dressing-down that it would be a long time before he would be able to handle a brush and paint offensive caricatures.

As a matter of fact, as soon as the blizzard began and the wind blew straight in their faces, Tchub expressed his regret, and pulling his hood further down on his head showered abuse on himself, the devil and his friend. His annoyance was feigned, however. Tchub was really glad of the snowstorm. They had still eight times as far to go as they had gone already before they would reach the sacristan's. They turned round. The wind blew on the back of their heads, but they could see nothing through the whirling snow.

"Stay, mate! I fancy we are going wrong," said Tchub, after walking on a little. "I do not see a single cottage. Oh, what a snowstorm! You go a little that way, mate, and see whether you find the road, and meanwhile I'll look this way. It was the foul fiend put it into my head to go trudging out in such a storm! Don't forget to shout when you find the road. Oh what a heap of snow Satan has driven into my eyes!"

The road was not to be seen, however. Tchub's friend, turning off, wandered up and down in his long boots, and at last came straight upon the tavern. This lucky find so cheered him that he forgot everything and, shaking the snow off, walked straight in, not worrying himself in the least about the friend he had left on the road. Meanwhile Tchub fancied that he had found the road. Standing still, he fell to shouting at the top of his voice, but, seeing that his friend did not appear, he made up his mind to go on alone. After walking on a little he saw his own cottage. Snowdrifts lay all about it and on the roof. Clapping his frozen hands together, he began knocking at the door and shouting peremptorily to his daughter to open it.

"What do you want here?" the blacksmith called grimly, as he came out.

Tchub, recognizing the blacksmith's voice, stepped back a little. "Ah, no, it's not my cottage," he said to himself. "The blacksmith doesn't come into my cottage. Though, as I come to look well, it is not the blacksmith's either. Whose cottage can it be? I know! I didn't recognize it! It's where lame Levtchenko lives, who has lately married a young wife. His is the only cottage that is like mine. I did think it was a little queer that I had reached home so soon. But Levtchenko is at the sacristan's now, I know that. Why is the blacksmith here . . . ? Ah, a-ha! he comes to see his young wife. So that's it! Good . . . ! Now I understand it all."

"Who are you and what are you hanging about at people's doors for?" said the blacksmith more grimly than before, coming closer up to him.

"No, I am not going to tell him who I am," thought Tchub. "He'll give me a good drubbing, I shouldn't wonder, the damned brute." And, disguising his voice, he answered: "It's I, good man! I have come for your diversion to sing carols under your windows."

"Go to the devil with your carols!" Vakula shouted angrily. "Why are you standing there? Do you hear! Be off with you."

Tchub already had that prudent intention; but it annoyed him to be forced to obey the blacksmith's orders. It seemed as though some evil spirit nudged his arm and compelled him to say something contradictory. "Why are you bawling like that?" he said in the same voice. "I want to sing carols, and that's enough!"

"A-ha! I see words aren't enough for you!" And upon that Tchub felt a very painful blow on his shoulder.

"So I see you are beginning to fight now!" he said, stepping back a little.

"Be off, be off!" shouted the blacksmith, giving Tchub another shove.

"Well, you are!" said Tchub in a voice that betrayed pain, annoyance and timidity. "You are fighting in earnest, I see, and hitting pretty hard, too."

"Be off, be off!" shouted the blacksmith, and slammed the door.

"Look, how he swaggered!" said Tchub when he was left alone in the road. "Just try going near him! What a fellow! He's a somebody! Do you suppose I won't have the law of you? No, my dear lad, I am going straight to the Commissar. I'll teach you! I don't care if you are a blacksmith and a painter. But I must look at my back and shoulders; I believe they are black and blue. The devil's son must have hit hard. It's a pity that it is cold, and I don't want to take off my pelisse. You wait, you fiend of a blacksmith; may the devil give you a drubbing and your smithy, too; I'll make you dance! Ah, the damned rascal! But, I say, he is not at home, now. I expect Soloha is all alone. H'm . . . it's not far off, I might go! It's such weather now that no one will come in on us. There's no saying what may happen. . . . Oh dear, how hard that damned blacksmith did whack!"

Here Tchub, rubbing his back, set off in a different direction.

The agreeable possibilities awaiting him in a tryst with Soloha took off the pain a little and made him insensible even to the frost, the crackling of which could be heard on all the roads in spite of the howling of the storm. At moments a look of mawkish sweetness came into his face, though the blizzard soaped his beard and moustaches with snow more briskly than any barber who tyrannically holds his victim by the nose. But if everything had not been hidden by the criss-cross of the snow, Tchub might have been seen long afterwards stopping and rubbing his back as he brought out: "The damned blacksmith did whack hard!" and then going on his way again.

While the nimble dandy with the tail and goat-beard was flying out of the chimney and back again into the chimney, the pouch which hung on a shoulder-belt at his side and in which he had put the stolen moon chanced to catch in something in the stove and came open—and the moon took advantage of this accident to fly up through the chimney of Soloha's cottage and to float smoothly through the sky. Everything was flooded with light. It was as though there had been no snowstorm. The snow sparkled, a broad silvery plain, studded with crystal stars. The frost seemed less cold. Groups of lads and girls appeared with sacks. Songs rang out, and under almost every cottage window were crowds of carol-singers.

How wonderful is the light of the moon! It is hard to put into words how pleasant it is on such a night to mingle in a group of singing, laughing girls and among lads ready for every jest and sport which the gaily smiling night can suggest. It is warm under the thick pelisse; the cheeks glow brighter than ever from the frost and Old Sly himself prompts to mischief.

Groups of girls with sacks burst into Tchub's cottage and gathered round Oksana. The blacksmith was deafened by the shouts, the laughter, the stories. They vied with one another in telling the beauty some bit of news, in emptying their sacks and boasting of the little loaves, the sausages and curd dump-

185

lings of which they had already gathered a fair harvest from their singing. Oksana seemed to be highly pleased and delighted, she chatted first with one and then with another and laughed without ceasing.

With what envy and vexation the blacksmith looked at this gaiety, and this time he cursed the carol-singing, though he was passionately fond of it himself.

"Oh, Odarka!" said the light-hearted beauty, turning to one of the girls, "you have some new slippers. Ah, how pretty! And with gold on them! It's nice for you, Odarka, you have a man who will buy you anything, but I have no one to get me such splendid slippers."

"Don't grieve, my precious Oksana!" put in the blacksmith. "I will get you slippers such as not many a lady wears."

"You!" said Oksana, with a rapid and haughty glance at him. "I should like to know where you'll get hold of slippers such as I could put on my feet. Perhaps you will bring me the very ones the Tsaritsa wears?"

"You see the sort she wants!" cried the crowd of girls, laughing.

"Yes!" the beauty went on proudly, "all of you be my witnesses: if the blacksmith Vakula brings me the very slippers the Tsaritsa wears, here's my word on it, I'll marry him that very day."

The girls carried off the capricious beauty with them.

"Laugh away! laugh away!" thought the blacksmith as he followed them out. "I laugh at myself! I wonder and can't think what I have done with my senses! she does not love me—well, let her go! As though there were no one in the world but Oksana. Thank God, there are lots of fine girls besides her in the village. And what is Oksana? She'll never make a good housewife; the only thing she is good at is dressing up. No, it's enough! It's time I gave up playing the fool!"

But at the very time when the blacksmith was making up his mind to be resolute, some evil spirit set floating before him the laughing image of Oksana saying mockingly, "Get me the Tsaritsa's slippers, blacksmith, and I will marry you!" Everything within him was stirred and he could think of nothing but Oksana.

The crowds of carol singers, the lads in one party and the girls in another, hurried from one street to the next. But the blacksmith went on and saw nothing, and took no part in the merrymaking which he had once loved more than any.

Meanwhile the devil was making love in earnest at Soloha's: he kissed her hand with the same airs and graces as the assessor does the priest's daughter's, put his hand on his heart, sighed and said bluntly that, if she would not consent to gratify his passion and reward his devotion in the usual way, he was ready for anything: would fling himself in the water and let his soul go straight to hell. Soloha was not so cruel; besides, the devil as we know was alone with her. She was fond of seeing a crowd hanging about her and was rarely without company. That evening, however, she was expecting to spend alone, because all the noteworthy inhabitants of the village had been invited to keep Christmas Eve at the sacristan's. But it turned out otherwise: the devil had only just urged his suit, when suddenly they heard a knock and the voice of the stalwart mayor. Soloha ran to open the door, while the nimble devil crept into a sack that was lying on the floor.

The mayor, after shaking the snow off his cap and drinking a glass of vodka from Soloha's hand, told her that he had not gone to the sacristan's because it had begun to snow; and, seeing a light in her cottage, had dropped in, meaning to spend the evening with her.

The mayor had hardly had time to say this when they heard a knock at the door and the voice of the sacristan. "Hide me somewhere," whispered the mayor. "I don't want to meet the sacristan now."

Soloha thought for some time where to hide so bulky a

187

visitor; at last she selected the biggest coal sack. She shot the coal out into a barrel, and the stalwart mayor, moustaches, head, pelisse and all, crept into the sack.

The sacristan walked in, clearing his throat and rubbing his hands, and told her that no one had come to his party and that he was heartily glad of this opportunity to enjoy a visit to her and was not afraid of the snowstorm. Then he went closer to her and, with a cough and a smirk, touched her plump bare arm with his long fingers and said with an air expressive both of slyness and satisfaction: "And what have you here, magnificent Soloha?" and saying this he stepped back a little.

"How do you mean? My arm, Osip Nikiforovitch!" answered Soloha.

"H'm! your arm! He—he—he!" cried the sacristan, highly delighted with his opening. And he paced up and down the room.

"And what have you here, most precious Soloha?" he said with the same air, going up to her again, lightly touching her neck and skipping back again in the same way.

"As though you don't see, Osip Nikiforovitch!" answered Soloha; "my neck and my necklace on my neck."

"H'm! A necklace on your neck! He—he—he!" and the sacristan walked again up and down the room, rubbing his hands.

"And what have you here, incomparable Soloha . . . ?" There's no telling what the sacristan (a carnal-minded man) might have touched next with his long fingers, when suddenly they heard a knock at the door and the voice of the Cossack Tchub.

"Oh dear, someone who's not wanted!" cried the sacristan in alarm. "What now if I am caught here, a person of my position . . . ! It will come to Father Kondrat's ears. . . ."

But the sacristan's apprehensions were really of a different nature; he was more afraid that his doings might come to the knowledge of his better half, whose terrible hand had already turned his thick mane into a very scanty one. "For God's sake, virtuous Soloha!" he said, trembling all over, "your lovingkind-

ness, as it says in the Gospel of St. Luke, chapter thirt . . . thirt
. . . What a knocking, oh dear, what a knocking! Ough, hide
me somewhere!"

Soloha turned the coal out of another sack, and the sacristan,
whose proportions were not too ample, crept into it and settled
at the very bottom, so that another half-sack of coal might have
been put in on the top of him.

"Good evening, Soloha!" said Tchub, as he came into the
cottage. "Maybe you didn't expect me, eh? You didn't, did you?
Perhaps I am in the way . . . ?" Tchub went on with a good
humored and significant expression on his face, which betrayed
that his slow-moving mind was at work and preparing to utter
some sarcastic and amusing jest.

"Maybe you had some entertaining companion here . . . !
Maybe you have some one in hiding already? Eh?" And enchanted by this observation of his, Tchub laughed, inwardly
triumphant at being the only man who enjoyed Soloha's favor.
"Come, Soloha, let me have a drink of vodka now. I believe
my throat's frozen stiff with this damned frost. God has sent
us weather for Christmas Eve! How it has come on, do you
hear, Soloha, how it has come on . . . ? Ah, my hands are stiff,
I can't unbutton my sheepskin! How the storm has come
on. . . ."

"Open the door!" a voice rang out in the street accompanied
by a thump on the door.

"Some one is knocking," said Tchub standing still.

"Open!" the shout rang out louder still.

"It's the blacksmith!" cried Tchub, catching up his pelisse.
"I say, Soloha, put me where you like; for nothing in the world
will I show myself to that damned brute. May he have a pimple
as big as a haycock under each of his eyes, the devil's son!"

Soloha, herself alarmed, flew about like one distraught and,
forgetting what she was doing, signed to Tchub to creep into
the very same sack in which the sacristan was already sitting.
The poor sacristan dared not betray his pain by a cough or a

groan when the heavy Cossack sat down almost on his head and put a frozen boot on each side of his face.

The blacksmith walked in, not saying a word nor removing his cap, and almost fell down on the bench. It could be seen that he was in a very bad humor.

At the very moment when Soloha was shutting the door after him, some one knocked at the door again. This was the Cossack Sverbyguz. He could not be hidden in the sack, because no sack big enough could be found anywhere. He was more corpulent than the mayor and taller than Tchub's neighbor Panas. And so Soloha led him into the kitchen garden to hear from him there all that he had to tell her.

The blacksmith looked absent-mindedly at the corners of his cottage, listening from time to time to the voices of the carol singers floating far away through the village. At last his eyes rested on the sacks. "Why are those sacks lying there? They ought to have been cleared away long ago. This foolish love has turned me quite silly. Tomorrow's Christmas and rubbish of all sorts is still lying about the cottage. I'll carry them to the smithy!"

Hereupon the blacksmith stooped down to the huge sacks, tied them up more tightly and prepared to hoist them on his shoulders. But it was evident that his thoughts were straying, God knows where; or he would have heard how Tchub gasped when the hair of his head was twisted in the string that tied the sack and the stalwart mayor began hiccupping quite distinctly.

"Can nothing drive that wretched Oksana out of my head?" the blacksmith was saying. "I don't want to think about her; but I keep thinking and thinking and, as luck will have it, of her and nothing else. How is it that thoughts creep into the mind against the will? The devil! the sacks seem to have grown heavier than they were! Something besides coal must have been put into them. I am a fool! I forget that now everything seems heavier to me. In old days I could bend and unbend again a

copper coin or a horseshoe with one hand, and now I can't lift
sacks of coal. I shall be blown over by the wind next. . . . No!"
he cried, pulling himself together after a pause, "I am not a
weak woman! I won't let anyone make a mock of me! If there
were ten such sacks, I would lift them all." And he briskly
hoisted on his shoulders the sacks which two stalwart men could
not have carried. "I'll take this one too," he went on, picking
up the little one at the bottom of which the devil lay curled up.
"I believe I put my tools in this one." Saying this he went out
of the hut whistling the song: "I can't be bothered with a wife."

The singing, laughter and shouts sounded louder and louder
in the streets. The crowds of jostling people were reinforced by
newcomers from neighboring villages. The lads were full of mischief and mad pranks. Often among the carols some gay song
was heard which one of the young Cossacks had made up on
the spot. All at once one of the crowd would let out a begging
New Year's song instead of a carol and bawl at the top of his
voice:

> "Christmas faring!
> Be not sparing
> A tart or pie, please!
> Bowl of porridge!
> String of sausage!"

A roar of laughter rewarded the wag. Little windows were
thrown up and the withered hand of an old woman (the old
women, together with the sedate fathers, were the only people
left indoors) was thrust out with a sausage or a piece of pie.
The lads and the girls vied with one another in holding out
their sacks and catching their booty. In one place the lads,
coming together from all sides, surrounded a group of girls.
There was loud noise and clamor; one flung a snowball, another
pulled away a sack full of all sorts of good things. In another

191

place, the girls caught a lad, gave him a kick and sent him flying headlong with his sack into the snow. It seemed as though they were ready to make merry the whole night through. And, as though of design, the night was so splendidly warm! And the light of the moon seemed brighter still from the glitter of the snow.

The blacksmith stood still with his sacks. He fancied he heard among the crowd of girls the voice and shrill laugh of Oksana. Every vein in his body throbbed; flinging the sacks on the ground so that the sacristan at the bottom groaned over the bruise he received, and the major gave a loud hiccup, he strolled with the little sack on his shoulders together with a group of lads after a crowd of girls, among whom he heard the voice of Oksana.

"Yes, it is she! She stands like a queen, her black eyes sparkling. A handsome lad is telling her something. It must be amusing, for she is laughing. But she is always laughing." As it were unconsciously, he could not say how, the blacksmith squeezed his way through the crowd and stood beside her.

"Oh, Vakula, you here! Good evening!" said the beauty, with the smile which almost drove Vakula mad. "Well, have you sung many carols? Oh, but what a little sack! And have you got the slippers that the Tsaritsa wears? Get me the slippers and I will marry you . . . !" And laughing she ran off with the other girls.

The blacksmith stood as though rooted to the spot. "No, I cannot bear it; it's too much for me . . ." he brought out at last. "But, my God, why is she so fiendishly beautiful? Her eyes, her words and everything, well, they scorch me, they fairly scorch me. . . . No, I cannot master myself. It's time to put an end to it all. Damn my soul, I'll go and drown myself in the hole in the ice and it will all be over!"

Then with a resolute step he walked on, caught up the group of girls, overtook Oksana and said in a firm voice: "Farewell, Oksana! Find any lover you like, make a fool of whom you like; but me you will not see again in this world."

The beauty seemed amazed and would have said something, but with a wave of his hand the blacksmith ran away.

"Where are you off to, Vakula?" said the lads, seeing the blacksmith running.

"Good-bye, mates!" the blacksmith shouted in answer. "Please God we shall meet again in the other world, but we shall not walk together again in this. Farewell! Do not remember evil against me! Tell Father Kondrat to sing a requiem service for my sinful soul. Sinner that I am, for the sake of worldly things, I did not finish painting the candles for the ikons of the Wonder-worker and the Mother of God. All the goods which will be found in my chest are for the church. Farewell!"

Saying this, the blacksmith fell to running again with the sack upon his back.

"He is gone crazy!" said the lads.

"A lost soul" an old woman, who was passing, muttered devoutly. "I must go and tell them that the blacksmith has hanged himself!"

Meanwhile, after running through several streets Vakula stopped to take breath. "Where am I running?" he thought, "as though everything were over already. I'll try one way more: I'll go to the Zaporozhets, Paunchy Patsyuk; they say he knows all the devils and can do anything he likes. I'll go to him, for my soul is lost anyway!"

At that the devil, who had lain for a long while without moving, skipped for joy in the sack; but the blacksmith, fancying that he had somehow twitched the sack with his hand and caused the movement himself, gave the sack a punch with his stalwart fist and, shaking it on his shoulders, set off to Paunchy Patsyuk.

This Paunchy Patsyuk certainly at one time had been a Zaporozhets; but no one knew whether he had been turned out of the camp or whether he had run away from Zaporozhye of his own accord.

For a long time, ten years or perhaps fifteen, he had been living in Dikanka. At first he had lived like a true Zaporozhets: he had done no work, slept three-quarters of the day, ate as much as six mowers and drank almost a whole pailful at a time. He had somewhere to put it all, however, for though Patsyuk was not very tall he was fairly bulky in width. Moreover, the trousers he used to wear were so full that, however long a step he took, no trace of his leg was visible, and it seemed as though a wine distiller's butt were moving down the street. Perhaps it was just this that gave rise to his nickname, Paunchy. Before many weeks had passed after his coming to the village, everyone had found out that he was a wizard. If anyone were ill, he called in Patsyuk at once: Patsyuk had only to whisper a few words and it was as though the ailment had been lifted off by his hand. If it happened that a hungry gentleman was choked by a fishbone, Patsyuk could punch him so skilfully on the back that the bone went the proper way without causing any harm to the gentleman's throat. Of late years he was rarely seen anywhere. The reason of that was perhaps sloth, though possibly also the fact that it was every year becoming increasingly difficult for him to pass through a doorway. People had of late been obliged to go to him if they had need of him.

Not without some timidity, the blacksmith opened the door and saw Patsyuk sitting Turkish-fashion on the floor before a little tub on which stood a bowl of dumplings. This bowl stood as though purposely on a level with his mouth. Without moving a single finger, he bent his head a little towards the bowl and sipped the soup, from time to time catching the dumplings with his teeth.

"Well," thought Vakula to himself, "this fellow's even lazier than Tchub: he does eat with a spoon, anyway, while this fellow won't even lift his hand!"

Patsyuk must have been entirely engrossed with the dumplings, for he seemed to be quite unaware of the entrance of the blacksmith, who made him a very low bow as soon as he stepped on the threshold.

"I have come to ask you a favor, Patsyuk!" said Vakula, bowing again.

Fat Patsyuk lifted his head and again began swallowing dumplings.

"They say that you—no offense meant . . ." the blacksmith said, taking heart, "I speak of this not by way of any insult to you—that you are a little akin to the devil."

When he had uttered these words, Vakula was alarmed, thinking that he had expressed himself too bluntly and had not sufficiently softened his language, and, expecting that Patsyuk would pick up the tub together with the bowl and fling them straight at his head, he turned aside a little and covered his face with his sleeve that the hot dumpling soup might not spatter it. But Patsyuk looked up and again began swallowing the dumplings.

The blacksmith, reassured, made up his mind to go on. "I have come to you, Patsyuk. God give you everything, goods of all sorts in abundance and bread in proportion!" (The blacksmith would sometimes throw in a fashionable word: he had got into the way of it during his stay in Poltava when he was painting the paling fence for the officer.) "There is nothing but ruin before me, a sinner! Nothing in the world will help! What will be, will be. I have to ask help from the devil himself. Well, Patsyuk," the blacksmith brought out, seeing his unchanged silence, "what am I to do?"

"If you need the devil, then go to the devil," answered Patsyuk, not lifting his eyes to him, but still making away with the dumplings.

"It is for that that I have come to you," answered the blacksmith, dropping another bow to him. "I suppose that nobody in the world but you knows the way to him!"

Patsyuk answered not a word, but ate up the remaining

dumplings. "Do me a kindness, good man, do not refuse me!" persisted the blacksmith. "Whether it is pork or sausage or buckwheat flour or linen, say—millet or anything else in case of need . . . as is usual between good people . . . we will not grudge it. Tell me at least how, for instance, to get on the road to him."

"He need not go far who has the devil on his shoulders!" Patsyuk pronounced carelessly, without changing his position.

Vakula fastened his eyes upon him as though the interpretation of those words were written on his brow. "What does he mean?" his face asked dumbly, while his mouth stood half open ready to swallow the first word like a dumpling.

But Patsyuk was still silent.

Then Vakula noticed that there were neither dumplings nor a tub before him; but two wooden bowls were standing on the floor instead—one was filled with turnovers, the other with some cream. His thoughts and his eyes unconsciously fastened on these dainties. "Let us see," he said to himself, "how Patsyuk will eat the turnovers. He certainly won't want to bend down to lap them up like the dumplings; besides he couldn't—he must first dip the turnovers in the cream."

He had hardly time to think this when Patsyuk opened his mouth, looked at the turnovers and opened his mouth wider still. At that moment a turnover popped out of the bowl, splashed into the cream, turned over on the other side, leapt upwards and flew straight into his mouth. Patsyuk ate it up and opened his mouth again, and another turnover went through the same performance. The only trouble he took was to munch it up and swallow it.

"My word, what a miracle!" thought the blacksmith, his mouth dropping open with surprise, and at the same moment he was aware that a turnover was creeping towards him and was already smearing his mouth with cream. Pushing away the turnover and wiping his lips, the blacksmith began to reflect what marvels there are in the world and to what subtle devices the evil spirit may lead a man, saying to himself at the same time that no one but Patsyuk could help him.

"I'll bow to him once more, maybe he will explain properly. . . . The devil, though! Why, today is a fast day and he is eating turnovers with meat in them! What a fool I am really. I am standing here and making ready to sin! Back . . . !" And the pious blacksmith ran headlong out of the cottage.

But the devil sitting in the sack and already gloating over his prey could not endure to let such a glorious capture slip through his fingers. As soon as the blacksmith put down the sack the devil skipped out of it and mounted astride on his neck.

A cold shudder ran over the blacksmith's skin; pale and scared, he did not know what to do; he was on the point of crossing himself. . . . But the devil, putting his dog's nose down to Vakula's right ear, said: "It's I, your friend; I'll do anything for a friend and comrade! I'll give you as much money as you like," he squeaked into his left ear. "Oksana shall be yours this very day," he whispered, turning his nose again to the right ear. The blacksmith stood still, hesitating.

"Very well," he said at last; "for such a price I am ready to be yours!"

The devil clasped his hands in delight and began galloping up and down on the blacksmith's neck. "Now the blacksmith is done for!" he thought to himself: "now I'll pay you out, my dear, for all your paintings and false tales thrown up at the devils! What will my comrades say now when they learn that the most pious man of the whole village is in my hands!"

Here the devil laughed with joy, thinking how he would taunt all the long-tailed crew in hell, how furious the lame devil, who was reckoned the most resourceful among them, would be.

"Well, Vakula!" piped the devil, not dismounting from his neck, as though afraid he might escape, "you know nothing is done without a contract."

"I am ready!" said the blacksmith. "I have heard that among

197

you contracts are signed with blood. Stay, I'll get a nail out of my pocket!"

Here he put his hand behind him and caught the devil by the tail.

"What a man you are for a joke!" cried the devil, laughing. "Come, let go, that's enough mischief!"

"Wait a bit, friend!" cried the blacksmith, "and what do you think of this?" As he said that he made the sign of the cross and the devil became as meek as a lamb. "Wait a bit," said the blacksmith, pulling him by the tail to the ground: "I'll teach you to entice good men and honest Christians into sin."

Here the blacksmith leaped astride on the devil and lifted his hand to make the sign of the cross.

"Have mercy, Vakula!" the devil moaned piteously; "I will do anything you want, anything; only let me off with my life: do not lay the terrible cross upon me!"

"Ah, so that's your note now, you damned German! Now I know what to do. Carry me at once on yourself! Do you hear? And fly like a bird!"

"Whither?" asked the melancholy devil.

"To Petersburg, straight to the Tsaritsa!" And the blacksmith almost swooned with terror, as he felt himself mounting into the air.

Oksana stood for a long time pondering on the strange sayings of the blacksmith. Already an inner voice was telling her that she had treated him too cruelly. "What if he really does make up his mind to do something dreadful! I shouldn't wonder! Perhaps his sorrow will make him fall in love with another girl, and in his vexation he will begin calling her the greatest beauty in the village. But no, he loves me. I am so beautiful! He will not give me up for anything; he is playing, he is pretending. In ten minutes he will come back to look at me, for certain. I really was cross. I must, as though it were against my will, let him kiss me. Won't he be delighted!" And the frivolous beauty went back to jesting with her companions.

"Stay," said one of them, "the blacksmith has forgotten his sacks: look what terrible great sacks! He has made more by his carol singing than we have. I fancy they must have put here quite a quarter of a sheep, and I am sure that there are no end of sausages and loaves in them. Glorious! we shall have enough to feast on for all Christmas week!"

"Are they the blacksmith's sacks?" asked Oksana. "We had better drag them to my cottage and have a good look at what he has put in them."

All the girls laughingly approved of this proposal.

"But we can't lift them!" the whole group cried, trying to move the sacks.

"Wait a minute," said Oksana; "let us run for a sledge and take them away on it!"

And the crowd of girls ran out to get a sledge.

The captives were dreadfully bored with staying in the sacks, although the sacristan had poked a fair-sized hole to peep through. If there had been no one about, he might have found a way to creep out; but to creep out of a sack before everybody, to be a laughingstock . . . that thought restrained him, and he made up his mind to wait, only uttering a slight groan under Tchub's ill-mannered boots.

Tchub himself was no less desirous of freedom, feeling that there was something under him that was terribly uncomfortable to sit upon. But as soon as he heard his daughter's plan, he felt relieved and did not want to creep out, reflecting that it must be at least a hundred paces and perhaps two hundred to his hut; if he crept out, he would have to set himself to rights, button up his sheepskin, fasten his belt—such a lot of trouble! Besides, his winter cap had been left at Soloha's. Let the girls drag him in the sledge.

But things turned out not at all as Tchub was expecting.

Just when the girls were running to fetch the sledge, his lean neighbor, Panas, came out of the tavern, upset and ill-humored. The woman who kept the tavern could not be persuaded to serve him on credit. He thought to sit on in the tavern in the hope that some godly gentleman would come along and stand him treat; but as ill luck would have it, all the gentlefolk were staying at home and like good Christians were eating rice and honey in the bosom of their families. Meditating on the degeneration of manners and the hard heart of the Jewess who kept the tavern, Panas made his way up to the sacks and stopped in amazement. "My word, what sacks somebody has flung down in the road!" he said, looking about him in all directions. "I'll be bound there is pork in them. Some carol singer is in luck to get so many gifts of all sorts! What terrible great sacks! Suppose they are only stuffed full of buckwheat cake and biscuits, that's worth having; if there should be nothing but flat cakes in them, that would be welcome, too; the Jewess would give me a dram of vodka for each cake. Let's make haste and get them away before any one sees."

Here he flung on his shoulder the sack with Tchub and the sacristan in it, but felt it was too heavy. "No, it'll be too heavy for one to carry," he said; "and here by good luck comes the weaver Shapuvalenko. Good evening, Ostap!"

"Good evening!" said the weaver, stopping.

"Where are you going?"

"Oh, nowhere in particular."

"Help me carry these sacks, good man! Some one has been singing carols, and has dropped them in the middle of the road. We'll go halves over the things."

"Sacks? sacks of what? White loaves or flatcakes?"

"Oh, all sorts of things, I expect."

They hurriedly pulled some sticks out of the fence, laid the sack on them and carried it on their shoulders.

"Where shall we take it? To the tavern?" the weaver asked on the way.

"That's just what I was thinking; but, you know, the damned Jewess won't trust us, she'll think we have stolen it somewhere; besides, I have only just come from the tavern. We'll take it to my hut. No one will hinder us there, the wife's not at home."

"Are you sure she is not at home?" the prudent weaver inquired.

"Thank God that I am not quite a fool yet," said Panas; "the devil would hardly take me where she is. I expect she will be trailing round with the other women till daybreak."

"Who is there?" shouted Panas's wife, opening the door of the hut as she heard the noise in the porch made by the two friends with the sack. Panas was dumbfoundered.

"Here's a go!" articulated the weaver, letting his hands fall.

Panas's wife was a treasure of a kind that is not uncommon in this world. Like her husband, she hardly ever stayed at home, but almost every day visited various cronies and well-to-do old women, flattered them and ate with good appetite at their expense; she only quarrelled with her husband in the mornings, as it was only then that she sometimes saw him. Their hut was twice as old as the district clerk's trousers; there was no straw in places on their thatched roof. Only the remnants of a fence could be seen, for every one, as he went out of his house, thought it unnecessary to take a stick for the dogs, relying on passing by Panas's kitchen garden and pulling one out of his fence. The stove was not heated for three days at a time. Whatever the tender wife managed to beg from good Christians she hid as far as possible out of her husband's reach, and often wantonly robbed him of his gains if he had not had time to spend them on drink. In spite of his habitual imperturbability Panas did not like to give way to her, and consequently left his house every day with both eyes blackened, while his better half, sighing and groaning, waddled off to tell her old friends of her husband's unmannerliness and the blows she had to put up with from him.

Now you can imagine how disconcerted were the weaver and

Panas by this unexpected apparition. Dropping the sack, they stood before it, and concealed it with their skirts, but it was already too late; Panas's wife, though she did not see well with her old eyes, had observed the sack.

"Well, that's good!" she said, with a face which betrayed the joy of a vulture. "That's good, that you have gained so much, singing carols! That's how it always is with good Christians; but no, I expect you have filched it somewhere. Show me your sack at once, do you hear, show me this very minute!"

"The bald devil may show you, but we won't," said Panas, assuming a dignified air.

"What's it to do with you?" said the weaver. "We've sung the carols, not you."

"Yes, you will show me, you wretched drunkard!" screamed the wife, striking her tall husband on the chin with her fist and forcing her way towards the sack. But the weaver and Panas manfully defended the sack and compelled her to beat a retreat. Before they recovered themselves the wife ran out again with an oven fork in her hands. She nimbly caught her husband a thwack on the arms and the weaver one on his back and reached the sack.

"Why did we let her pass?" said the weaver, coming to himself.

"Ay, we let her pass! Why did you let her pass?" said Panas coolly.

"Your oven fork is made of iron, seemingly!" said the weaver after a brief silence, rubbing his back. "My wife bought one last year at the fair, gave twenty-five kopecks; that one's all right . . . it doesn't hurt. . . . "

Meanwhile the triumphant wife, setting the pot-lamp on the floor, untied the sack and peeped into it.

But her old eyes, which had so well descried the sack, this time certainly deceived her.

"Oh, but there is a whole pig lying here!" she shrieked, clapping her hands in glee.

"A pig! Do you hear, a whole pig!" The weaver nudged Panas. "And it's all your fault."

"It can't be helped!" replied Panas, shrugging his shoulders.

"Can't be helped! Why are we standing still? Let us take away the sack! Here, come on! Go away, go away, it's our pig!" shouted the weaver stepping forward.

"Go along, go along, you devilish woman! It's not your property!" said Panas, approaching.

His spouse picked up the oven fork again, but at that moment Tchub crawled out of the sack and stood in the middle of the room, stretching like a man who has just woken up from a long sleep. Panas's wife shrieked, slapping her skirts, and they all stood with open mouths.

"Why did she say it was a pig, the silly! It's not a pig!" said Panas, gazing open-eyed.

"My word! What a man has been dropped into a sack!" said the weaver, staggering back in alarm. "You may say what you please, you can burst if you like, but the foul fiend has had a hand in it. Why, he would not go through a window!"

"It's Tchub!" cried Panas, looking more closely.

"Why, who did you think it was?" said Tchub, laughing. "Well, haven't I played you a fine trick? I'll be bound you meant to eat me by way of pork! Wait a bit, I'll console you: there is something in the sack, if not a whole pig, it's certainly a little porker or some live beast. Something was continually moving under me."

The weaver and Panas flew to the sack, the lady of the house clutched at the other side of it, and the battle would have been renewed, had not the sacristan, seeing that now he had no chance of concealment, scrambled out of the sack of his own accord.

The woman, astounded, let go of the leg by which she was beginning to drag the sacristan out of the sack.

"Here's another of them!" cried the weaver in horror, "the devil knows what has happened to the world. . . . My head's going round. . . . Men are put into sacks instead of cakes or sausages!"

"It's the sacristan!" said Tchub, more surprised than any of them. "Well, there! you're a nice one, Soloha! To put one in a sack. . . . I thought at the time her hut was very full of sacks. . . . Now I understand it all: she had a couple of men hidden in each sack. While I thought it was only me she . . . So there you have her!"

The girls were a little surprised on finding that one sack was missing.

"Well, there is nothing for it, we must be content with this one," murmured Oksana.

The mayor made up his mind to keep quiet, reasoning that if he called out to them to untie the sack and let him out, the silly girls would run away in all directions; they would think that the devil was in the sack—and he would be left in the street till next day. Meanwhile the girls, linking arms together, flew like a whirlwind with the sledge over the crunching snow. Many of them sat on the sledge for fun; others even clambered on to the top of the mayor. The mayor made up his mind to endure everything.

At last they arrived, threw open the door into the outer room of the hut and dragged in the sack amid laughter.

"Let us see what is in it," they all cried, hastening to untie it.

At this point the hiccup which had tormented the mayor became so much worse that he began hiccupping and coughing loudly.

"Ah, there is some one in it!" they all shrieked, and rushed out of doors in horror.

"What the devil is it? Where are you tearing off to as though you were all possessed?" said Tchub, walking in at the door.

"Oh, daddy!" cried Oksana, "there is some one in the sack!"

"In the sack? Where did you get this sack?"

"The blacksmith threw it in the middle of the road," they all said at once.

"So that's it; didn't I say so?" Tchub thought to himself. "What are you frightened at? Let us look. Come now, my man —I beg you won't be offended at our not addressing you by your proper name—crawl out of the sack!"

The mayor did crawl out.

"Oh!" shrieked the girls.

"So the mayor got into one, too," Tchub thought to himself in bewilderment, scanning him from head to foot. "Well, I'm blessed!" He could say nothing more.

The mayor himself was no less confused and did not know how to begin. "I expect it is a cold night," he said, addressing Tchub.

"There is a bit of a frost," answered Tchub. "Allow me to ask you what you rub your boots with, goose fat or tar?" He had not meant to say that; he had meant to ask: "How did you get into that sack, mayor?" and he did not himself understand how he came to say something utterly different.

"Tar is better," said the mayor. "Well, good-night, Tchub!" and, pulling his winter cap down over his head, he walked out of the hut.

"Why was I such a fool as to ask him what he rubbed his boots with?" said Tchub, looking towards the door by which the mayor had gone out.

"Well, Soloha is a fine one! To put a man like that in a sack . . . ! My word, she is a devil of a woman! While I, poor fool . . . But where is that damned sack?"

"I flung it in the corner, there is nothing more in it," said Oksana.

"I know all about that; nothing in it, indeed! Give it here; there is another one in it! Shake it well. . . . What, nothing? My word, the cursed woman! And to look at her she is like a saint, as though she had never tasted anything but lenten fare . . . !"

205

But we will leave Tchub to pour out his vexation at leisure and will go back to the blacksmith, for it must be past eight o'clock.

At first it seemed dreadful to Vakula, particularly when he rose up from the earth to such a height that he could see nothing below, and flew like a fly so close under the moon that if he had not bent down he would have caught his cap in it. But in a little while he gained confidence and even began mocking at the devil. (He was extremely amused by the way the devil sneezed and coughed when he took the little cyprus wood cross off his neck and held it down to him. He purposely raised his hand to scratch his head, and the devil, thinking he was going to make the sign of the cross over him, flew along more swiftly than ever). It was quite light at that height. The air was transparent, bathed in a light silvery mist. Everything was visible, and he could even see a wizard whisk by them like a hurricane, sitting in a pot, and the stars gathering together to play hide-and-seek, a whole swarm of spirits whirling away in a cloud, a devil dancing in the light of the moon and taking off his cap at the sight of the blacksmith galloping by, a broom flying back home, from which evidently a witch had just alighted at her destination. . . . And many nasty things besides they met. They all stopped at the sight of the blacksmith to stare at him for a moment, and then whirled off and went on their way again. The blacksmith flew on till all at once Petersburg flashed before him, glittering with lights. (There happened to be an illumination that day.) The devil, flying over the city gate, turned into a horse and the blacksmith found himself mounted on a fiery steed in the middle of the street.

My goodness! the clatter, the uproar, the brilliant light; the walls rose up, four stories on each side; the thud of the horses' hoofs and the rumble of the wheels echoed and resounded from every quarter; houses seemed to start up out of the ground at every step; the bridges trembled; carriages raced along; sledge drivers and postillions shouted; the snow crunched under the thousand sledges flying from all parts; people passing along on foot huddled together, crowded under the houses which were studded with little lamps, and their immense shadows flitted over the walls with their heads reaching the roofs and the chimneys.

The blacksmith looked about him in amazement. It seemed to him as though all the houses had fixed their innumerable fiery eyes upon him, watching. Good Lord! he saw so many gentlemen in cloth fur-lined overcoats that he did not know whom to take off his cap to. "Good gracious, what a lot of gentry here!" thought the blacksmith. "I fancy every one who comes along the street in a fur coat is the assessor and again the assessor! And those who are driving about in such wonderful chaises with glass windows, if they are not police captains they certainly must be commissars or perhaps something grander still." His words were cut short by a question from the devil:

"Am I to go straight to the Tsaritsa?"

"No, I'm frightened," thought the blacksmith. "The Zaporozhtsy, who marched in the autumn through Dikanka, are stationed here, where I don't know. They came from the camp with papers for the Tsaritsa; anyway I might ask their advice. Hey, Satan! creep into my pocket and take me to the Zaporozhtsy!"

And in one minute the devil became so thin and small that he had no difficulty in creeping into the blacksmith's pocket. And before Vakula had time to look round he found himself in front of a big house, went up a staircase, hardly knowing what he was doing, opened a door and drew back a little from the brilliant light on seeing the smartly furnished room; but he regained confidence a little when he recognized the Zaporozhtsy who had ridden through Dikanka and now, sitting on silk-covered sofas, their tar-smeared boots tucked under them, were smoking the strongest tobacco, usually called "root."

"Good-day to you, gentlemen! God be with you, this is where we meet again," said the blacksmith, going up to them and swinging off a low bow.

"What man is that?" the one who was sitting just in front of the blacksmith asked another who was further away.

"You don't know me?" said the blacksmith. "It's I, Vakula, the blacksmith! When you rode through Dikanka in the autumn you stayed nearly two days with me. God give you all health and long years! And I put a new iron hoop on the front wheel of your chaise!"

"Oh!" said the same Zaporozhets, "it's that blacksmith who paints so well. Good day to you, neighbor! How has God brought you here?"

"Oh, I just wanted to have a look round. I was told . . ."

"Well, neighbor," said the Zaporozhets, drawing himself up with dignity and wishing to show he could speak Russian too, "well, it's a big city."

The blacksmith, too, wanted to keep up his credit and not to seem like a novice. Moreover, as we have had occasion to see before, he too could speak like a book.

"A considerable town!" he answered carelessly. "There is no denying the houses are very large, the pictures that are hanging up are uncommonly good. Many of the houses are painted with letters in gold leaf to exuberance. The configuration is superb, there is no other word for it!"

The Zaporozhtsy, hearing the blacksmith express himself so freely, drew the most flattering conclusions in regard to him.

"We will have a little more talk with you, neighbor; now we are going at once to the Tsaritsa."

"To the Tsaritsa? Oh, be so kind, gentlemen, as to take me with you!"

"You?" a Zaporozhets pronounced in the tone in which an old man speaks to his four-year-old charge when the latter asks to be sat on a real, big horse. "What would you do there? No, we can't do that. We are going to talk about our own affairs to the Tsaritsa." And his face assumed an expression of great significance.

"Do take me!" the blacksmith persisted.

"Ask them to!" he whispered softly to the devil, banging on the pocket with his fist.

He had hardly said this, when another Zaporozhets brought out: "Do let us take him, mates!"

"Yes, do let us take him!" others joined in.

"Put on the same dress as we are wearing, then."

The blacksmith was hastily putting on a green tunic when all at once the door opened and a man covered with gold lace said it was time to go.

Again the blacksmith was moved to wonder, as he was whisked along in an immense coach swaying on springs, as four-storied houses raced by him on both sides and the rumbling pavement seemed to be moving under the horses' hoofs.

"My goodness, how light it is!" thought the blacksmith to himself. "At home it is not so light as this in the daytime."

The coaches stopped in front of the palace. The Zaporozhtsy got out, went into a magnificent vestibule and began ascending a brilliantly lighted staircase.

"What a staircase!" the blacksmith murmured to himself, "it's a pity to trample it with one's feet. What decorations! They say the stories tell lies! The devil a bit they do! My goodness! what banisters, what workmanship! Quite fifty roubles must have gone on the iron alone!"

When they had mounted the stairs, the Zaporozhtsy walked through the first drawing room. The blacksmith followed them timidly, afraid of slipping on the parquet at every footstep. They walked through three drawing rooms, the blacksmith still overwhelmed with admiration. On entering the fourth, he could not help going up to a picture hanging on the wall. It was the Holy Virgin with the Child in her arms.

"What a picture! What a wonderful painting!" he thought. "It seems to be speaking! It seems to be alive! And the Holy Child! It's pressing its little hands together and laughing, poor thing! And the colors! My goodness, what colors! I fancy there is not a kopeck-worth of ochre on it, it's all emerald green and crimson lake. And the blue simply glows! A fine piece of work! I expect the background was put in with the most expensive white lead. Wonderful as that painting is, though, this copper handle," he went on, going up to the door and fingering the lock, "is even more wonderful. Ah, what a fine finish! That's all done, I expect, by German blacksmiths and most expensive."

Perhaps the blacksmith would have gone on reflecting for a long time, if a flunkey in livery had not nudged his arm and reminded him not to lag behind the others. The Zaporozhtsy passed through two more rooms and then stopped. They were told to wait in the third, in which there was a group of several generals in gold-laced uniforms. The Zaporozhtsy bowed in all directions and stood all together.

A minute later, a rather thick-set man of majestic stature, wearing the uniform of a Hetman and yellow boots, walked in, accompanied by a regular suite. His hair was in disorder, he squinted a little, his face wore an expression of haughty dignity and the habit of command could be seen in every movement. All the generals, who had been walking up and down rather superciliously in their gold uniforms, bustled about and seemed with low bows to be hanging on every word he uttered and even on his slightest gesture, so as to fly at once to carry out his wishes. But the Hetman did not even notice all that: he barely nodded to them and went up to the Zaporozhtsy.

The Zaporozhtsy all bowed down to the ground.

"Are you all here?" he asked deliberately, speaking a little through his nose.

"All, little father!" answered the Zaporozhtsy, bowing again.

"Don't forget to speak as I have told you!"

"No, little father, we will not forget."

"Is that the Tsar?" asked the blacksmith of one of the Zaporozhtsy.

"Tsar, indeed! It's Potyomkin himself," answered the other.

Voices were heard in the other room, and the blacksmith did not know which way to look for the number of ladies who walked in, wearing satin gowns with long trains, and courtiers in gold-laced coats with their hair tied in a tail at the back. He could see a blur of brilliance and nothing more.

The Zaporozhtsy all bowed down at once to the floor and cried out with one voice: "Have mercy, little mother, mercy!"

The blacksmith, too, though seeing nothing, stretched himself very zealously on the floor.

"Get up!" An imperious and at the same time pleasant voice sounded above them. Some of the courtiers bustled about and nudged the Zaporozhtsy.

"We will not get up, little mother! We will not get up! We will die, but we will not get up!" shouted the Zaporozhtsy.

Potyomkin bit his lips. At last he went up himself and whispered peremptorily to one of the Zaporozhtsy. They rose to their feet.

Then the blacksmith, too, ventured to raise his head, and saw standing before him a short and, indeed, rather stout woman with blue eyes, and at the same time with that majestically smiling air which was so well able to subdue everything and could only belong to a queen.

"His Excellency has promised to make me acquainted today with my people whom I have not hitherto seen," said the lady with the blue eyes, scrutinizing the Zaporozhtsy with curiosity.

"Are you well cared for here?" she went on, going nearer to them.

"Thanks, little mother! The provisions they give us are excellent, though the mutton here is not at all like what we have in Zaporozhye . . . What does our daily fare matter . . . ?"

Potyomkin frowned, seeing that the Zaporozhtsy were saying something quite different from what he had taught them. . . .

One of the Zaporozhtsy, drawing himself up with dignity, stepped forward:

"Be gracious, little mother! How have your faithful people angered you? Have we taken the hand of the vile Tatar? Have we come to agreement with the Turk? Have we been false to

211

you in deed or in thought? How have we lost your favor? First we heard that you were commanding fortresses to be built everywhere against us; then we heard you mean to turn us into carbineers; now we hear of new oppressions. Wherein are your Zaporozhye troops in fault? In having brought your army across the Perekop and helped your generals to slaughter the Tatars in the Crimea . . . ?"

Potyomkin carelessly rubbed with a little brush the diamonds with which his hands were studded and said nothing.

"What is it you want?" Catherine asked anxiously.

The Zaporozhtsy looked meaningly at one another.

"Now is the time! The Tsaritsa asks what we want!" the blacksmith said to himself, and he suddenly flopped down on the floor.

"Your Imperial Majesty, do not command me to be punished! Show me mercy! Of what, be it said without offense to your Imperial Graciousness, are the little slippers made that are on your feet? I fancy there is no Swede nor a shoemaker in any kingdom in the world can make them like that. Merciful heavens, if only my wife could wear slippers like that!"

The Empress laughed. The courtiers laughed too. Potyomkin frowned and smiled both together. The Zaporozhtsy began nudging the blacksmith under the arm, wondering whether he had gone out of his mind.

"Stand up!" the Empress said graciously. "If you wish so much to have slippers like these, it is very easy to arrange it. Bring him at once the very best slippers with gold on them! Indeed, this simple-heartedness greatly pleases me! Here you have a subject worthy of your witty pen!" the Empress went on, turning to a gentleman with a full but rather pale face, who stood a little apart from the others and whose modest coat with big mother-of-pearl buttons on it showed that he was not one of the courtiers.

"You are too gracious, your Imperial Majesty. It needs a La Fontaine at least to do justice to it!" answered the man with the mother-of-pearl buttons, bowing.

"I tell you sincerely, I have not yet got over my delight at your *Brigadier*. You read so wonderfully well! I have heard, though," the Empress went on, turning again to the Zaporozhtsy, "that none of you are married in the Syetch."

"What next, little mother! Why, you know yourself, a man cannot live without a wife," answered the same Zaporozhets who had talked to the blacksmith, and the blacksmith wondered, hearing him address the Tsaritsa as though purposely in coarse language, speaking like a peasant, as it is commonly called, though he could speak like a book.

"They are sly fellows!" he thought to himself. "I'll be bound he does not do that for nothing."

"We are not monks," the Zaporozhets went on, "but sinful folk. Ready like all honest Christians to fall into sin. There are among us many who have wives, but do not live with them in the Syetch. There are some who have wives in Poland; there are some who have wives in Ukraine; there are some who have wives even in Turkey."

At that moment they brought the blacksmith the slippers.

"My goodness, what fine embroidery!" he cried joyfully, taking the slippers. "Your Imperial Majesty! If the slippers on your feet are like this—and in them your Honor, I expect, goes sliding on the ice—what must the feet themselves be like! They must be made of pure sugar at least, I should think!"

The Empress, who had in fact very well-shaped and charming feet, could not help smiling at hearing such a compliment from the lips of a simple-hearted blacksmith, who in his Zaporozhets dress might be reckoned a handsome fellow in spite of his swarthy face.

Delighted with such gracious attention, the blacksmith would have liked to have cross-questioned the pretty Tsaritsa thoroughly about everything: whether it was true that tsars eat nothing but honey, fat bacon and suchlike; but, feeling that the Zaporozhtsy were digging him in the ribs, he made up his mind to keep quiet. And when the Empress, turning to the older men, began questioning them about their manner of life and customs in the Syetch, he, stepping back, stooped down to his pocket and said softly: "Hurry me away from here and make haste!" And at once he found himself outside the city gates.

"He is drowned! On my word he is drowned! May I never leave this spot if he is not drowned!" lisped the weaver's fat wife, standing with a group of Dikanka women in the middle of the street.

"Why, am I a liar then? Have I stolen any one's cow? Have I put the evil eye on some one, that I am not to be believed?" shouted a purple-nosed woman in a Cossack tunic, waving her arms. "May I never want to drink water again if old Dame Perepertchih didn't see with her own eyes the blacksmith hanging himself!"

"Has the blacksmith hanged himself? Well, I never!" said the mayor, coming out of Tchub's hut, and he stopped and pressed closer to the group.

"You had better say, may you never want to drink vodka, you old drunkard!" answered the weaver's wife. "He had need to be as mad as you to hang himself! He drowned himself! He drowned himself in the hole in the ice! I know that as well as I know that you were in the tavern just now."

"You disgrace! See what she throws up against me!" the woman with the purple nose retorted wrathfully. "You had better hold your tongue, you wretch! Do you think I don't know that the sacristan comes to see you every evening?"

The weaver's wife flared up.

"What about the sacristan? Whom does the sacristan go to? What lies are you telling?"

"The sacristan?" piped the sacristan's wife, squeezing her way up to the combatants, in an old blue cotton coat lined with hareskin. "I'll let the sacristan know! Who was it said the sacristan?"

"Well, this is the lady the sacristan visits!" said the woman with the purple nose, pointing to the weaver's wife.

"So it's you, you bitch!" said the sacristan's wife, stepping up to the weaver's wife. "So it's you, is it, witch, who cast a spell over him and gave him a foul poison to make him come to you!"

"Get thee behind me, Satan!" said the weaver's wife, staggering back.

"Oh, you cursed witch, may you never live to see your children! Wretched creature! Tfoo!"

Here the sacristan's wife spat straight into the other woman's face.

The weaver's wife endeavored to do the same, but spat instead on the unshaven chin of the mayor, who had come close up to the combatants that he might hear the quarrel better.

"Ah, nasty woman!" cried the mayor, wiping his face with the skirt of his coat and lifting his whip.

This gesture sent them all flying in different directions, scolding loudly.

"How disgusting!" repeated the mayor, still wiping his face. "So the blacksmith is drowned! My goodness! What a fine painter he was! What good knives and reaping-hooks and ploughs he could forge! What a strong man he was! Yes," he went on musing, "there are not many fellows like that in our village. To be sure, I did notice while I was in that damned sack that the poor fellow was very much depressed. So that is the end of the blacksmith! He was and is not! And I was meaning to have my dapple mare shod . . . !" And filled with such Christian reflections, the mayor quietly made his way to his own cottage.

Oksana was much troubled when the news reached her. She put little faith in Dame Perepertchih's having seen it and in the women's talk; she knew that the blacksmith was rather too pious a man to bring himself to send his soul to perdition. But what if he really had gone away, intending never to return to the village? And, indeed, in any place it would be hard to find as

fine a fellow as the blacksmith. And how he loved her! He had
borne with her caprices longer than any one of them. . . . All
night long the beauty turned over from her right side to her left
and her left to her right, and could not go to sleep. Now tossing
in bewitching nakedness which the darknes concealed even from
herself, she reviled herself almost aloud; now growing quieter,
made up her mind to think of nothing—and kept thinking all
the time. She was in a perfect fever, and by the morning head
over ears in love with the blacksmith.

Tchub expressed neither pleasure nor sorrow at Vakula's fate.
His thoughts were absorbed by one subject: he could not forget
the treachery of Soloha and never left off abusing her even in his
sleep.

Morning came. Even before daybreak the church was full of
people. Elderly women in white linen wimples, in white cloth
tunics, crossed themselves piously at the church porch. Ladies
in green and yellow blouses, some even in dark blue overdresses
with gold streamers behind, stood in front of them. Girls who
had a whole shopful of ribbons twined on their heads, and neck-
laces, crosses, and coins round their necks, tried to make their
way closer to the ikon stand. But in front of all stood the
gentlemen and humble peasants with moustaches, with fore-
locks, with thick necks and newly shaven chins, for the most
part wearing hooded cloaks, below which peeped a white or
sometimes a dark blue jacket. Wherever one looked every face
had a festive air. The mayor was licking his lips in anticipation
of the sausage with which he would break his fast; the girls were
thinking how they would slide with the lads on the ice; the old
women murmured prayers more zealously than ever. All over
the church one could hear the Cossack Sverbyguz bowing to the
ground. Only Oksana stood feeling unlike herself: she prayed
without praying. So many different feelings, each more amazing,
each more distressing than the other, crowded upon her heart
that her face expressed nothing but overwhelming confusion;
tears quivered in her eyes. The girls could not think why it was

216

and did not suspect that the blacksmith was responsible. However, not only Oksana was concerned about the blacksmith. All the villagers observed that the holiday did not seem like a holiday, that something was lacking. To make things worse, the sacristan was hoarse after his travels in the sack and he wheezed scarcely audibly; it is true that the chorister who was on a visit to the village sang the bass splendidly, but how much better it would have been if they had had the blacksmith too, who used always when they were singing *Our Father* or the *Holy Cherubim* to step up into the choir and from there sing it with the same chant with which it is sung in Poltava. Moreover, he alone performed the duty of a churchwarden. Matins were already over; after matins mass was over. . . . Where indeed could the blacksmith have vanished to?

It was still night as the devil flew even more swiftly back with the blacksmith, and in a trice Vakula found himself inside his own cottage. At that moment the cock crowed.

"Where are you off to?" cried the blacksmith, catching the devil by his tail as he was about to run away. "Wait a bit, friend, that's not all: I haven't thanked you yet." Then, seizing a switch, he gave him three lashes and the poor devil set to running like a peasant who has just had a hiding from the tax assessor. And so, instead of tricking, tempting and fooling others, the enemy of mankind was fooled himself. After that Vakula went into the outer room, made himself a hole in the hay and slept till dinnertime. When he woke up he was frightened at seeing that the sun was already high. "I've overslept myself and missed matins and mass!"

Then the worthy blacksmith was overwhelmed with distress, thinking that no doubt God, as a punishment for his sinful intention of damning his soul, had sent this heavy sleep, which had prevented him from even being in church on this solemn holiday. However, comforting himself with the thought that next week he would confess all this to the priest and that from that day he would begin making fifty bows a day for a whole

217

year, he glanced into the cottage; but there was no one there. Apparently Soloha had not yet returned.

Carefully he drew out from the breast of his coat the slippers and again marvelled at the costly workmanship and the wonderful adventure of the previous night. He washed and dressed himself in his best, put on the very clothes which he had got from the Zaporozhtsy, took out of a chest a new cap of good astrakhan with a dark blue top not once worn since he had bought it while staying in Poltava; he also took out a new girdle of rainbow colors; he put all this together with a whip in a kerchief and set off straight to see Tchub.

Tchub opened his eyes wide when the blacksmith walked into his cottage, and did not know what to wonder at most, the blacksmith's having risen from the dead, the blacksmith's having dared to come to see him, or the blacksmith's being dressed up such a dandy, like a Zaporozhets. But he was even more astonished when Vakula untied the kerchief and laid before him a new cap and a girdle such as had never been seen in the village, and then plumped down on his knees before him, and said in a tone of entreaty: "Have mercy, father! Be not wroth! Here is a whip; beat me as much as your heart may desire. I give myself up, I repent of everything! Beat, but only be not wroth. You were once a comrade of my father's, you ate bread and salt together and drank the cup of goodwill."

It was not without secret satisfaction that Tchub saw the blacksmith, who had never knocked under to any one in the village and who could twist five-kopeck pieces and horseshoes in his hands like pancakes, lying now at his feet. In order to keep up his dignity still further, Tchub took the whip and gave him three strokes on the back. "Well, that's enough; get up! Always obey the old! Let us forget everything that has passed between us. Come, tell me now what is it that you want?"

"Give me Oksana to wife, father!"

Tchub thought a little, looked at the cap and the girdle. The cap was delightful and the girdle, too, was not inferior to it; he thought of the treacherous Soloha and said resolutely: "Good! send the matchmakers!"

"Aïe!" shrieked Oksana, as she crossed the threshold and saw Vakula; she gazed at him with astonishment and delight.

"Look, what slippers I have brought you!" said Vakula, "they are the same as the Tsaritsa wears!"

"No, no! I don't want slippers!" she said, waving her arms and keeping her eyes fixed upon him. "I am ready without slippers. . . ." She blushed and could say no more.

The blacksmith went up to her and took her by the hand; the beauty looked down. Never before had she looked so exquisitely lovely. The enchanted blacksmith gently kissed her; her face flushed crimson and she was even lovelier still.

The bishop of blessed memory was driving through Dikanka. He admired the site on which the village stands, and as he drove down the street stopped before a new cottage.

"And whose is this cottage so gaily painted?" asked his reverence of a beautiful woman, who was standing near the door with a baby in her arms. "The blacksmith Vakula's!" Oksana, for it was she, told him, bowing.

"Splendid! splendid work!" said his reverence, examining the doors and windows. The windows were all outlined with a ring of red paint; everywhere on the doors there were Cossacks on horseback with pipes in their teeth.

But his reverence was even warmer in his praise of Vakula when he learned that by way of church penance he had painted free of charge the whole of the left choir green with red flowers.

But that was not all. On the wall, to one side as you go in at the church, Vakula had painted the devil in hell—such a loathsome figure that every one spat as he passed. And the women would take a child up to the picture, if it would go on crying in their arms, and would say: "There, look! What a fright!" And the child, restraining its tears, would steal a glance at the picture and nestle closer to its mother.

The Christmas Lovers

FRANÇOIS COPPÉE

ÉSIRÉ MUGUET, designer and engraver of anatomical plates, the man who has reproduced so many brains, lungs, livers, spleens and intestines for Testevuide and Company, the celebrated publishers of medical works in the Rue Antoine-Dubois, had not taken up an artisic career—as you may well imagine—with any preconceived idea of choosing this useful but objectionable specialty.

When, as a young student in the night classes of the drawing school, he was working in charcoal on Houdon's "Ecorché"— that terrible object with skin peeled off like the skin of an orange, giving a view of the bare muscles—he had not even a presentiment of his fate. Bashful and well-bred youth that he was, he was not in sympathy with the "Ecorché." It was much too undressed for his taste; and when, after making some little progress, he obtained permission to give up this man without dermis or epidermis, and to begin work on the Apollo Belvedere and the Venus de Milo, he was greatly relieved. He found much pleasure in drawing these two divinities, who, although lacking in flowing draperies and fig leaves, had at least the decency to keep on their skins.

Like many another, Désiré, in his young artist life, had dreams of glory. But a man has to fight these dreams when he stops to consider the price of butter. I once knew a young poet who used scornfully to shrug his shoulders at the mention of Victor Hugo's name, yet he now has to earn his forty sous a day by composing each morning, at his shaving mirror, a rhymed couplet extolling the virtues of a certain kind of soap. And I don't know that he is to be pitied. A franc a line is a good price.

220

Unfortunately the soap speculator will not accept more than two lines a day, because it costs too much to put the advertisements in the daily papers. On one occasion, when the unfortunate poet risked a quatrain, he barely escaped having his wages docked.

Désiré Muguet had had his springtime hopes, and had been taken very seriously at the École des Beaux-Arts. He would have asked nothing better than to sell his pictures, as Meissonier did, for three or four thousand francs the square inch. But, alas! At twenty-nine, the age limit, he failed to get the Prix de Rome. Yet what a fine subject he had! "Themistocles begging for the hospitality of Admetus, King of the Molossians." His composition was good, but—fatal mistake!—he had forgotten the Molossian dogs. The jury decided that he was lacking in imagination and selected Pitraz, who—merely because he happened that day to think of the famous dogs—has since been able to make his way, has had great orders, has become a member of the Institute, has received a row of decorations—everything you can think of—and today paints the portraits of our most illustrious contemporaries; all so pale and on such dark backgrounds that they seem to have been painted with starch in the depths of a cellar.

"No luck," is the device which Désiré Muguet might have had in black and shining letters on his writing paper, if the poor devil had not had to be content, for his decidedly infrequent correspondence, with a two-penny sheet bought from the grocer opposite.

However, he had had, on coming into the world, one great piece of good fortune, perhaps, in my humble opinion, the greatest. His father and mother were honest people. What is that I hear you say? That that is not uncommon, indeed, quite an everyday occurrence? Do not smile, you materialist! You have bored us long enough with the laws of heredity. Why do you not admit that love of goodness as well as gout may be transmitted, and that through atavism, it is possible to be arthritic and virtous at the same time? I do not defend my theory beyond a certain point; it is not infallible, but this much is certain, that Désiré received from the authors of his being a conscience made of good solid material, all honor and goodness—something that would not wear out, something that was all wool, something that would keep his heart warm all his life.

Désiré's father, an old soldier, occupied the modest but respectable position of paying teller in a banking house. Is there a natural relation between scrupulous honesty on the one hand and long-tailed grayish-blue coats and soft hats on the other? Probably. For you may safely trust a pocketbook filled with thousand-franc notes to any man dressed in this way, even if he has very little in his own purse for his own personal pleasures; and you may trust him from morning until night amid all the temptations of Paris, and never—or at any rate very seldom— will it occur to the man in grayish-blue clothes to skip to Brussels by the fast express—a blessed proof that the sons of Adam are not such rascals as we like to paint them. As for Father Muguet, he was a model for the other fellows at the bank; and such a good husband and father of a family that he heroically denied himself tobacco when he saw his wife, an excellent seamstress, working by lamplight until midnight, and losing her eyesight in trying to make up the extra expenses caused by the birth of their little Désiré.

This mother, although she was but a humble working woman, had transmitted to her son an extreme sensitiveness, a delicate, aristocratic—if we may use the word—manner of feeling and thinking. Such natures are not infrequent among the common people in Paris. When her son showed a decided taste for drawing, this woman was very happy. "Perhaps he will be a great artist," she said to her husband, who, although a trifle disturbed at the child's bent, was nevertheless very proud on his birthday, when the little one presented him with two sheets filled with noses and ears, and a crayon Vitellius from the round.

All sorts of privations were necessary to enable Désiré to go on with his art studies, privations which lasted through years. His father's beard grew gray, his mother's fine face was marked with deep lines, and still Désiré was a mere student not even earning his salt. It made the poor boy wretched; he reproached himself for compelling his parents to a life of self-sacrifice. Many a time he proposed to give up his hopes, to learn a trade, but the good people steadfastly refused, so confident were they in the future of their son, so deceived by his success in the school.

Désiré, who was naturally modest, very soon learned to distrust himself. In truth, there was nothing of the genius about him, nothing original. At the most, after great effort and strength of will, he might have managed to acquire a certain facility; he might, for example, have made fairly good conscientious portraits. His master, a pupil of Ingres, nicknamed by the students "Chief of the Fire Department," held him up to the others as an example, because of the correctness of his drawing. These praises did not spoil him; on the contrary, they made him blush. They did give him some illusions, however; they interfered with his progress, made him satisfied with the mediocre triumph of the technically strong, and content with an honorable place at the examinations, with a medal, or with the "Very good," of his professor.

He was not wholly dependent upon his family. With the best will in the world he continually sought employment, and here and there he found some poorly paid work—a portrait, a few lessons. He tried drawing for the illustrated papers, but was rarely successful. He lacked facility and was not capable of rapid invention.

What a dismal life it was, after all! A model son, he was obliged to see his dearly loved parents grow old in poverty for his sake, renouncing for him all pleasure, all diversion; so that he often asked himself with a shudder if he had not made a great mistake in choosing his calling.

A sudden misfortune gave him his answer.

His father died, and his mother had to give up work altogether, because of a serious trouble with her eyes, which in a few months' time made her almost blind. Désiré was then thirty years old, and had just missed getting the Prix de Rome, by forgetting the dogs of the King of the Molossians. Misfortunes did not some singly. But adversity is a great spur to people whose hearts are in the right place.

Désiré at once gave up his ambitions as an artist, and his dreams of glory, which in any case, let us confess it, had small chances of realization. First of all, it was his duty to think of his mother, was it not? To do, no matter what; to earn his daily bread like a workman, if necessary. He had already had an offer to draw and engrave anatomical plates, and knew something about the use of the graver's tool. In this calling his good drawing became invaluable to him. He accepted the offer of Testevuide and Company. Poor Désiré Muguet, who bore the name of a flower, who had the soul of a flower, and who used almost to faint at the sight of blood, when he merely cut his finger in sharpening his charcoal, overcame his repugnance, went every day to the medical college and took his place, his paper on his lap, near the dissecting table, where he copied from life all sorts of hateful things.

It was horrible, but in this way Désiré could earn his twelve or fifteen francs a day. From eight until eleven o'clock he was in the dissecting rooms, studying a heart worn out from aneurism, a stomach eaten by a cancer, or a pair of lungs covered with tubercles. He did his drawing conscientiously, minutely, as he had the antiques when he was working from the Polyhymnia or the Discobolus. Then, when he went home to the little fourth-floor lodging in the Rue de la Harpe, the poor fellow, after getting something to eat, would bend over his copperplate and engrave until nightfall more enlarged hearts, more cancerous stomachs, more consumptive lungs. Cheerful? No, it was not cheerful! But they at least had coal for their stove, bread for their cupboard, and a piece of meat gently boiling for their dinner. And close to her devoted, industrious son, sat the mother, peacefully knitting a woollen stocking, her eyes protected by a green shade.

Had the satisfaction of a duty performed killed in the spirit of Désiré Muguet all regret for the past? Not entirely, it must be said. For in abandoning high art and setting up as a portrayer of viscera and entrails, he had renounced, not only his chances for success in the Ecole des Beaux-Arts and the periodical compliments of the "Chief of the Fire Department," but in addition—and this was hardest of all—he had to tear from his heart a newborn love.

He became acquainted with Mademoiselle Clara at the Louvre. She was a poor artist like himself, who supported herself by copying and giving lessons. She lived in a little apartment away out in Neuilly, with her old paralytic father, a former employee of the government who had a small pension. On the occasion when Désiré Muguet made the discovery that Mademoiselle Clara had pretty eyes, she had placed her easel in front of the "Woman sick of the dropsy." But he was so bashful that she had time to finish—oh, how imperfectly!—Gerard Douw's chef-d'œuvre before her fellow student had dared to address a word to her; and she had already prepared a new canvas for Titian's "Entombment of Christ" before Désiré, on the pretext of borrowing from her a tube of Veronese green, ventured upon a conversation. Their idyl was of slow growth, and had always a famous picture as a background. They told their love in front of Ruysdael's "Thicket," he made her accept a little engagement ring in the presence of the "Lisa Gioconda," and Clara was just beginning to undertake a "Cruche cassée," after Greuze when Désiré told her of the disasters that had come to him; of the death of his father, of his mother's threatened blindness; and they had to acknowledge that they were too poor, and had too many burdens to marry. So they said farewell like good children, each trying not to see the tears in the other's eyes.

Ten years had passed since then, and still Désiré had not forgotten the sweet young copyist. He had heard but vague reports of her; he knew only that she had lost her father, and that she was now a drawing teacher in a young ladies' boarding school.

At length, to all the other sadness in Désiré's life was added an affliction with a touch of the ridiculous about it. Although he was barely forty, his beard began to grow white. If it had changed as other beards do, he would have paid no attention to it. But curiously enough, it turned white on one side only, the left side, the heart side, in such a way that with this divided beard the poor man looked like an advertisement for a barber who had invented a hair-dye. Désiré, who economically made his hats and coats last three years, Désiré, who, if he looked in the glass at all, never found the least thing pleasing in his poor melancholy visage, was absolutely without vanity. But this physical peculiarity which gave him two profiles, on the right that of a young man, on the left that of an old one, distressed him. He felt a little like a monster. On the street everybody looked at him; it made him nervous, and he found himself longing for fresh troubles which should eventually whiten the rest of his beard.

Gradually, however, he settled down. Testevuide and Company were much pleased with him. His latest plates—a sarcoma of the kidney and a lupus vorax of the face—had won him the congratulations of the publisher. He was able to lay by something and could indulge his dear old mother in a few comforts. Yet what a sad life he led, after all! One night, it was Christmas Eve, after staying in his little room in the Rue de la Harpe, where he had lived for more than twenty years, until after eleven o'clock, leaning over his plates and engraving by lamplight a disordered brain, Désiré turned to his mother, who had fallen asleep by the stove, and said with an appeal both to her piety and her love of eating: "Mother, if you feel like it, I will take you to the midnight Mass at Saint-Severin, and on the way back— you know the butchers do not close to-night—we will buy something stuffed with truffles, and have a regular Christmas feast."

226

Either the good woman was not in a mood for it, or else she did not dare to venture out.

"Go alone, my dear Désiré. You can pray for us both, and I will read Mass by the fire and wait for you to come back. Bring a galantine and a bag of chestnuts with you."

Then as he kissed her brow before leaving her, she drew him to her and pressed him to her heart.

"My poor child," she murmured, "Christmas ought to give you a little happiness."

What a night! The cold was black, damp, and penetrating. Big snowflakes fell and mingled with the mud of the pavements. But in the narrow streets which wind about the old church and which date from the Middle Ages, more than one shop was lighted on account of the Christmas festival, and the quarter had a gala look. Housekeepers with baskets on their arms were bustling in and out of grocers' and cook-shops. At the doors of the cafés, where the sound of voices singing could be heard, great piles of oyster shells were heaped.

In his heart Désiré rejoiced at the joy of the poor.

A tall girl with brazen eyes and a big hat with feathers, who passed on the arm of a student, stared at the artist. "Look at that," she cried with a burst of laughter. "Why has it snowed only on one side of his beard?"

With a sudden feeling of sadness at the thought of his physical peculiarity, Désiré Muguet entered Saint-Severin.

The church, one of the Gothic gems of old Paris, was swarming with people, and innumerable wax tapers shed a glimmering golden light. Just as the brightness of the Venite Adoremus burst forth from the cloud of perfumed incense which filled the choir, Désiré Muguet, standing near a pillar in one of the side chapels, was trying to recall a prayer. For even though he had not preserved the outward forms of religion, this simple, uncomplaining soul had always kept a little faith and hope. He remembered his mother's words.

Yes, Christmas ought to bring him a happy surprise, some-

227

thing like the cornucopia of candies that he used to find in his shoe when he was a small boy. Was it his lot to grow old and to die without ever having known anything of life but work and duty? He was not exacting, unreasonable, no. But frankly, in the matter of happiness his portion had been pitifully small, and it seemed to him that God was his debtor.

He had nothing—nothing—not even a little love. He began to think of Clara and of their poor little romance among the masterpieces of the Louvre; and of that day in the Salon des Sept-Cheminées under the stern eye of Géricault's "Wounded Cuirassier," when, trembling all over, he had slipped his first love letter into the young girl's color box. Alas! after he had confessed his love, after he had given her the engagement ring, they had had to renounce their dearest hopes because of the duty they owed to their families. And later, when Désiré, found by his mother in tears, confessed it all to her, the good woman cried too, but she said, "After all, my poor child, you did well. It would not have been wise."

What could have become of his sweetheart? He had heard that she had lost her father, that she still gave drawing lessons, going about from house to house, in rain and in shine. Ah! she too must have known poverty. Poor child! She had cared for him—he was sure of that—and at his request, out of friendship for him, she had kept his ring when they parted; a poor little ring that he had bought—how well he remembered it—of a small Jewish tradesman in the Rue de Rambuteau.

This rush of memories was heartrending for poor Désiré. He left the church, went to a cook shop, had a slice of galantine cut, at the corner bought a pound of chestnuts hot enough to burn his pocket, and then once more climbed his four flights of stairs.

But what was the matter? The door was ajar, and he heard women's voices and sobbing. At one o'clock in the morning! *Grand Dieu!* something had happened! Perhaps his mother is ill! He enters the room and stops in amazement.

228

In the old armchair is seated a pale woman in tattered black; Mamma Muguet, on her knees on a little footstool, is rubbing the poor thing's hands as if to warm them. Is it a dream? He recognizes her now. Poor creature! The outlines of her face, thinner but pure as of old, those eyes, so hollow but so gentle, they are the outlines, the eyes, of that Clara whom he has not seen for ten long years, but whom he has never forgotten!

"Clara!" Désiré calls with a great sob.

His mother has already risen, has put both her hands on her son's shoulders.

"Yes, it is Clara, your poor Clara," she says, with a trembling voice; "it is your Clara, and she has been telling me her life, which has been that of a brave and honest girl. She lost her father two years ago, and has tried in vain to earn her bread by giving lessons; she has suffered the keenest poverty; for three days,—oh, it is heart-breaking!—she has slept at the 'Refuge Home,' and when they would not take her there again to-night —you know three days is the limit—she was on the point of throwing herself into the Seine! Then in her despair she had a happy thought: she remembered that this was Christmas, the day the God of Charity was born, and so she came to ask help from the mother of her former lover—from the old woman who, without realizing it or meaning to do so, separated you, my poor children! She is at home now; is she not, Désiré, and we will take care of her, poor dear, shall we not? From this night she shall share my bed and have her meals with us."

Ah, Désiré no longer knew where he was. Here was his Christmas surprise! He kissed his mother, and fell at Clara's feet, took her hand, covered it with kisses, then all at once he saw a ring shining there.

With deep emotion he raised his eyes to those of his sad friend. Trying to smile,—oh, the pathetic smile that shows the teeth—she murmured in a feeble voice, "Yes, I would have died with hunger rather than part with it."

It is needless to tell you that Désiré did not sleep a wink that night, for thinking of poor Clara in the next room on the same pillow with his old mother.

Oh, how glad he was that he had fifteen hundred francs in the savings bank, and three louis in his money box! There would be something with which to pay for the wedding as soon as Clara's cheeks should fill out a little. And after? Well, he would work for three, that is all. For some time he had scarcely been able to keep up with Testevuide's orders. Ah, now they may show him brains, lungs, hearts, livers, spleens and intestines without end! Consumed by frightful diseases into the bargain! He will draw and engrave for them everything they want, and never wince at the dissecting table.

Happy Désiré! Surely Christmas seemed bound to overwhelm him with joy. For the next morning, when he looked in his glass before shaving, he saw that the right side of his beard had turned white during this night of emotion; and when Clara, with his mother on her arm, appeared again, rested, not too greatly changed, not too much older, almost like the Clara of other days in spite of all her suffering, he was able to show her a face that no longer resembled a hair-dyer's advertisement—a good, kind face, with a white beard, it is true, but with eyes that shone with youth and love.

230

Dulce Domum

KENNETH GRAHAME

THE SHEEP ran huddling together against the hurdles, blowing out thin nostrils and stamping with delicate fore-feet, their heads thrown back and a light steam rising from the crowded sheep-pen into the frosty air, as the two animals hastened by in high spirits, with much chatter and laughter. They were returning across country after a long day's outing with Otter, hunting and exploring on the wide uplands where certain streams tributary to their own river had their first small beginnings; and the shades of the short winter day were closing in on them, and they had still some distance to go. Plodding at random across the plough, they had heard the sheep and had made for them; and now, leading from the sheep-pen, they found a beaten track that made walking a lighter business, and re-sponded, moreover, to that small inquiring something which all animals carry inside them, saying unmistakably, "Yes, quite right; *this* leads home!"

"It looks as if we were coming to a village," said the Mole somewhat dubiously, slackening his pace, as the track, that had in time become a path and then had developed into a lane, now handed them over to the charge of a well-metalled road. The animals did not hold with villages, and their own highways, thickly frequented as they were, took an independent course, regardless of church, post office, or public-house.

"Oh, never mind" said the Rat. "At this season of the year they're all safe indoors by this time, sitting round the fire; men, women, and children, dogs and cats and all. We shall slip through all right, without any bother or unpleasantness, and we can have a look at them through their windows if you like, and see what they're doing."

The rapid nightfall of mid-December had quite beset the little village as they approached it on soft feet over a thin fall of powdery snow. Little was visible but squares of a dusky orange-red on either side of the street, where the firelight or lamplight of each cottage overflowed through the casements into the dark world without. Most of the low latticed windows were innocent of blinds, and to the lookers-in from outside, the inmates, gathered round the tea-table, absorbed in handiwork, or talking with laughter and gesture, had each that happy grace which is the last thing the skilled actor shall capture—the natural grace which goes with perfect unconsciousness of observation. Moving at will from one theatre to another, the two spectators, so far from home themselves, had something of wistfulness in their eyes as they watched a cat being stroked, a sleepy child picked up and huddled off to bed, or a tired man stretch and knock out his pipe on the end of a smouldering log.

But it was from one little window, with its blind drawn down, a mere blank transparency on the night, that the sense of home and the little curtained world within walls—the larger stressful world of outside Nature shut out and forgotten—most pulsated. Close against the white blind hung a bird-cage, clearly silhouetted, every wire, perch, and appurtenance distinct and recognisable, even to yesterday's dull-edged lump of sugar. On the middle perch the fluffy occupant, head tucked well into feathers, seemed so near to them as to be easily stroked, had they tried; even the delicate tips of his plumped-out plumage pencilled plainly on the illuminated screen. As they looked, the sleepy little fellow stirred uneasily, woke, shook himself, and raised his head. They could see the gape of his tiny beak as he yawned in a bored sort of way, looked round, and then settled his head into his back again, while the ruffled feathers gradually subsided into perfect stillness. Then a gust of bitter wind took them in the back of the neck, a small sting of frozen sleet on the skin woke them as from a dream, and they knew their toes to be cold and their legs tired, and their own home distant a weary way.

Once beyond the village, where the cottages ceased abruptly, on either side of the road they could smell through the darkness the friendly fields again; and they braced themselves for the last long stretch, the home stretch, the stretch that we know is bound to end, some time, in the rattle of the door-latch, the sudden fire-light, and the sight of familiar things greeting us as long-absent travellers from far oversea. They plodded along steadily and silently, each of them thinking his own thoughts. The Mole's ran a good deal on supper, as it was pitchdark, and it was all a strange country to him as far as he knew, and he was following obediently in the wake of the Rat, leaving the guidance entirely to him. As for the Rat, he was walking a little way ahead, as his habit was, his shoulders humped, his eyes fixed on the straight grey road in front of him; so he did not notice poor Mole when suddenly the summons reached him, and took him like an electric shock.

We others, who have long lost the more subtle of the physical senses, have not even proper terms to express an animal's inter-communications with his surroundings, living or otherwise, and have only the word "smell," for instance, to include the whole range of delicate thrills which murmur in the nose of the animal night and day, summoning, warning, inciting, repelling. It was one of these mysterious fairy calls from out the void that sud-denly reached Mole in the darkness, making him tingle through and through with its very familiar appeal, even while as yet he could not clearly remember what it was. He stopped dead in his tracks, his nose searching hither and thither in its efforts to recapture the fine filament, the telegraphic current, that had so strongly moved him. A moment, and he had caught it again; and with it this time came recollection in fullest flood.

Home! That was what they meant, those caressing appeals, those soft touches wafted through the air, those invisible little hands pulling and tugging, all one way! Why, it must be quite close by him at that moment, his old home that he had hurriedly forsaken and never sought again, that day when he first found the river! And now it was sending out its scouts and its messengers to capture him and bring him in. Since his escape on that bright morning he had hardly given it a thought, so absorbed had he been in his new life, in all its pleasures, its surprises, its fresh and captivating experiences. Now, with a rush of old memories, how clearly it stood up before him, in the darkness! Shabby indeed, and small and poorly furnished, and yet his, the home he had made for himself, the home he had been so happy to get back to after his day's work. And the home had been happy with him, too, evidently, and was missing him, and wanted him back, and was telling him so, through his nose, sorrowfully, reproachfully, but with no bitterness or anger; only with plaintive reminder that it was there, and wanted him.

The call was clear, the summons was plain. He must obey it instantly, and go. "Ratty!" he called, full of joyful excitement, "hold on! Come back! I want you, quick!"

"O, *come* along, Mole, do!" replied the Rat cheerfully, still plodding along.

"*Please* stop, Ratty!" pleaded the poor Mole, in anguish of heart. "You don't understand! It's my home, my old home! I've just come across the smell of it, and it's close by here, really quite close. And I *must* go to it, I must, I must! O, come back, Ratty! Please, please come back!"

The Rat was by this time very far ahead, too far to hear clearly what the Mole was calling, too far to catch the sharp note of painful appeal in his voice. And he was much taken up with the weather, for he too could smell something—something suspiciously like approaching snow.

"Mole, we mustn't stop now, really!" he called back. "We'll come for it to-morrow, whatever it is you've found. But I daren't stop now—it's late, and the snow's coming on again, and I'm not sure of the way! And I want your nose, Mole, so come on

234

quick, there's a good fellow!" And the Rat pressed forward on his way without waiting for an answer.

Poor Mole stood alone in the road, his heart torn asunder, and a big sob gathering, gathering, somewhere low down inside him, to leap up to the surface presently, he knew, in passionate escape. But even under such a test as this his loyalty to his friend stood firm. Never for a moment did he dream of abandoning him. Meanwhile, the wafts from his old home pleaded, whispered, conjured, and finally claimed him imperiously. He dared not tarry longer within their magic circle. With a wrench that tore his very heartstrings he set his face down the road and followed submissively in the track of the Rat, while faint, thin little smells, still dogging his retreating nose, reproached him for his new friendship and his callous forgetfulness.

With an effort he caught up the unsuspecting Rat, who began chattering cheerfully about what they would do when they got back, and how jolly a fire of logs in the parlor would be, and what a supper he meant to eat; never noticing his companion's silence and distressful state of mind. At last, however, when they had gone some considerable way further, and were passing some tree-stumps at the edge of a copse that bordered the road, he stopped and said kindly, "Look here, Mole, old chap, you seem dead tired. No talk left in you, and your feet dragging like lead. We'll sit down here for a minute and rest. The snow has held off so far, and the best part of our journey is over."

The Mole subsided forlornly on a tree-stump and tried to control himself, for he felt it surely coming. The sob he had fought with so long refused to be beaten. Up and up, it forced its way to the air, and then another, and another, and others thick and fast; till poor Mole at last gave up the struggle, and cried freely and helplessly and openly, now that he knew it was all over and he had lost what he could hardly be said to have found.

The Rat, astonished and dismayed at the violence of Mole's

paroxysm of grief, did not dare to speak for a while. At last he said, very quietly and sympathetically, "What it is, old fellow? Whatever can be the matter? Tell us your trouble, and let me see what I can do."

Poor Mole found it difficult to get any words out between the upheavals of his chest that followed one upon another so quickly and held back speech and choked it as it came. "I know it's a— shabby, dingy little place," he sobbed forth at last, brokenly: "not like—your cosy quarters—or Toad's beautiful hall—or Badger's great house—but it was my own little home—and I was fond of it—and I went away and forgot all about it—and then I smelt it suddenly—on the road, when I called and you wouldn't listen, Rat—and everything came back to me with a rush—and I *wanted* it!—O dear, O dear!—and when you *wouldn't* turn back, Ratty—and I had to leave it, though I was smelling it all the time—I thought my heart would break.—We might have just gone and had one look at it, Ratty—only one look—it was close by—but you wouldn't turn back, Ratty, you wouldn't turn back! O dear, O dear!"

Recollection brought fresh waves of sorrow, and sobs again took full charge of him, preventing further speech.

The Rat stared straight in front of him, saying nothing, only patting Mole gently on the shoulder. After a time he muttered gloomily, "I see it all now! What a *pig* I have been! A pig— that's me! Just a pig—a plain pig!"

He waited till Mole's sobs became gradually less stormy and more rhythmical; he waited till at last sniffs were frequent and sobs only intermittent. Then he rose from his seat, and, remarking carelessly, "Well, now we'd really better be getting on, old chap!" set off up the road again, over the toilsome way they had come.

"Wherever are you (hic) going to (hic), Ratty?" cried the tearful Mole, looking up in alarm.

"We're going to find that home of yours, old fellow," replied the Rat pleasantly; "so you had better come along, for it will take some finding, and we shall want your nose."

"O, come back, Ratty, do!" cried the Mole, getting up and hurrying after him. "It's no good, I tell you! It's too late, and too dark, and the place is too far off, and the snow's coming! And—and I never meant to let you know I was feeling that way about it—it was all an accident and a mistake! And think of River Bank, and your supper!"

"Hang River Bank, and supper too!" said the Rat heartily. "I tell you, I'm going to find this place now, if I stay out all night. So cheer up, old chap, and take my arm, and we'll very soon be back there again."

Still snuffling, pleading, and reluctant, Mole suffered himself to be dragged back along the road by his imperious companion, who by a flow of cheerful talk and anecdote endeavored to beguile his spirits back and make the weary way seem shorter. When at last it seemed to the Rat that they must be nearing that part of the road where the Mole had been "held up," he said, "Now, no more talking. Business! Use your nose, and give your mind to it."

They moved on in silence for some little way, when suddenly the Rat was conscious, through his arm that was linked in Mole's, of a faint sort of electric thrill that was passing down that animal's body. Instantly he disengaged himself, fell back a pace, and waited, all attention.

The signals were coming through!

Mole stood a moment rigid, while his uplifted nose, quivering slightly, felt the air.

Then a short, quick run forward—a fault—a check—a try back; and then a slow, steady, confident advance.

The Rat, much excited, kept close to his heels as the Mole, with something of the air of a sleepwalker, crossed a dry ditch, scrambled through a hedge, and nosed his way over a field open and trackless and bare in the faint starlight.

Suddenly, without giving warning, he dived; but the Rat was on the alert, and promptly followed him down the tunnel to which his unerring nose had faithfully led him.

It was close and airless, and the earthy smell was strong, and it seemed a long time to Rat ere the passage ended and he could stand erect and stretch and shake himself. The Mole struck a match, and by its light the Rat saw that they were standing in an open space, neatly swept and sanded underfoot, and directly facing them was Mole's little front door, with "Mole End" painted, in Gothic lettering, over the bell-pull at the side.

Mole reached down a lantern from a nail on the wall and lit it, and the Rat, looking round him, saw that they were in a sort of fore-court. A garden-seat stood on one side of the door, and on the other, a roller; for the Mole, who was a tidy animal when at home, could not stand having his ground kicked up by other animals into little runs that ended in earth-heaps. On the walls hung wire baskets with ferns in them, alternating with brackets carrying plaster statuary—Garibaldi, and the infant Samuel, and Queen Victoria, and other heroes of modern Italy. Down one side of the fore-court ran a skittle-alley, with benches along it and little wooden tables marked with rings that hinted at beer-mugs. In the middle was a small round pond containing goldfish and surrounded by a cockle-shell border. Out of the centre of the pond rose a fanciful erection clothed in more cockle-shells and topped by a large silvered glass ball that reflected everything all wrong and had a very pleasing effect.

Mole's face beamed at the sight of all these objects so dear to him, and he hurried Rat through the door, lit a lamp in the hall, and took one glance round his old home. He saw the dust lying thick on everything, saw the cheerless, deserted look of the long-neglected house, and its narrow, meagre dimensions, its worn and shabby contents—and collapsed again on a hall-chair, his nose in his paws. "O, Ratty!" he cried dismally, "why ever did I do it? Why did I bring you to this poor, cold little place, on a night like this, when you might have been at River Bank by this time, toasting your toes before a blazing fire, with all your own nice things about you!"

The Rat paid no heed to his doleful self-reproaches. He was running here and there, opening doors, inspecting rooms and cupboards, and lighting lamps and candles and sticking them up everywhere. "What a capital little house this is!" he called out cheerily. "So compact! So well planned! Everything here and everything in its place! We'll make a jolly night of it. The first thing we want is a good fire; I'll see to that—I always know where to find things, So this is the parlor? Splendid! Your own idea, those little sleeping-bunks in the wall? Capital! Now, I'll fetch the wood and the coals, and you get a duster, Mole—you'll find one in the drawer of the kitchen table—and try and smarten things up a bit. Bustle about, old chap!"

Encouraged by his inspiriting companion, the Mole roused himself and dusted and polished with energy and heartiness, while the Rat, running to and fro with armfuls of fuel, soon had a cheerful blaze roaring up the chimney. He hailed the Mole to come and warm himself; but Mole promptly had another fit of the blues, dropping down on a couch in dark despair and burying his face in his duster.

"Rat," he moaned, "how about your supper, you poor, cold, hungry, weary animal? I've nothing to give you—nothing—not a crumb!"

"What a fellow you are for giving in!" said the Rat reproachfully. "Why, only just now I saw a sardine-opener on the kitchen dresser, quite distinctly; and everybody knows that means there are sardines about somewhere in the neighborhood. Rouse yourself! pull yourself together, and come with me and forage."

They went and foraged accordingly, hunting through every cupboard and turning out every drawer. The result was not so very depressing after all, though of course it might have been better; a tin of sardines—a box of captain's biscuits, nearly full —and a German sausage encased in silver paper.

239

"There's a banquet for you!" observed the Rat, as he arranged the table. "I know some animals who would give their ears to be sitting down to supper with us tonight!"

"No bread!" groaned the Mole dolorously; "no butter, no——"

"No *pâté de foie gras*, no champagne!" continued the Rat, grinning. "And that reminds me—what's that little door at the end of the passage? Your cellar, of course! Every luxury in this house! Just you wait a minute."

He made for the cellar door, and presently reappeared, somewhat dusty, with a bottle of beer in each paw and another under each arm. "Self-indulgent beggar you seem to be, Mole," he observed. "Deny yourself nothing. This is really the jolliest little place I ever was in. Now, wherever did you pick up those prints? Make the place look so home-like, they do. No wonder you're so fond of it, Mole. Tell us all about it, and how you came to make it what it is."

Then, while the Rat busied himself fetching plates, and knives and forks, and mustard which he mixed in an egg-cup, the Mole, his bosom still heaving with the stress of his recent emotion, related—somewhat shyly at first, but with more freedom as he warmed to his subject—how this was planned, and how that was thought out, and how this was got through a windfall from an aunt, and that was a wonderful find and a bargain, and this other thing was bought out of laborious savings and a certain amount of "going without." His spirits finally quite restored, he must needs go and caress his possessions, and take a lamp and show off their points to his visitor and expatiate on them, quite forgetful of the supper they both so much needed; Rat, who was desperately hungry but strove to conceal it, nodding seriously, examining with a puckered brow, and saying, "Wonderful," and "Most remarkable," at intervals, when the chance for an observation was given him.

At last the Rat succeeded in decoying him to the table, and had just got seriously to work with the sardine-opener when sounds were heard from the fore-court without—sounds like the scuffling of small feet in the gravel and a confused murmur of tiny voices, while broken sentences reached them—"Now, all in a line—hold the lantern up a bit, Tommy—clear your throats first—no coughing after I say one, two, three.—Where's young Bill?—Here, come on, do, we're all a-waiting——"

"What's up?" inquired the Rat, pausing in his labors.

I think it must be the field-mice," replied the Mole, with a touch of pride in his manner. "They go round carol-singing regularly at this time of the year. They're quite an institution in these parts. And they never pass me over—they come to Mole End last of all; and I used to give them hot drinks, and supper too sometimes, when I could afford it. It will be like old times to hear them again."

"Let's have a look at them!" cried the Rat, jumping up and running to the door.

It was a pretty sight, and a seasonable one, that met their eyes when they flung the door open. In the fore-court, lit by the dim rays of a horn lantern, some eight or ten little field-mice stood in a semicircle, red worsted comforters round their throats, their fore-paws thrust deep into their pockets, their feet jigging for warmth. With bright beady eyes they glanced shyly at each other, sniggering a little, sniffing and applying coat-sleeves a good deal. As the door opened, one of the elder ones that carried the lantern was just saying, "Now then, one, two, three!" and forthwith their shrill little voices uprose on the air, singing one of the old-time carols that their forefathers composed in fields that were fallow and held by frost, or when snow-bound in chimney corners, and handed down to be sung in the miry streets to lamp-lit windows at Yule time.

CAROL

Villagers all, this frosty tide,
Let your doors swing open wide,

Though wind may follow, and snow beside,
Yet draw us in by your fire to bide;
  Joy shall be yours in the morning!

Here we stand in the cold and the sleet,
Blowing fingers and stamping feet,
Come from far away you to greet—
You by the fire and we in the street—
  Bidding you joy in the morning!

For ere one half of the night was gone,
Sudden a star has led us on,
Raining bliss and benison—
Bliss tomorrow and more anon,
  Joy for every morning!

Goodman Joseph toiled through the snow—
Saw the star o'er a stable low;
Mary she might not further go—
Welcome thatch, and litter below!
  Joy was hers in the morning!

And then they heard the angels tell
"Who were the first to cry Nowell?
Animals all, as it befell,
In the stable where they did dwell!
  Joy shall be theirs in the morning!"

The voices ceased, the singers, bashful but smiling, exchanged sidelong glances, and silence succeeded—but for a moment only. Then, from up above and far away, down the tunnel they had so lately travelled was borne to their ears in a faint musical hum the sound of distant bells ringing a joyful and clangorous peal.

"Very well sung, boys!" cried the Rat heartily. "And now

come along in, all of you, and warm yourselves by the fire, and have something hot!"

"Yes, come along, field-mice," cried the Mole eagerly. "This is quite like old times! Shut the door after you. Pull up that settle to the fire. Now, you just wait a minute, while we—— O, Ratty!" he cried in despair, plumping down on a seat, with tears impending. "Whatever are we doing? We've nothing to give them!"

"You leave all that to me," said the masterful Rat. "Here, you with the lantern! Come over this way. I want to talk to you. Now, tell me, are there any shops open at this hour of the night?"

"Why, certainly, sir," replied the field-mouse respectfully. "At this time of the year our shops keep open to all sorts of hours."

"Then look here!" said the Rat. "You go off at once, you and your lantern, and you get me——"

Here much muttered conversation ensued, and the Mole only heard bits of it, such as—"Fresh, mind!—no, a pound of that will do—see you get Buggins's, for I won't have any other—no, only the best—if you can't get it there, try somewhere else— yes, of course, home-made, no tinned stuff—well then, do the best you can!" Finally, there was a chink of coin passing from paw to paw, the field-mouse was provided with an ample basket for his purchases, and off he hurried, he and his lantern.

The rest of the field-mice, perched in a row on the settle, their small legs swinging, gave themselves up to enjoyment of the fire, and toasted their chilblains till they tingled; while the Mole, failing to draw them into easy conversation, plunged into family history and made each of them recite the names of his numerous brothers, who were too young, it appeared, to be allowed to go out a-carolling this year, but looked forward very shortly to winning the parental consent.

The Rat, meanwhile, was busy examining the label on one of the beer bottles. "I perceive this to be Old Burton," he remarked approvingly. "*Sensible* Mole! The very thing! Now we shall be

243

able to mull some ale! Get the things ready, Mole, while I draw the corks."

It did not take long to prepare the brew and thrust the tin heater well into the red heart of the fire; and soon every field-mouse was sipping and coughing and choking (for a little mulled ale goes a long way) and wiping his eyes and laughing and forgetting he had ever been cold in all his life.

"They act plays too, these fellows," the Mole explained to the Rat. "Make them up all by themselves, and act them afterwards. And very well they do it, too! They gave us a capital one last year, about a field-mouse who was captured at sea by a Barbary corsair, and made to row in a galley; and when he escaped and got home again, his lady-love had gone into a convent. Here, *you!* You were in it, I remember. Get up and recite a bit."

The field-mouse addressed got up on his legs, giggled shyly, looked round the room, and remained absolutely tongue-tied. His comrades cheered him on, Mole coaxed and encouraged him, and the Rat went so far as to take him by the shoulders and shake him; but nothing could overcome his stage-fright. They were all busily engaged on him like water men applying the Royal Humane Society's regulations to a case of long submersion, when the latch clicked, the door opened, and the field-mouse with the lantern reappeared, staggering under the weight of his basket.

There was no more talk of play-acting once the very real and solid contents of the basket had been tumbled out on the table. Under the generalship of Rat, everybody was set to do something or to fetch something. In a very few minutes supper was ready, and Mole, as he took the head of the table in a sort of dream, saw a lately barren board set thick with savoury comforts; saw his little friends' faces brighten and beam as they fell to without delay; and then let himself loose—for he was famished indeed—on the provender so magically provided, thinking what a happy homecoming this had turned out, after all. As they ate, they talked of old times, and the field-mice gave him the local gossip up to date, and answered as well as they could the hundred questions he had to ask them. The Rat said little or nothing, only taking care that each guest had what he wanted, and plenty of it, and that Mole had no trouble or anxiety about anything.

They clattered off at last, very grateful and showering wishes of the season, with their jacket pockets stuffed with remembrances for the small brothers and sisters at home. When the door had closed on the last of them and the chink of the lanterns had died away, Mole and Rat kicked the fire up, drew their chairs in, brewed themselves a last nightcap of mulled ale, and discussed the events of the long day. At last the Rat, with a tremendous yawn, said, "Mole, old chap, I'm ready to drop. Sleepy is simply not the word. That your own bunk over on that side? Very well, then, I'll take this. What a ripping little house this is! Everything so handy!"

He clambered into his bunk and rolled himself well up in the blankets, and slumber gathered him forthwith, as a swath of barley is folded into the arms of the reaping-machine.

The weary Mole also was glad to turn in without delay, and soon had his head on his pillow, in great joy and contentment. But ere he closed his eyes he let them wander round his old room, mellow in the glow of the firelight that played or rested on familiar and friendly things which had long been unconsciously a part of him, and now smilingly received him back, without rancor. He was now in just the frame of mind that the tactful Rat had quietly worked to bring about in him. He saw clearly how plain and simple—how narrow, even—it all was; but clearly, too, how much it all meant to him, and the special value of some such anchorage in one's existence. He did not at all want to abandon the new life and its splendid spaces, to turn his back on sun and air and all they offered him and creep home and stay there; the upper world was all

245

too strong, it called to him still, even down there, and he knew he must return to the larger stage. But it was good to think he had this to come back to, this place which was all his own, these things which were so glad to see him again and could always be counted upon for the same simple welcome.

From *The Wind in the Willows*

Two by Saki

REGINALD'S CHRISTMAS REVEL

THEY SAY (said Reginald) that there's nothing sadder than victory except defeat. If you've ever stayed with dull people during what is alleged to be the festive season, you can probably revise that saying. I shall never forget putting in a Christmas at the Babwolds'. Mrs. Babwold is some relation of my father's—a sort of to-be-left-till-called-for cousin —and that was considered sufficient reason for my having to accept her invitation at about the sixth time of asking; though why the sins of the father should be visited by the children— you won't find any notepaper in that drawer; that's where I keep old menus and first-night programmes.

Mrs. Babwold wears a rather solemn personality, and has never been known to smile, even when saying disagreeable things to her friends or making out the Stores list. She takes her pleasures sadly. A state elephant at a Durbar gives one a very similar impression. Her husband gardens in all weathers. When a man goes out in the pouring rain to brush caterpillars off rose trees, I generally imagine his life indoors leaves something to be desired; anyway, it must be very unsettling for the caterpillars.

Of course there were other people there. There was a Major Somebody who had shot things in Lapland, or somewhere of that sort; I forgot what they were, but it wasn't for want of reminding. We had them cold with every meal almost, and he was continually giving us details of what they measured from tip to tip, as though he thought we were going to make them warm under-things for the winter. I used to listen to him with a rapt attention that I thought rather suited me, and then one day

I quite modestly gave the dimensions of an okapi I had shot in the Lincolnshire fens. The Major turned a beautiful Tyrian scarlet (I remember thinking at the time that I should like my bathroom hung in that colour), and I think that at that moment he almost found it in his heart to dislike me. Mrs. Babwold put on a first-aid-to-the-injured expression, and asked him why he didn't publish a book of his sporting reminiscences; it would be *so* interesting. She didn't remember till afterwards that he had given her two fat volumes on the subject, with his portrait and autograph as a frontispiece and an appendix on the habits of the Arctic mussel.

It was in the evening that we cast aside the cares and distractions of the day and really lived. Cards were thought to be too frivolous and empty a way of passing the time, so most of them played what they called a book game. You went out into the hall—to get an inspiration, I suppose—then you came in again with a muffler tied round your neck and looked silly, and the others were supposed to guess that you were *Wee MacGreegor*. I held out against the inanity as long as I decently could, but at last, in a lapse of good-nature, I consented to masquerade as a book, only I warned them that it would take some time to carry out. They waited for the best part of forty minutes while I went and played wineglass skittles with the page-boy in the pantry; you play it with a champagne cork, you know, and the one who knocks down the most glasses without breaking them wins. I won, with four unbroken out of seven; I think William suffered from over-anxiousness. They were rather mad in the drawing-room at my not having come back, and they weren't a bit pacified when I told them afterwards that I was *At the end of the passage.*

"I never did like Kipling," was Mrs. Babwold's comment, when the situation dawned upon her. "I couldn't see anything clever in *Earthworms out of Tuscany*—or is that by Darwin?"

Of course these games are very educational, but, personally, I prefer bridge.

On Christmas evening we were supposed to be specially festive in the Old English fashion. The hall was horribly draughty,
but it seemed to be the proper place to revel in, and it was
decorated with Japanese fans and Chinese lanterns, which gave
it a very Old English effect. A young lady with a confidential
voice favoured us with a long recitation about a little girl who
died or did something equally hackneyed, and then the Major
gave us a graphic account of a struggle he had with a wounded
bear. I privately wished that the bears would win sometimes on
these occasions; at least they wouldn't go vapouring about it
afterwards. Before we had time to recover our spirits, we were
indulged with some thought-reading by a young man whom
one knew instinctively had a good mother and an indifferent
tailor—the sort of young man who talks unflaggingly through
the thickest soup, and smooths his hair dubiously as though he
thought it might hit back. The thought-reading was rather a
success; he announced that the hostess was thinking about
poetry, and she admitted that her mind was dwelling on one of
Austin's odes. Which was near enough. I fancy she had been
really wondering whether a scrag-end of mutton and some cold
plum-pudding would do for the kitchen dinner next day. As a
crowning dissipation, they all sat down to play progressive
halma, with milk-chocolate for prizes. I've been carefully
brought up, and I don't like to play games of skill for milk-
chocolate, so I invented a headache and retired from the scene.
I had been preceded a few minutes earlier by Miss Langshan-
Smith, a rather formidable lady, who always got up at some uncomfortable hour in the morning, and gave you the impression
that she had been in communication with most of the European
Governments before breakfast. There was a paper pinned on her
door with a signed request that she might be called particularly
early on the morrow. Such an opportunity does not come twice
in a lifetime. I covered up everything except the signature with
another notice, to the effect that before these words should
meet the eye she would have ended a misspent life, was sorry for

the trouble she was giving, and would like a military funeral. A few minutes later I violently exploded an air-filled paper bag on the landing, and gave a stage moan that could have been heard in the cellars. Then I pursued my original intention and went to bed. The noise those people made in forcing open the good lady's door was positively indecorous; she resisted gallantly, but I believe they searched her for bullets for about a quarter of an hour, as if she had been a historic battlefield.

I hate travelling on Boxing Day, but one must occasionally do things that one dislikes.

BERTIE'S CHRISTMAS EVE

IT WAS Christmas Eve, and the family circle of Luke Steffink, Esq., was aglow with the amiability and random mirth which the occasion demanded. A long and lavish dinner had been partaken of, waits had been round and sung carols, the house-party had regaled itself with more carolling on its own account, and there had been romping which, even in a pulpit reference, could not have been condemned as ragging. In the midst of the general glow, however, there was one black unkindled cinder.

Bertie Steffink, nephew of the aforementioned Luke, had early in life adopted the profession of ne'er-do-weel; his father had been something of the kind before him. At the age of eighteen Bertie had commenced that round of visits to our Colonial possessions, so seemly and desirable in the case of a Prince of the Blood, so suggestive of insincerity in a young man

250

of the middle-class. He had gone to grow tea in Ceylon and fruit in British Columbia, and to help sheep to grow wool in Australia. At the age of twenty he had just returned from some similar errand in Canada, from which it may be gathered that the trial he gave to these various experiments was of the summary drum-head nature. Luke Steffink, who fulfilled the troubled rôle of guardian and deputy-parent to Bertie, deplored the persistent manifestation of the homing instinct on his nephew's part, and his solemn thanks earlier in the day for the blessing of reporting a united family had no reference to Bertie's return.

Arrangements had been promptly made for packing the youth off to a distant corner of Rhodesia, whence return would be a difficult matter; the journey to this uninviting destination was imminent, in fact a more careful and willing traveller would have already begun to think about his packing. Hence Bertie was in no mood to share in the festive spirit which displayed itself around him, and resentment smouldered within him at the eager, self-absorbed discussion of social plans for the coming months which he heard on all sides. Beyond depressing his uncle and the family circle generally by singing "Say au revoir, and not good-bye," he had taken no part in the evening's conviviality.

Eleven o'clock had struck some half-hour ago, and the elder Steffinks began to throw out suggestions leading up to that process which they called retiring for the night.

"Come, Teddie, it's time you were in your little bed, you know," said Luke Steffink to his thirteen-year-old son.

"That's where we all ought to be," said Mrs. Steffink.

"There wouldn't be room," said Bertie.

The remark was considered to border on the scandalous; everybody ate raisins and almonds with the nervous industry of sheep feeding during threatening weather.

"In Russia," said Horace Bordenby, who was staying in the house as a Christmas guest, "I've read that the peasants believe that if you go into a cow-house or stable at midnight on

251

Christmas Eve you will hear the animals talk. They're supposed to have the gift of speech at that one moment of the year."

"Oh, *do* let's *all* go down to the cow-house and listen to what they've got to say!" exclaimed Beryl, to whom anything was thrilling and amusing if you did it in a troop.

Mrs. Steffink made a laughing protest, but gave a virtual consent by saying, "We must all wrap up well, then." The idea seemed a scatterbrained one to her, and almost heathenish, but it afforded an opportunity for "throwing the young people together," and as such she welcomed it. Mr. Horace Bordenby was a young man with quite substantial prospects, and he had danced with Beryl at a local subscription ball a sufficient number of times to warrant the authorized inquiry on the part of the neighbors whether "there was anything in it." Though Mrs. Steffink would not have put it in so many words, she shared the idea of the Russian peasantry that on this night the beast might speak.

The cow-house stood at the junction of the garden with a small paddock, an isolated survival, in a suburban neighborhood, of what had once been a small farm. Luke Steffink was complacently proud of his cow-house and his two cows; he felt that they gave him a stamp of solidity which no number of Wyandottes or Orpingtons could impart. They even seemed to link him in a sort of inconsequent way with those patriarchs who derived importance from their floating capital of flocks and herds, he-asses and she-asses. It had been an anxious and momentous occasion when he had had to decide definitely between "the Byre" and "the Ranch" for the naming of his villa residence. A December midnight was hardly the moment he would have chosen for showing his farm-building to visitors, but since it was a fine night, and the young people were anxious for an excuse for a mild frolic, Luke consented to chaperon the expedition. The servants had long since gone to bed, so the house was left in charge of Bertie, who scornfully declined to stir out on the pretext of listening to bovine conversation.

"We must go quietly," said Luke, as he headed the procession of giggling young folk, brought up in the rear by the shawled and hooded figure of Mrs. Steffink; "I've always laid stress on keeping this a quiet and orderly neighborhood."

It was a few minutes to midnight when the party reached the cow-house and made its way in by the light of Luke's stable lantern. For a moment every one stood in silence, almost with a feeling of being in church.

"Daisy—the one lying down—is by a shorthorn bull out of a Guernsey cow," announced Luke in a hushed voice, which was in keeping with the foregoing impression.

"Is she?" said Bordenby, rather as if he had expected her to be by Rembrandt.

"Myrtle is—"

Myrtle's family history was cut short by a little scream from the women of the party.

The cow-house door had closed noiselessly behind them and the key had turned gratingly in the lock; then they heard Bertie's voice pleasantly wishing them good night and his footsteps retreating along the garden path.

Luke Steffink strode to the window; it was a small square opening of the old-fashioned sort, with iron bars let into the stonework.

"Unlock the door this instant," he shouted, with as much air of menacing authority as a hen might assume when screaming through the bars of a coop at a marauding hawk. In reply to his summons the hall-door closed with a defiant bang.

A neighboring clock struck the hour of midnight. If the cows had received the gift of human speech at that moment they would not have been able to make themselves heard. Seven or eight other voices were engaged in describing Bertie's present

253

conduct and his general character at a high pressure of excitement and indignation.

In the course of half an hour or so everything that it was permissible to say about Bertie had been said some dozens of times, and other topics began to come to the front—the extreme mustiness of the cow-house, the possibility of it catching fire, and the probability of it being a Rowton House for the vagrant rats of the neighbourhood. And still no sign of deliverance came to the unwilling vigil-keepers.

Towards one o'clock the sound of rather boisterous and undisciplined carol-singing approached rapidly, and came to a sudden anchorage, apparently just outside the garden gate. A motor-load of youthful "bloods," in a high state of conviviality, had made a temporary halt for repairs; the stoppage, however, did not extend to the vocal efforts of the party, and the watchers in the cow-shed were treated to a highly unauthorized rendering of "Good King Wenceslas," in which the adjective "good" appeared to be very carelessly applied.

The noise had the effect of bringing Bertie out into the garden, but he utterly ignored the pale, angry faces peering out at the cow-house window, and concentrated his attention on the revellers outside the gate.

"Wassail, you chaps!" he shouted.

"Wassail, old sport!" they shouted back; "we'd jolly well drink y'r health, only we've nothing to drink it in."

"Come and wassail inside," said Bertie hospitably; "I'm all alone, and there's heaps of 'wet.' "

They were total strangers, but his touch of kindness made them instantly his kin. In another moment the unauthorized version of King Wenceslas, which, like many other scandals, grew worse on repetition, went echoing up the garden path; two of the revellers gave an impromptu performance on the way by executing the staircase waltz up the terraces of what Luke Steffink, hitherto with some justification, called his rock-garden. The rock part of it was still there when the waltz had been accorded its third encore. Luke, more than ever like a cooped hen behind the cow-house bars, was in a position to realize the feelings of concert-goers unable to countermand the call for an encore which they neither desire nor deserve.

The hall door closed with a bang on Bertie's guests, and the sounds of merriment became faint and muffled to the weary watchers at the other end of the garden. Presently two ominous pops, in quick succession, made themselves distinctly heard.

"They've got at the champagne!" exclaimed Mrs. Steffink.

"Perhaps it's the sparkling Moselle," said Luke hopefully.

Three or four more pops were heard.

"The champagne *and* the sparkling Moselle," said Mrs. Steffink.

Luke uncorked an expletive which, like brandy in a temperance household, was only used on rare emergencies. Mr. Horace Bordenby had been making use of similar expressions under his breath for a considerable time past. The experiment of "throwing the young people together" had been prolonged beyond a point when it was likely to produce any romantic result.

Some forty minutes later the hall door opened and disgorged a crowd that had thrown off any restraint of shyness that might have influenced its earlier actions. Its vocal efforts in the direction of carol singing were now supplemented by instrumental music; a Christmas tree that had been prepared for the children of the gardener and other household retainers had yielded a rich spoil of tin trumpets, rattles, and drums. The life story of King Wenceslas had been dropped, Luke was thankful to notice, but it was intensely irritating for the chilled prisoners in the cow-house to be told that it was "a hot time in the old town tonight," together with some accurate but entirely superfluous information as to the imminence of Christmas morning. Judging by the protests which began to be shouted from the upper windows of neighboring houses, the sentiments prevailing in the cow-house were heartily echoed in other quarters.

The revellers found their car, and, what was more remarkable,

255

managed to drive off in it, with a parting fanfare of tin trumpets. The lively beat of a drum disclosed the fact that the master of the revels remained on the scene.

"Bertie!" came in an angry, imploring chorus of shouts and screams from the cow-house window.

"Hullo," cried the owner of the name, turning his rather errant steps in the direction of the summons; "are you people still there? Must have heard everything cows got to say by this time. If you haven't, no use waiting. After all, it's a Russian legend, and Russian Chrismush Eve not due for 'nother fortnight. Better come out."

After one or two ineffectual attempts he managed to pitch the key of the cow-house door in through the window. Then, lifting his voice in the strains of "I'm afraid to go home in the dark," with a lusty drum accompaniment, he led the way back to the house. The hurried procession of the released that followed in his steps came in for a good deal of the adverse comment that his exuberant display had evoked.

It was the happiest Christmas Eve he had ever spent. To quote his own words, he had a rotten Christmas.

Old Folks' Christmas

RING LARDNER

TOM and Grace Carter sat in their living-room on Christmas Eve, sometimes talking, sometimes pretending to read and all the time thinking things they didn't want to think. Their two children, Junior, aged nineteen, and Grace, two years younger, had come home that day from their schools for the Christmas vacation. Junior was in his first year at the university and Grace attending a boarding-school that would fit her for college.

I won't call them Grace and Junior any more, though that is the way they had been christened. Junior had changed his name to Ted and Grace was now Caroline, and thus they insisted on being addressed, even by their parents. This was one of the things Tom and Grace the elder were thinking of as they sat in their living-room Christmas Eve.

Other university freshmen who had lived here had returned on the twenty-first, the day when the vacation was supposed to begin. Ted had telegraphed that he would be three days late owing to a special examination which, if he passed it, would lighten the terrific burden of the next term. He had arrived at home looking so pale, heavy-eyed and shaky that his mother doubted the wisdom of the concentrated mental effort, while his father secretly hoped the stuff had been nonpoisonous and would not have lasting effects. Caroline, too, had been behind schedule, explaining that her laundry had gone astray and she had not dared trust others to trace it for her.

Grace and Tom had attempted, with fair success, to conceal their disappointment over this delayed home-coming and had continued with their preparations for a Christmas that would thrill their children and consequently themselves. They had bought an imposing lot of presents, costing twice or three times as much as had been Tom's father's annual income when Tom was Ted's age, or Tom's own income a year ago, before General Motors' acceptance of his new weather-proof paint had enabled him to buy this suburban home and luxuries such as his own parents and Grace's had never dreamed of, and to give Ted and Caroline advantages that he and Grace had perforce gone without.

Behind the closed door of the music-room was the elaborately decked tree. The piano and piano bench and the floor around the tree were covered with beribboned packages of all sizes, shapes and weights, one of them addressed to Tom, another to Grace, a few to the servants and the rest to Ted and Caroline. A huge box contained a sealskin coat for Caroline, a coat that had cost as much as the Carters had formerly paid a year for rent. Even more expensive was a "set" of jewelry consisting of an opal brooch, a bracelet of opals and gold filigree, and an opal ring surrounded by diamonds.

Grace always had preferred opals to any other stone, but now that she could afford them, some inhibition prevented her from buying them for herself; she could enjoy them much more adorning her pretty daughter. There were boxes of silk stockings, lingerie, gloves and handkerchiefs. And for Ted, a three-hundred-dollar watch, a de-luxe edition of Balzac, an expensive bag of shiny, new steel-shafted golf-clubs and the last word in portable phonographs.

But the big surprise for the boy was locked in the garage, a black Gorham sedan, a model more up to date and better-looking than Tom's own year-old car that stood beside it. Ted could use it during the vacation if the mild weather continued and could look forward to driving it around home next spring and summer, there being a rule at the university forbidding undergraduates the possession or use of private automobiles.

Every year for sixteen years, since Ted was three and Caroline

258

one, it had been the Christmas Eve custom of the Carters to
hang up their children's stockings and fill with inexpensive toys.
Tom and Grace had thought it would be fun to continue the
custom this year; the contents of the stockings—a mechanical
negro dancing doll, music boxes, a kitten that meowed when
you pressed a spot on her back, et cetera—would make the "kids"
laugh. And one of Grace's first pronouncements to her returned
offspring was that they must go to bed early so Santa Claus
would not be frightened away.

But it seemed they couldn't promise to make it so terribly
early. They both had long-standing dates in town. Caroline was
going to dinner and a play with Beatrice Murdock and Beatrice's
nineteen-year-old brother Paul. The latter would call for her
in his car at half past six. Ted had accepted an invitation to see
the hockey match with two classmates, Herb Castle and Bernard
King. He wanted to take his father's Gorham, but Tom told him
untruthfully that the foot-brake was not working; Ted must be
kept out of the garage till tomorrow morning.

Ted and Caroline had taken naps in the afternoon and gone
off together in Paul Murdock's stylish roadster, giving their word
that they would be back by midnight or a little later and that
tomorrow night they would stay home.

And now their mother and father were sitting up for them,
because the stockings could not be filled and hung till they were
safely in bed, and also because trying to go to sleep is a painful
and hopeless business when you are kind of jumpy.

"What time is it?" asked Grace, looking up from the third
page of a book that she had begun to "read" soon after dinner.

"Half past two," said her husband. (He had answered the
same question every fifteen or twenty minutes since midnight.)

"You don't suppose anything could have happened?" said
Grace.

"We'd have heard if there had," said Tom.

"It isn't likely, of course," said Grace, "but they might have
had an accident some place where nobody was there to report

it or telephone or anything. We don't know what kind of a driver the Murdock boy is."

"He's Ted's age. Boys that age may be inclined to drive too fast, but they drive pretty well."

"How do you know?"

"Well, I've watched some of them drive."

"Yes, but not all of them."

"I doubt whether anybody in the world has seen every nineteen-year-old boy drive."

"Boys these days seem so kind of irresponsible."

"Oh, don't worry! They probably met some of their young friends and stopped for a bite to eat or something." Tom got up and walked to the window with studied carelessness. "It's a pretty night," he said. "You can see every star in the sky."

But he wasn't looking at the stars. He was looking down the road for headlights. There were none in sight and after a few moments he returned to his chair.

"What time is it?" asked Grace.

"Twenty-two of," he said.

"Of what?"

"Of three."

"Your watch must have stopped. Nearly an hour ago you told me it was half past two."

"My watch is all right. You probably dozed off."

"I haven't closed my eyes."

"Well, it's time you did. Why don't you go to bed?"

"Why don't *you?*"

"I'm not sleepy."

"Neither am I. But honestly, Tom, it's silly for you to stay up. I'm just doing it so I can fix the stockings, and because I feel so wakeful. But there's no use of your losing your sleep."

"I couldn't sleep a wink till they're home."

"That's foolishness! There's nothing to worry about. They're just having a good time. You were young once yourself."

"That's just it! When I was young, I was young." He picked up his paper and tried to get interested in the shipping news.

"What time is it?" asked Grace.

"Five minutes of three."

"Maybe they're staying at the Murdocks' all night."

"They'd have let us know."

"They were afraid to wake us up, telephoning."

At three-twenty a car stopped at the front gate.

"There they are!"

"I told you there was nothing to worry about."

Tom went to the window. He could just discern the outlines of the Murdock boy's roadster, whose lighting system seemed to have broken down.

"He hasn't any lights," said Tom. "Maybe I'd better go out and see if I can fix them."

"No, don't!" said Grace sharply. "He can fix them himself. He's just saving them while he stands still."

"Why don't they come in?"

"They're probably making plans."

"They can make them in here. I'll go out and tell them we're still up."

"No, don't!" said Grace as before, and Tom obediently remained at the window.

It was nearly four when the car lights flashed on and the car drove away. Caroline walked into the house and stared dazedly at her parents.

"Heavens! What are you doing up?"

Tom was about to say something, but Grace forestalled him.

"We were talking over old Christmases," she said. "Is it very late?"

"I haven't any idea," said Caroline.

"Where is Ted?"

"Isn't he home? I haven't seen him since we dropped him at the hockey place."

"Well, you go right to bed," said her mother. "You must be worn out."

"I am, kind of. We danced after the play. What time is breakfast?"

"Eight o'clock."

"Oh, Mother, can't you make it nine?"

"I guess so. You used to want to get up early on Christmas."

"I know, but—"

"Who brought you home?" asked Tom.

"Why, Paul Murdock—and Beatrice."

"You look rumpled."

"They made me sit in the 'rumple' seat."

She laughed at her joke, said good night and went upstairs. She had not come even within hand-shaking distance of her father and mother.

"The Murdocks," said Tom, "must have great manners, making their guest ride in that uncomfortable seat."

Grace was silent.

"You go to bed, too," said Tom. "I'll wait for Ted."

"You couldn't fix the stockings."

"I won't try. We'll have time for that in the morning; I mean, later in the morning."

"I'm not going to bed till you do," said Grace.

"All right, we'll both go. Ted ought not to be long now. I suppose his friends will bring him home. We'll hear him when he comes in."

There was no chance not to hear him when, at ten minutes before six, he came in. He had done his Christmas shopping late and brought home a package.

Grace went downstairs again at half past seven, telling the servants breakfast would be postponed till nine. She nailed the stockings beside the fireplace, went into the music-room to see that nothing had been disturbed and removed Ted's hat and overcoat from where he had carefully hung them on the hall floor.

Tom appeared a little before nine and suggested that the children ought to be awakened.

"I'll wake them," said Grace, and went upstairs. She opened Ted's door, looked and softly closed it again. She entered her daughter's room and found Caroline semiconscious.

"Do I have to get up now? Honestly I can't eat anything. If you could just have Molla bring me some coffee. Ted and I are both invited to the Murdock's for breakfast at half past twelve, and I could sleep for another hour or two."

"But dearie, don't you know we have Christmas dinner at one?"

"It's a shame, Mother, but I thought of course our dinner would be at night."

"Don't you want to see your presents?"

"Certainly I do, but can't they wait?"

Grace was about to go to the kitchen to tell the cook that dinner would be at seven instead of one, but she remembered having promised Signe the afternoon and evening off, as a cold, light supper would be all anyone wanted after the heavy midday meal.

Tom and Grace breakfasted alone and once more sat in the living room, talking, thinking and pretending to read.

"You ought to speak to Caroline," said Tom.

"I will, but not today. It's Christmas."

"And I intend to say a few words to Ted."

"Yes, dear, you must. But not today."

"I suppose they'll be out again tonight."

"No, they promised to stay home. We'll have a nice cozy evening."

"Don't bet too much on that," said Tom.

At noon the "children" made their entrance and responded to their parents' salutations with almost the proper warmth.

263

Ted declined a cup of coffee and he and Caroline apologized for making a "breakfast" date at the Murdocks'.

"Sis and I both thought you'd be having dinner at seven, as usual."

"We've always had it at one o'clock on Christmas," said Tom.

"I'd forgotten it was Christmas," said Ted.

"Well, those stockings ought to remind you."

Ted and Caroline looked at the bulging stockings.

"Isn't there a tree?" asked Caroline.

"Of course," said her mother. "But the stockings come first."

"We've only a little time," said Caroline. "We'll be terribly late as it is. So can't we see the tree now?"

"I guess so," said Grace, and led the way into the music-room.

The servants were summoned and the tree stared at and admired.

"You must open your presents," said Grace to her daughter.

"I can't open them all now," said Caroline. "Tell me which is special."

The cover was removed from the huge box and Grace held up the coat.

"Oh, Mother!" said Caroline. "A sealskin coat!"

"Put it on," said her father.

"Not now. We haven't time."

"Then look at this!" said Grace, and opened the case of jewels.

"Oh, Mother! Opals!" said Caroline.

"They're my favorite stone," said Grace quietly.

"If nobody minds," said Ted, "I'll postpone my personal investigation till we get back. I know I'll like everything you've given me. But if we have no car in working order, I've got to call a taxi and catch a train."

"You can drive in," said his father.

"Did you fix the brake?"

"I think it's all right. Come up to the garage and we'll see."

Ted got his hat and coat and kissed his mother good-by.

"Mother," he said, "I know you'll forgive me for not having

264

any presents for you and Dad. I was so rushed the last three days at school. And I thought I'd have time to shop a little when we got in yesterday, but I was in too much of a hurry to be home. Last night, everything was closed."

"Don't worry," said Grace. "Christmas is for young people. Dad and I have everything we want."

The servants had found their gifts and disappeared, expressing effusive Scandinavian thanks.

Caroline and her mother were left alone.

"Mother, where did the coat come from?"

"Lloyd and Henry's."

"They keep all kinds of furs, don't they?"

"Yes."

"Would you mind horribly if I exchanged this?"

"Certainly not, dear. You pick out anything you like, and if it's a little more expensive, it won't make any difference. We can go in town tomorrow or next day. But don't you want to wear your opals to the Murdocks'?"

"I don't believe so. They might get lost or something. And I'm not—well, I'm not so crazy about—"

"I think they can be exchanged, too," said Grace. "You run along now and get ready to start."

Caroline obeyed with alacrity, and Grace spent a welcome moment by herself.

Tom opened the garage door.

"Why, you've got two cars!" said Ted.

"The new one isn't mine," said Tom.

"Whose is it?"

"Yours. It's the new model."

"Dad, that's wonderful! But it looks just like the old one."

"Well, the old one's pretty good. Just the same, yours is better. You'll find that out when you drive it. Hop in and get started. I had her filled with gas."

"I think I'd rather drive the old one."

"Why?"

265

"Well, what I really wanted, Dad, was a Barnes sport roadster, something like Paul Murdock's, only a different color scheme. And if I don't drive this Gorham at all, maybe you could get them to take it back or make some kind of a deal with the Barnes people."

Tom didn't speak till he was sure of his voice. Then: "All right, son. Take my car and I'll see what can be done about yours."

Caroline, waiting for Ted, remembered something and called to her mother. "Here's what I got for you and Dad," she said. "It's two tickets to 'Jolly Jane,' the play I saw last night. You'll love it!"

"When are they for?" asked Grace.

"Tonight," said Caroline.

"But dearie," said her mother, "we don't want to go out tonight, when you promised to stay home."

"We'll keep our promise," said Caroline, "but the Murdocks may drop in and bring some friends and we'll dance and there'll be music. And Ted and I both thought you'd rather be away somewhere so our noise wouldn't disturb you."

"It was sweet of you to do this," said her mother, "but your father and I don't mind noise as long as you're enjoying yourselves."

"It's time anyway that you and Dad had a treat."

"The real treat," said Grace, "would be to spend a quiet evening here with just you two."

"The Murdocks practically invited themselves and I couldn't say no after they'd been so nice to me. And honestly, Mother, you'll love this play!"

"Will you be home for supper?"

"I'm pretty sure we will, but if we're a little late, don't you and Dad wait for us. Take the seven-twenty so you won't miss anything. The first act is really the best. We probably won't be hungry, but have Signe leave something out for us in case we are."

Tom and Grace sat down to the elaborate Christmas dinner

266

and didn't make much impression on it. Even if they had had any appetite, the sixteen-pound turkey would have looked almost like new when they had eaten their fill. Conversation was intermittent and related chiefly to Signe's excellence as a cook and the mildness of the weather. Children and Christmas were barely touched on.

Tom merely suggested that on account of its being a holiday and their having theatre tickets, they ought to take the six-ten and eat supper at the Metropole. His wife said no; Ted and Caroline might come home and be disappointed at not finding them. Tom seemed about to make some remark, but changed his mind.

The afternoon was the longest Grace had ever known. The children were still absent at seven and she and Tom taxied to the train. Neither talked much on the way to town. As for the play, which Grace was sure to love, it turned out to be a rehash of "Cradle Snatchers" and "Sex," retaining the worst features of each.

When it was over, Tom said: "Now I'm inviting you to the Cove Club. You didn't eat any breakfast or dinner or supper and I can't have you starving to death on a feast-day. Besides, I'm thirsty as well as hungry."

They ordered the special *table d'hôte* and struggled hard to get away with it. Tom drank six high-balls, but they failed to produce the usual effect of making him jovial. Grace had one high-ball and some kind of cordial that gave her a warm, contented feeling for a moment. But the warmth and contentment left her before the train was half way home.

The living-room looked as if Von Kluck's army had just passed through. Ted and Caroline had kept their promise up to a certain point. They had spent part of the evening at home, and the Murdocks must have brought all their own friends and everybody else's, judging from the results. The tables and floors were strewn with empty glasses, ashes and cigaret stubs. The stockings had been torn off their nails and the wrecked contents were all

267

over the place. Two sizable holes had been burnt in Grace's favorite rug.

Tom took his wife by the arm and led her into the music-room.

"You never took the trouble to open your own present," he said.

"And I think there's one for you, too," said Grace. "They didn't come in here," she added, "so I guess there wasn't much dancing or music."

Tom found his gift from Grace, a set of diamond studs and cuff buttons for festive wear. Grace's present from him was an opal ring.

"Oh, Tom!" she said.

"We'll have to go out somewhere tomorrow night, so I can break these in," said Tom.

"Well, if we do that, we'd better get a good night's rest."

"I'll beat you upstairs," said Tom.

Twelfth Night

PHILIP BOOTH

At Twelfth Night twilight now
the greens burn bright: the dry-spined wreath
and bittersweet returned to frozen earth,
    Canada fir
    become the fire
that wreathes a ritual circle in the snow.

  The decorations are first
to flame: old mistletoe and holly
go up in a burst of charred berry, their holy
    roots tossed on,
    a burnt seed sown,
long after the symbol and song are lost.

  Uprooted meanings flare
like watchfires in this cold backyard.
A single star outshines the ice. Unheard,
    the Magi raise
    their prayer; a blaze
of balsam climbs the still and brittle air.

  At Twelfth Night twilight now
the tree must be the final torch,
a coronal to melt the dark; the branch
    that angels swung on,
    Christ hung on,
quick tinder lit to ebb the tidal snow.

269

From slow bright smoke the tree
explodes in fire-veins, star-sparks rain
like fallen Pleiades. The green grain
      burns to warn
      the burner, turn
his back on ceremonial memory.

No god's made manifest
from this raw bush. But who will light
a legend that he will not celebrate?
      In the quick match,
      the winter watch,
the burner is both burned and blessed.

The Broken Christmas

EDWARD FENTON

ARTIN lay there alone, still more than half asleep, dimly wondering why Jane's place in the bed beside him was already empty. He rolled over onto his side, flinging his arm out across the void where she had been. Even the warmth of her body had gone.

Still dimly, he was aware of sounds, muted and scurrying, from the other side of the bedroom door. He knew that there was something else; something connected with her absence; something which he felt he ought to remember. But it kept slipping away from him. His mind wandered after it through the coils of sleep, the layers of soft bedclothes and the chill rays of the morning slanting through the windows. It still eluded him. With Jane, it seemed to have risen from his bed before he had even stirred; and now they had both left him to find his way alone into the winter morning's early brightness.

A bare branch scrabbled against the window, driving him more nearly awake. Now the sounds from beyond the bedroom door cut through more clearly to his ear so that he could tell them apart, like the upper and lower levels of a fugue. There were Jane's mules clapping firmly against the floor of the hall. Little Martin's woolly slippers skittered along beside them.

Now Martin could hear them talking, although he was unable to make out the words.

The footsteps stopped. Above the muffled whispering rose the urgent voice of Little Martin. "Now, Mommy? Now?"

Then suddenly Martin remembered. The morning pivoted into focus. The next moment the bedroom door burst open and Little Martin and Jane were in the room, shouting "Merry

Christmas!" Little Martin clambered across the bed to present a moist, enthusiastic kiss. Jane stood over them both, smiling. Then Martin reached out for her. She bent down and kissed him too, saying, "Merry Christmas, darling," in his ear, while Little Martin, watching them, shrieked, "And there's a angel on the top of the tree and it goes around and around . . ."

Martin swung his feet to the floor. "I'll be quick," he said, adding with a grin, "At least I won't have to hang around until you're finished in the bathroom."

"Listen to the Downtrodden Male!"

Little Martin squirmed out of his mother's arms. "There's presents downstairs," he proclaimed. "And there's—"

"Sh!" Jane warned him. "It's a secret. Martin doesn't know yet. She grabbed him by the seat of his bathrobe and propelled him out into the hall. "Come on, let's let Martin shave."

He could hear Little Martin patter down the hall. "Will he be s'prised when he opens them?" Jane's voice carried back from the staircase, calm and clear. "We'll watch him. He'd just better be surprised."

The bathroom door swung closed behind him, shutting out their voices. Martin stood regarding his own face in the mirror while he lathered it. Another Christmas morning, another growth of stubble! He could still remember, though, how Christmas had used to matter to him. When he was a kid he had always been excited by the anticipation of its delights. And then New Year's followed so closely, bringing another year to his life. It meant he was that much closer to being grown up and to all that seemed to go with it: going wherever he wanted on the face of the earth without having to answer to anyone. There had always been the hope, too, that on Christmas day something would happen to him, the way it did to people in books, to signalize it from all the other days of the year. Somehow, though, it never quite turned out the way he hoped.

But then there had never been much of a fuss made over Christmas when he was a boy. For one thing, most of the time he had been away at distant schools. Home, where his mother lived, had always been a hotel. And his father, with whom they had both long been out of touch, was usually in Europe somewhere, or South America, with his new wife—was it the third by now?

It would have been different, he reflected, if he had been one of a large and undivided family, like Jane's, where there were always celebrations going on, each with its elaborate and intimate network of accumulated traditions. But, as he recalled them, his Christmases (and birthdays too, for that matter) had always, for one reason or another, turned out to be pretty dreary.

He wet his razor and began shaving. He handled it with especial care, remembering how much it upset Jane whenever he cut himself. As he stood before the basin in his crumpled flannel pajamas, drawing the blade across his wet skin, his mind flew back to some of those other Christmases.

He was ten the time his mother sent that beautiful new bike out to him. He was at the ranch school then, staying over for Christmas with the other boys who lived too far east for them to go home for the holidays. She had promised to come out in time to spend the day with him. He waited for her impatiently. It wasn't only that he wanted to be with her himself. He wanted the other kids to see her: he knew that she was younger and prettier than most of their mothers.

He showed the bike around proudly all morning. Glowing in the flash of popularity it had brought with it, he let everyone try it out. There was a big feast at midday, with "Pop" and Mrs. Warner presiding over the long table, the potted poinsettia, the glazed turkey and the blazing plum pudding. The afternoon was one of warm surfeit, punctuated with a carol sing around the piano, with Mrs. Warner leading in her tremulous contralto, and excruciating references to the alcoholic content of the plum pudding.

It was evening when his mother's telegram finally got to him. It was sent from Chicago and it explained why she hadn't been

273

able to come. She was married again. She knew he would be glad, because it was to Mr. Hoyt who liked him so much and was going to take care of both of them. They were coming to the school to see him New Year's Day, on their way to the West Coast. She hoped he liked the bicycle. It ended: "Wreaths of Christmas kisses, darling, from your adoring Mummy."

He stuffed the yellow paper into the pocket of his trousers and wandered off beyond the football field. He walked for a long time, following the arroyo trail. When he got back to the dormitory it was an hour after lights out, and Pop, who had been waiting up for him, worried, gave him three days' no desserts as a punishment.

He still rode the bike around after that, but he didn't feel about it the way he had when it first came. By the time the summer vacation came along, both tires were flat.

Martin remembered, too, the first Christmas he spent at the University. He had gone there on his own, working nights and

274

weekends at a big cafeteria on Massachusetts Avenue. His mother had quarreled with him about that, but her arguments had only made him more firmly determined to go ahead in his own way. The cafeteria had given him the day off as a Christmas bonus. He waited around the rooming house all day but there was no message from anyone to show it was Christmas, not even a card. He had a dollar bill in his wallet. He spent some of it going to a double feature at the Tremont with one of the other boys from the rooming house. When they got out he walked into a Western Union office, where with care and deliberation he wrote out a message to his mother. One of the city's church towers was pealing a carol. The notes rang clear and immemorial while he spelled out a bitter, cutting paraphrase of the words. It took all that was left of his dollar to send it, and the clerk looked at him curiously as she took the money.

When Christmas came around the following year it was shadowed by the thought of that telegram. But there was nothing he could do about it then. His mother had been dead for over a month.

Martin drew his jaw down, stretched the skin tighter. Strange, he thought, how all the past Christmases which came to mind were lonely ones.

But they became different after he met Jane. He thought of the first one, just after they were married. They had walked in the snow all afternoon, following the canal for miles down the towpath, Jane with her energetic stride always a few steps ahead of him and looking back. They walked until they came to a place where the snow had been brushed away from the stone steps leading down from the towpath. When they opened the door of the inn and went inside there was an open fire. The place was loud with the snapping of dry logs. They sat across from each other in the dining-room, quietly drinking hot buttered rum. They were the only ones there except for a large family party in the corner. When the food finally came, it was good and worth taking time over. They ate it, suffused with a grave happiness.

275

Then they smoked cigarettes and drank some more until it was dark outside. And all the way back to the stone cottage where they were staying there was no sound between them and the stars except for the occasional snapping of a dry twig underfoot beneath the snow.

Martin smiled at the recollection and nearly nicked himself with the razor. That was how many years ago, now? Not so very many, after all. Martin looked at his shaved face in the mirror and wiped a blob of lather from his ear. It was Jane who made the difference now. He had her. They had a house which suited them. He liked his job in town. They had more books and phonograph records than they really had room for, a painting which they both loved, over their mantlepiece, and a few good friends who liked pretty much the same things they did. When nobody was around, they still enjoyed being together, each reading quietly or squabbling fiercely over the backgammon board. And then there was Little Martin. He made the biggest difference. After all, Martin admitted to himself, his own Christmases didn't count any more. The ones which really mattered now were Little Martin's.

Jane and Little Martin were calling up to him from downstairs. "Okay, okay," he shouted back. With a quick gesture he brushed his hair. Then he went to his closet and stepped out of his pajamas. His gray flannels were back from the cleaner's: Jane had hung them just inside the door where he would be sure to find them. He slipped into them, pulled a flannel shirt over his head, pushed his bare feet into his moccasins and started downstairs. He was halfway down when he realized that he was running; that his heart was pounding with anticipation the way it always had when he used to run to open his presents when he was a boy.

They were waiting for him in the dining room. The tree stood in front of the window, bright with lights. Beneath it was a litter of packages which Little Martin had torn open, examined and then flung aside. On the very top of the tree the flaxen-haired angel revolved slowly, the light glinting on her tinsel wings, while all the other ornaments tinkled softly. Breakfast was set out on the polished table. Everything glistened: glass, silver, china, all reflecting the lighted tree. Little Martin's face was shiny with excitement and his eyes shone. Beside Martin's plate was a small stack of envelopes and beyond that a pile of brightly wrapped boxes. There was another at Jane's place. In the table's center stood a silver pitcher filled with sweet peas.

"See the flowers! Mommy and I picked them at the store!"

Martin lifted his son into a chair. Then he and Jane sat at either side, opposite each other.

Martin turned to the boy. "Well," he said, "since you've opened all your presents already, you might suggest what I'm to do first."

"First?"

Martin nodded.

Little Martin looked around the table mysteriously. Then he said, "Look in the basket!"

The basket was set in front of Martin's place, its contents covered with a linen napkin. With exaggerated suspicion he lifted a corner of the napkin. The brown popovers underneath were warm to his touch.

"They're wonderful!" Martin exclaimed. "Jane, when did you manage to make them?"

Jane laughed, turning to Little Martin. "I told you he'd be surprised," she said.

"Now open the letters!" Little Martin commanded.

He watched while Jane and Martin opened the greeting cards, one by one. In Martin's pile there was a comic one from the office which Little Martin immediately claimed; one with a picture of a setter from Jane's Aunt Harriet; there were the usual arty cards, clever ones, old English coaching scenes, reproductions of old masters; and finally, one from Martin's elderly cleaning woman in New York. The printed message read: *To a Friend: It's Someone like you who makes Life Worthwhile.* The design was of forget-me-nots and satin ribbons, and there were tiny bits of glass glued to it.

"Now open the presents!"

After a questioning look at Jane, Martin opened the biggest first. His fingers fumbled through the tissue paper to find a soft blue sweater. Martin rose with it in his hands and went over to Jane and kissed her.

"But you don't even know if it fits," Jane protested. "I spent days hunting it down." She took it from him and held it up against his chest.

"Perfect," Martin declared. He kissed her again. "Mmm, and so soft!"

Jane giggled. "Stop it, Martin. Now open the others or your child will burst."

There were some sheer monogrammed handkerchiefs from his secretary; a book which he had already read from Jane's father; and a couple of Jelly-Roll Morton records from John and Norma Prince. With the opening of each package, the excitement had mounted in Little Martin's face. It became unbearable now. "Open mine," he cried. "Martin, open mine!"

Deliberately, Martin pushed back the sea of tissue paper, spilled contents of boxes and the greeting cards to clear a space for Little Martin's present.

He squinted cautiously at it. "There's nothing in there that will pop out and smack me?"

The little boy thought the question excruciatingly funny. He twisted his tongue in the corner of his mouth and shook his head.

Martin glanced for a moment at the small, intent face waiting for him to open the squarish box. Then he turned, carefully undid the green ribbon and slowly lifted the lid. Inside, nested in a bed of green cellophane straw, stood a pink marzipan pig.

"I picked it out all by myself, Martin. You can eat it! Are you s'prised?" He turned to his mother. "Is he?" Jane nodded, smiling. Happily, the child lifted his face for his father to kiss.

Martin looked down at his son, seeing him in a way he never

had before: seeing him open and amazing as the pale flowers in their silver pitcher. He found himself marveling at the mysterious delicacy of the skull with its unruly soft hair, the clear eyes, the lashes around them, the untouched skin, the fine bones of the shoulders. Now, brushed with excitement, the child's face was raised to his, waiting. Martin bent and touched it lightly with his lips.

"And now it's high time we all had some breakfast," Jane said. "The rest of the presents can wait, but those popovers won't stay warm all morning."

Little Martin sat thoughtfully while Jane poured out Martin's coffee. "Mommy," Little Martin broke out suddenly, "are we going to have a Christmas cake? A *burning* one?"

The words curved across Martin's mind, releasing another memory. It was something he had forgotten while he was upstairs shaving: his one real Christmas party.

It was the earliest Christmas he could remember. He was six then; or was it seven? It was when they still lived in the big frame house on Wistaria Street. His father had gone away, and Mama Heinlein was taking care of him, as well as the house.

The party was Mama Heinlein's idea. His mother had said, "All right, Mrs. Heinlein, if you're sure it won't make too much extra work for you." Mama Heinlein had laughed and said, "Ach, work!" She spent all morning in the kitchen making the plum pudding. After more than twenty years Martin could still see it standing on a silver plate in the middle of the dining-room table: stuck all about with twigs of prickly holly, and blue flames licking greedily at its sides.

Some of the other little boys of the neighborhood had been invited. They arrived scrubbed and embarrassed in high starched Eton collars. There were scarlet snappers at each place and pistachio ice cream. And in the parlor where the big tree stood, hung with silken-tailed birds and peppermints with wire stems and strung with popcorn, there was a donkey game pinned to the wall. There were lots of presents. He couldn't remember now what they had all been, except for one. It was the best of all: a wonderful wooden box which the expressman brought on his wagon especially for him. When Martin opened it there was a whole circus inside, carved out of wood: a jointed man who circled around a trapeze, a lady with a fluffy skirt who rode on a dappled horse, clowns, animals and a proud tall ringmaster with a whip and a real mustache. Mama Heinlein clapped her hands and cried, "Ach, it's from Nuremberg! Your daddy sent it to you all the way from Europe." And there was a music box which went with it. It played a tune while the lady went around the ring on her horse.

Martin could remember how all the other little boys stood around gaping while he showed it to them. He was saying, "My daddy sent me this from Europe."

And then his mother, laughing and pretty with tea roses stuck in her belt, came in with Mr. Hoyt to watch. Suddenly he saw that she was looking at him in a strange way. He felt her hand grip his tightly, so that it hurt, and he wondered guiltily what he had done wrong. Then he watched her go over to Mama Heinlein and say something to her. His mother looked angry, but Mama Heinlein shrugged her shoulders and called everyone in for the donkey game.

When the tails had all been pinned on, Martin came back to play with the circus again. It wasn't anywhere to be seen. The lady on the horse was gone, the ringmaster with the real mustache, the acrobats, even the wooden box they lived in, were all gone.

Martin ran into the pantry to tell Mama Heinlein . . . and there she stood holding the circus. His mother was there too, a dark look on her face which he had never seen before. She was saying, "You shouldn't have let him have it." And he heard Mama Heinlein answer, "But Madame, from his own father! It would be a shame for the child not to have it—"

She saw Martin then and stopped with her mouth still open.

280

But his mother had not seen him. She wrenched the box from Mama Heinlein's hands and threw it to the floor.

Martin cried out, but it was too late. Everything lay in a heap. The lady on the horse was broken. The ringmaster's mustachioed head had snapped off and the music box wouldn't play any more . . . .

"Martin, your popover will get cold. Aren't you going to eat it?"

Martin started. It was Jane speaking to him, but for a moment he heard his mother's voice again: "Well, Martin, it won't burn you now. Aren't you going to eat it?"

"Oh," Martin said. There was a popover in his hand. It was already broken and he had spooned strawberry jam into it. He stared at it. Then his eyes traveled across the table littered with cards and opened boxes; across the sweater, the handkerchiefs, the book. The fat flaxen-haired angel at the top of the tree rotated stolidly. The marzipan pig that he could eat stood beside his plate, staring out of its green cellophane pen. Jane was looking at him, smiling, from the other side of the table. His eyes passed the flowers in the silver pitcher and met those of Little Martin, watching him out of that still untouched, expectant face.

He bit into the popover. He could feel the sweetness in his throat, refusing to melt or go down. Across all the intervening years and all the Christmases, irretrievably passed, he could still taste Mama Heinlein's blazing Christmas pudding, choking him.

The Carpenter's Christmas

PETER ROSEGGER

A T LAST it was over, this vigorous sweeping and scrubbing and chasing of dirt, this week-long turmoil during which nothing, not a piece of furniture, not a single wall decoration, remained in its place, until every piece of wood had been cleaned, every stone whitewashed, every bit of metal polished. Now the house shone in purest cleanliness.

The calm after a storm has a solemn effect in any case, but particularly when the Christ child is about to arrive. Somewhere in the house stands the cradle in which the God child sleeps. Those who wear shoes take them off; and those in their stocking feet must walk on tiptoe, for—He sleeps.

The goodwife bustled around in her rooms purposefully; she had to see that everything was right without marking the floor; check all the chests and closets and windows without touching anything, so that everything would retain its pristine beauty. The wind rattled the windowpanes, blowing snow into every nook and cranny, and the darkness of the skies almost turned the room into night. In the living room, on a table covered with white linen, were a crucifix, a burning blessed candle, and a crock holding a branch cut from the cherry tree three weeks ago on St. Barbara's Day, which was to bloom that night. Its buds glistened and swelled and would burst into flower any moment.

The goodwife ran to the door, opened it softly, raised her forefinger and hissed, "Pssst!" into the kitchen, where the servant girl wasn't quiet enough with the dishes. "Pssst! The Christ child is asleep!"

The woman was in a deeply pious mood. Her graying hair

was wound around her head in two braids; she had donned her red kerchief and her silk apron. With a rosary in her folded hands she sat in the armchair next to the table and could think of nothing except: Christmas Eve! The Christ child!

Suddenly there was a noise in the corner. Her husband, the carpenter, who was lying on the bench against the wall, turned around and bumped his elbow so hard against the back rest of the chair that it crashed to the floor.

"Pssst!" she hissed, getting up. "Man alive, but what a restless person you are!"

"I? Restless?" He brushed his hand over his face. "Can't a person sleep any more? Can't you leave me alone?"

"If you don't want to pray, you should at least be quiet, man. And you shouldn't sleep, either!"

"But, old lady, when a man sleeps he makes the least noise."

"So you think! That's when you make the most noise, when you sleep! If you're not upsetting a chair beating about with your arms you're poking a hole in the wall. Anyone would think there were at least two sawmills and a threshing machine in here."

"Yea, the sawmills and that threshing machine ought to be turned off on Christmas Eve," he answered calmly, sitting up.

"Oh, don't talk nonsense, please! Here, find yourself a nice Christmas prayer!" She reached for the prayer book on the shelf, wiped the old, worn binding with her apron—yes, it was already dusty again!—and laid it on the table.

"What's the matter with you?" he asked tranquilly. "When they ring the bell, I'll pray all right. Just now I want to sleep some more."

"Stop arguing!" she cried impatiently, kicking at a footstool below the table.

He looked at her and grinned. "Woman," he said. "Not even old age helps you—you simply won't change!"

"You're the one to talk!" she answered. "A man ought to remember at least on a day like this that he has holy water on

283

him. Haven't you any piety in you at all? Don't you know that tomorrow is Christmas?"

"Am I doing anything wrong?"

"Nor are you doing anything right, either. Go on, find that Christmas prayer!"

"I've never let anyone order me to be pious. If it doesn't come by itself . . ."

"Come by itself? To you? Mary Joseph, that'd be a long wait! All week long you are so unchristian that it's a scandal. Holidays are made for piety!"

"Oh, phhhht!" the carpenter replied crossly. "If a man works hard all week and does his duty in God's name and does nobody any wrong, he's supposed to be extra-pious on Sundays, eh? Why, woman, how is a man to do that?"

"Pray, I said, and keep quiet! Holy Christ will be awakened soon enough when He comes to judge the quick and the dead. . . . Jesus Mary, what's that?!"

For a moment it was quite dark in the room, as if a black cloth had been drawn across the window; then, a heavy thud, and the wild whirling of the snow outside. The carpenter went to the window and looked out. The storm had broken off a heavy limb from the old fir tree standing in front of the house.

"Oh God, oh God, what a day!" the woman whined, wringing her hands. "That's a bad sign for a year without peace!"

"If the devil doesn't fetch you, it'll be just that," the carpenter growled amiably.

"Today I refuse to argue with you!" she answered with cold superiority. "But just you wait until the day is over. Then you'll see whom the devil will fetch!"

She took the little vessel of holy water from the door-jamb and sprinkled everything in the room, especially her husband. He stared at her grumpily and refused to stir.

"He doesn't even make the sign of the cross when he is sprinkled with holy water!"

She rushed to the kitchen, returned with a basin of glowing

embers, sprinkled incense over it and carried it around, according to the old Christmas custom, close to the table, to the bed and, finally, to her husband, whose nostrils the incense attacked so vehemently that he began to curse and opened a window.

He opened the window just in time. From the road, over the whistling of the wind, came excited voices. The wind had done quite a bit of damage in the village. "Ditch-Cenzi's" roof had been torn off so that you could look from above it into the crawling children's warren.

"That's because they don't pray, those people," the carpenter's wife sneered. "Mary Joseph, that's how it is in this world. The entire Christmas Eve spoiled! And instead of saying his Christmas prayers now, he runs away! Who, I ask you, is to protect us, if not our dear Lord in heaven?"

"Ditch-Cenzi" was a widow with three small children, the oldest of which was sick in bed with scarlet fever. She wasn't much liked in the village and it was said that in the fall she sometimes harvested potatoes where she hadn't planted any. Now the roof of her hut was torn down, with the shingles lying in the road. Cenzi stumbled around with her children in the darkness and succeeded, just barely succeeded, in placing them with neighbors. Nobody wanted to harbor the child sick with scarlet fever until the teacher offered to take it in; but the teacher was ruled out because he might carry the infection into the school. The childless wife of the carpenter, too, was approached, but she didn't want her Christmas Eve spoiled by a sick child. Finally, the village priest remembered that He who was expected that very night had said that whoever takes in a child, takes in Him—even though he wasn't quite certain how the quotation really ran. And so, with kindness and the help of the quotation, he arranged with his housekeeper for the sick child to stay at the vicarage until the roof of the old home could be fixed at least temporarily.

The carpenter had gone outside. His voice was louder than the wind as he called together his neighbors and his journeymen. They came with ladders, tools and boards. There was a hammering and sawing in the village that lasted all night under the light of the improvised torches—very much to the horror of Mrs. Carpenter, who esteemed the holy calm and heavenly peace of this night above all else.

"How can the cherry branch bloom in all this turmoil? And how is the Christ child to rest?"

When the bells in the church tower began to chime for Midnight Mass the men still shouted and hammered on Ditch-Cenzi's roof. And while the parish sang in the church, the pounding and the clanking of nails and tools still vied so with the noise of the storm that the women, thus cheated out of their Christmas humor, were positively horrified. At last, when all the bells tolled in unison and the organ jubilated at the high point of the Midnight Mass, the men who were helping to build the roof jumped down and strolled into the church, too; and the carpenter found himself alone with two of his journeymen on the skeleton of the roof. The storm seemed to blow harder now, to tear down again what the hands of men had just put up.

The Carpenter's Christmas

The carpenter had expected to have the roof ready before morning. When he saw that most of the others had deserted him and that even the boys who had held the torches had thrown them in the snow and run to church, he began to curse mightily.

"To——with these——hypocrites! I like that! Here they practically chew off the toes of our good Lord, and in the meantime these poor wretches can go and die with the cold. Who cares? They squat around the corners of the church until they rot. He up there in heaven can really be proud of this brood! Hear them sing, 'Praise God in the highest!' They kiss the waxen image of the Christ child and cuddle it like a doll—and let these poor little human creatures—croak, I almost said, God forgive me my sins!"

When Midnight Mass was over and the people came out of the church, the carpenter was still cursing and kicking up on his roof. One man said to the other, "Poor fellow, he'll go completely mad if we don't help him; and maybe we are a little to blame for his swearing at that! Come on, let's pitch in. We can have that roof up in less than an hour."

Then another planted himself firmly in front of the speaker and said: "Do you really think, neighbor, that I would be so unchristian as to work on Holy Christmas Morn?" But his manner was so overbearing that the effect was far from what he intended.

"Did you hear that one?" someone asked. "In the face of such hypocrisy, I prefer the carpenter and all his cussing; and I for one am going to help him finish that roof!"

Others joined him. The torches were lit again and the sawing and hammering began once more with such renewed vigor that the carpenter's wife, in desperation, covered both her ears with her hands.

"You can't sleep and you can't pray with all this noise going on. And that—that heathen husband of mine prefers this beggar woman to our Jesus Child, so that he won't even let Him rest in His cradle. . . . God forgive him!"

On Christmas day when the sun rose, the icy wind still rushed over the rooftops, and over many a gable snow clouds still danced. But the roof of the Ditch-Cenzi house was fixed and nailed down tight, a good fire crackled in her stove, and the woman with her children had returned to their home. The carpenter was lying on his bed, jacket and boots and all, snoring with a right good will. His wife stood in the doorway, staring at him in disgust.

She herself could not settle down. She was miserable. Even before the solemn High Mass she went over to the vicarage, but she could hardly say a single word between her sobs. What an unhappy woman she was, she finally managed to stammer, to have such a husband! True, he was usually quiet and industrious, but he simply had no religion! Just no religion at all! And if she were to live to be a hundred, she would never forget that night!

"Not a single Our Father did he say, nor did he welcome the Christ child with so much as a single little prayer! What an end such a man will come to! Even this morning people are going from house to house telling each other that they have never heard anyone curse as much as this husband of mine on Holy Night! You must have heard it yourself, Your Reverence, after Midnight Mass! I was actually shivering in my soul!"

The priest sat with his hands folded in his lap and smiled benevolently at the distracted woman.

"To be sure, I heard something," he said. "But I thought it was a prayer!"

"Prayer?" the woman moaned, raising her hands and folding them high above her head, then letting them fall again as if she had had a stroke.

"My dear woman," the priest replied. "Some people have queer ways of praying. The Jews, for example. They wind their prayer-belts around their heads and arms when they pray. Others just turn the leaves of their prayer books. And still others pass the beads of their rosaries through their fingers. Well, our carpenter simply hammers nails into wooden shingles during his Our Father."

The woman again clasped her hands in despair.

"Did you say 'Our Father,' Your Reverence? Some Our Father that would be! How he cursed and shouted during Holy Mass! If our dear Lord weren't so kind, the earth would have opened up and swallowed him!"

"I admit," the priest replied, "that his words may have been chosen somewhat—unfortunately. But his intentions were certainly good. And that's really what counts. All the while he was cursing and shouting, I'm sure he didn't have another thought in his head other than to provide a roof for the poor widow and her children and his conviction that other men ought to be helping him. We probably all prayed devoutly last night, but I have an idea that the carpenter's prayer with his saw and hammer pleased our Good Lord the most."

"And now," the woman cried, "when the others are on their way to High Mass, he lies sleeping like a . . . a dormouse!"

"Let him sleep, my dear woman. Just as his work was a prayer, so is his rest."

As the carpenter's wife departed she kept shaking her head. She could make neither head nor tail of all this. What was the world coming to? If cursing was praying, what then was praying?

But she didn't get quite that far in her meditations.

Bethlehem

CHARLES PEGUY

JEANNETTE

He was born in Bethlehem in a poor stable.

MADAME GERVAISE

The gifts which the shepherds and kings had brought him.
He saw once more the lowly cradle at Bethlehem
In which his body was laid for the first time;
The gifts which the shepherds and kings had made him,
    were making him.

Bethlehem, Bethlehem, and you Jerusalem.
Life begun at Bethlehem and finished at Jerusalem.
Life included between Bethlehem and Jerusalem.
Life inscribed between Bethlehem and Jerusalem.
He saw once more the lowly cradle of his childhood.

Life begun at Bethlehem and not ending at Jerusalem.

The swaddling clothes on the straw waiting to be washed;
Another set of swaddling clothes was ready for the change.
The shepherds falling down before him offered wool.

Wool from their sheep, child; wool from the sheep
    of those days.
Wool like what we spin.

JEANNETTE

Wool like this.

Lucas Cranach. Angel Harping

Charles Péguy

MADAME GERVAISE

The wise kings offered gold, incense and myrrh. Gold
as to their king.

JEANNETTE

Incense as to their God·

MADAME GERVAISE

Myrrh as to a mortal man.

JEANNETTE

Who one day would be embalmed.

MADAME GERVAISE

The wise kings Gaspar, Melchior and Balthasar.

JEANNETTE

Gaspar and Balthasar and Melchior the wise kings.

MADAME GERVAISE

All that took place in the light of heaven;
The angels had formed into choirs in the night.
The angels sang like flowers in the night.
Above the shepherds, above the wise kings.
The angels in the night sang everlastingly.

Under the kindness of heaven, under its youthfulness,
under its eternity.
Of the firmament he called heaven.

Like song flowers, like hymn flowers, like prayer flowers,
like grace flowers.

Like a flowering, like a leafing, like a fruition of
prayer and grace.

292

Bethlehem

All that took place below the angel choirs.
All that took place below the kindness of heaven.
The star in the night shone like a gold nail.
The star in the night shone everlastingly .
The star in the night shone like a gold pin.

JEANNETTE

A star had appeared, a star had risen which will
then never again show itself.

The Clothes Mender

N. S. LESKOV

ISN'T IT a silly sort of custom to wish everyone new happiness every New Year's Eve, and yet—you know—sometimes something like that does happen. May I tell you, in this connecabout a little occurrence which really has quite a Yuletide flavor?

During one of my trips to Moscow—many years ago now that would be—I was kept there longer than I had expected, and I grew heartily tired of my hotel. The psalmodist of one of the Palace churches, hearing me complain to a friend of mine—a priest of the same church—about all the inconveniences I had to put up with, suddenly chimed in:

"Now, wouldn't he be just the person, Father, for my relative? He's got a room to let straight away—facing the street."

"What relative of yours would that be?" asked the priest.

"Vasilii Konych."

"Ha—that's 'Maître Tailleur Lepoutan'!"

"The same, sir."

"Well, that's not at all a bad idea."

And the priest went on to explain both that he knew the people and that the room was an excellent one, while the psalmodist added yet another advantage.

"If," said he, "you should tear your clothes or if the bottoms of your trousers get frayed, you'll find everything put right in no time—so well that you won't see a thing."

I decided that all further investigations were superfluous, and I did not even go to see the place first. I gave the psalmodist the key to my hotel room with a message scribbled on my card and asked him to settle my bill, collect my things and take them round to his relative. Then I asked him to call back for me and lead me to my new abode.

2

The psalmodist managed everything very quickly, and in a little over an hour he came round for me at the priest's.

"Come along," he said. "Everything has been unpacked already and arranged in your room, and they've got your window open—they have—and the door onto the verandah and the garden, and we've even had tea on the verandah. It's very nice there," he told me. "There are all kinds of flowers, and the dicky birds making their nests in the gooseberries, and a nightingale trilling in a cage under the window. It's better than the country, because it's all green all round you and yet everything about the house is shipshape, and if a button or what not gets loose, or the bottoms of your trousers get frayed—it'll be put right in no time."

The psalmodist was a very tidy person and a great dandy, and so he repeatedly emphasized this aspect of the advantage of my new quarters.

And the priest too backed him up.

"Yes," he said, "tailleur Lepoutan is such a craftsman in this particular line—you won't find another like him in Moscow or St. Petersburg."

"A specialist, that's what he is," the psalmodist said impressively, as he helped me into my coat.

Who this Lepoutan was I did not quite make out—besides, it was none of my business.

3

We set out on foot.

The psalmodist assured me that it was not worth taking a cab, because, according to him, it was only "a stone's throw away by way of *promenage*."

As a matter of fact, it turned out to be a good half-hour's

walk, but the psalmodist wanted to take a *promenage*, perhaps because he also wanted to show off his cane, which was decorated with a mauve silk tassel.

The district in which the house of Lepoutan was situated lay beyond the Moskva River, towards the Yausa, somewhere near its bank. I've now forgotten even what parish it was in and what the lane was called. As a matter of fact, it wasn't even a lane, but rather a sort of little cul-de-sac, like an old-fashioned church-yard. There was a little church there, and a kind of drive which ran at an angle to it, and in this drive stood six or seven houses, all of very modest proportions, of a gray color, built of wood, while one had a stone semi-basement. This one looked more showy and larger than the others, and right across its façade was nailed a large iron sign upon which, on a black background, in letters of gold, was prominently painted in large characters: "Maître Tailleur Lepoutan."

Obviously, this was my new abode, but I thought it strange that my host, who enjoyed the Christian name of Vasilii Konych, should call himself "Maître Tailleur Lepoutan." When the priest had called him that, I thought it was only a joke, and I did not take much notice of it, but now, on beholding this sign, I had to alter my view. Apparently—and quite seriously—it *was* his name, and I even asked my guide:

"Vasilii Konych—is he Russian or French?"

The psalmodist looked surprised and did not seem to grasp my question.

"Why—what d'you men? Why should he be French?—A pure-bred Russian, that's what he is. Why, even the clothes he makes for the market are all pure Russian—sleeveless topcoats, and all that kind of stuff—but he is better known all over Moscow for his mending: any amount of old clothes have passed through his hands and are being sold as new in the markets."

"Still," I said, feeling puzzled, "he must be of French descent?"

Again the psalmodist expressed surprise.

"No," he retorted—"why should he be? He's a regular local man—a Russian—and acts as godfather at christenings, and of course we Churchmen are all pure Orthodox. And why should you imagine that he has anything to do with the French nation?"

"That signboard—it has a French name on it."

"Oh, that," explained my companion. "That's nothing. That's just all splash. And, also, the main sign is in French, it's true, but there, next to the gate—see—there's another, a Russian sign. That's the more correct one."

I looked to where he pointed, and indeed beheld another signboard, which depicted a sleeveless topcoat, a coat as worn by Russian peasants, and two black waistcoats with silver buttons that sparkled like stars, with the following legend below:

"Clothing of Russian and Clerical Fashion Made. Specialist in Nap, Turning, and Mending."

Beneath this second sign the name of the man who made clothing, and turned and mended was not stated, but was merely indicated by two initials: "V.L."

4

The room and the owner proved indeed above all praise and description, so that I at once felt perfectly at home, and soon grew quite fond of my kindly host, Vasilii Konych. Presently he and I began to meet over tea and to have long conversations and debates on various subjects. Thus, one day, as we sat sipping our tea on the verandah, we debated upon the absorbing theme of the vanity of everything under the sun and of our undying propensity to labor in the service of vanity. That is how we got onto the subject of Lepoutan.

I don't remember now by what stages we reached a point in our conversation when Vasilii Konych expressed a wish to tell me the strange story of how, and why, he appeared "under a French title."

The tale has some relation to social morals and to literature, even though it is displayed on a signboard.

Konych began simply, but in a most intriguing manner.

"My name, sir," he said, "is not Lepoutan at all, but quite a different one—and under this French title I was placed by Destiny itself.

5

"I am Moscow-born and Moscow-bred, and of the poorest parentage. My grandad used to sell soles by the Rogozhinsky Barrier; some of the more ancient type of Old Believers used to wear these soles inside their boots. He was a fine old man, was my grandad—like a saint—all white, like a hare in moult, and he used to feed himself by the toil of his hands till his very death. He would buy some felt, cut it up into little pieces shaped like soles, string a pair on a thread, and would do the round of 'The Christians.' And you should have heard him sing out, as sweet as sweet could be: 'Soles, soles, who wants soles?' And so he would wander all over Moscow, with just about a copper's-worth of goods, and yet he earned his keep. My father was a tailor, making clothes according to the old rules. He made coats for all the most righteous Old Believers, with three pleats, as they should be, and taught me the craft as well. But ever since I was a child I possessed a special gift, and that was mending. I am not very bright at cutting, but when it comes to patching—that's my line. And I got so good at it—I'd mend a tear in the most prominent spot and you wouldn't know it had been there.

The old men used to say to my father:

'That youngster's got his talent from God, and where a man's talent is, there his happiness lies also.'

And that's how it all turned out, but before you get to your luck, you know, you need humble patience, and I was sent two serious trials: firstly, my parents died and left me when I was still very young; and secondly, the room where I lived was burnt out one Christmas Eve while I was at Mass—and I lost all my equipment: my iron and my tailor's dummy, and clothes belonging to various people, which I had there for mending. So I found myself right up against it; and yet, that's when my first step towards my new luck occurred.

6

"One customer, who lost his overcoat in my fire, came to me and said:

'My loss is pretty hard, and it is not pleasant to be left without a greatcoat over Christmas, but I see you can't make good the loss, and you need help yourself. If you're a reliable lad, I'll put you on the right road, but on one condition: by and by you must make up the cost of the coat.'

I answered him:

'God willing, I shall be glad to do what I can. I'll see that you get repaid before anything else.'

He told me to get dressed, and brought me to a hotel that was opposite the house of the Commander-in-Chief, and introduced me to the assistant barman and said to him in my presence:

'Here is the apprentice I told you of, who can be very useful in our line of business.'

And their business was to press all the clothes which were in the visitors' luggage and got crumpled, and also to do all kinds of necessary mending.

The assistant barman gave me a thing to do to try me out, saw that I did it well, and told me to stay.

'Now,' he said to me, 'it's Christmas, and the place is full of gentry, and they're all drinking and having high jinks, and there's still New Year to come and Twelfth-night—there will be some goings-on worse than ever—so you stay put—see?'

I said to him:

'I agree.'

And the chap who brought me there said to me:

'Well, there you are—you can make money here. Only you just do what he (that is, the assistant barman) tells you, always. If God is with you, He sends His prophet too.'

I was given a little corner with a small window in a back passage, and I got busy. There were lots and lots—I couldn't tell you how many lots of gentlemen I patched up, and it would be a sin to complain—I patched myself up pretty well too, because there was any amount of work and the pay was good. The ordinary kind of people did not put up there—only 'Trumps' used to stay there, who used to like feeling they were on the same level with the Commander-in-Chief—from window to window, that is.

The pay was particularly good for patching and mending when the damage was suddenly discovered in something that had to be worn straight away. I felt pretty uncomfortable at times: the hole would be the size of a ten-kopeck piece, and if I managed to mend it so that you couldn't tell, I'd get a gold piece.

They would never pay less than ten roubles, however small the tear. Well, naturally, there was real art in the work: just as one drop of water might run into another and you can't say there's two drops, so the clothes had to be done so that you couldn't tell they had ever been mended.

Of the money that was paid, I got a third, while another third went to the assistant barman, and the other to the servants who unpacked the gentlemen's bags in the rooms when they arrived, and brushed and cleaned the clothes. They, of course, were at the bottom of it all, because they would crumple and rub the things and sometimes jab a little hole in them; so they got two-thirds and I got one-third. Even then, there was more than enough for me in what I got, so that I even shifted my quarters from the corner in the passage, and rented a quiet little room all to myself across the yard; and a year later, the sister of the assistant barman came up on a visit from the country, and I married her—my present wife, as you see her—that's her: she's reached old age with honor, and maybe it was to her lot that God sent everything. And as for marrying her, it was like this. The assistant barman said: 'She's an orphan and you must make her happy, and then, through it all, you'll meet with great happiness too.' And she also would say: 'I—I am a lucky one,' she would say; 'God will reward you on my account.' And suddenly, as though indeed all this was the cause, there came a most unexpected surprise.

7

"It was Christmas time again, and New Year's Eve. I was in my little room in the evening, mending something or other, and was about to knock off work and go to bed, when in dashed a waiter from the rooms and said:

'Come on—get a move on; there's a terrible Trump in Number One—he's walloped just about everyone, and whoever he swipes he gives a gold piece to; now he wants you—quick.'

'What's he want me for?' I asked.

'He was dressing for a ball, and just about the last moment he finds someone's burnt a hole in his dress clothes—right in the middle; he's walloped the lad who cleaned them, and he's given him three gold pieces. You stir your stumps—he's cross —looks like all the beasts in the world at once.'

I just shook my head, because I knew how they spoilt the clothes of the visitors on purpose—just for their own profit from the work; but I dressed and went to have a look at the Trump who looked like all the beasts in the world put together.

The payment, I knew, would be pretty good, because Number One is reckoned a Trump number in every hotel, and it was only luxury people who stopped there; while in our hotel the price of Number One was fifteen roubles a day—that's at today's rate, and in those days it was fifty-two roubles fifty kopecks, in paper money—and whoever had it was known as 'The Trump.'

The one I was brought to now looked as terrifying as anything —he was so big and dark-faced and wild, and in truth he did look like all the beasts put together.

'You,' he said with a snarl: 'can you mend a hole so well that it can't be noticed?'

I replied:

'Depends what it's in. If the material's got a nap, it can be done very well, but if it's shiny satin or silk moiré stuff—I wouldn't undertake it.'

'Moiré yourself,' said he. 'Some swine, I suppose it was yesterday, sat behind me—went and burnt a hole in my dress-coat. There—have a look at it and see for yourself.'

I had a look at it and said:

'That can be done well.'

'And how long will it take?'

'I'll have it done in about an hour.'

'Go on, then,' he said, 'and if you do it well you'll get a mint of money, and if you don't, I'll give you such a hiding. You go and ask the lads here what I did to them, and you can be sure you'll get it a hundred times worse.'

8

"Off I went to mend the coat, and I can't say I was feeling at all happy about it, because you can't always be sure how it will turn out; if the cloth is soft it will work together better, and if it's stiffer it is hard to work in the nap so that you don't notice it.

However, I did the job well; but I didn't take it to him myself, because I didn't like his manner at all. The work is tricky—however well you do it, anyone who wants to find fault can easily make things unpleasant for you.

I sent my wife with the coat to her brother and told her to give it to him and get home herself as quick as she could; and as soon as she was back we put the door on a hook from inside and went to bed.

In the morning I got up and started on my day's job as usual; I busied myself with my work and waited to see what I should get from the Trump gent—whether it would be a mint of money or a crack over the head.

And suddenly, soon after one, a waiter came and said:

'The gent from Number One wants to see you.'

I said:

'I'm not going—he can do what he pleases.'

'Why?'

'Just because—I'm not going, that's all; I'd rather my work went for nothing—I don't want to see him.'

But the waiter said:

'You've nothing to be in a funk about: he's very pleased with you and he was seeing the New Year in in your dress suit and no one noticed any hole in it. And now he's got guests with him, they're wishing him a Happy New Year and have had a few and have got talking about your work and betting they'd find the mend, but no one's done so. And they're as pleased as can be; they're drinking toasts to your Russian artistry and want to see you. Hurry up—it'll bring you new luck in the New Year.'

And my wife also got on to me.

'Go on, go on,' says she. 'My heart feels that our new luck is about to begin.'

Well, I listened to them, and went.

9

"I saw about ten gentlemen in Number One, and they'd all had a lot to drink, and no sooner did I come in than they gave me a glass of wine and said:

'Drink with us for your Russian craftsmanship through which you can make our country famous.'

That was the sort of thing they said—they were drunk. The job, of course, wasn't all that good.

I naturally bowed and thanked them and had two glasses—one for Russia and one for their good health—'and more,' said I, 'I won't take, because I'm not used to sweet wine and also don't deserve such company.'

Then the terrible gent from Number One said:

'You're an ass and a fool and an animal, brother—you don't realize your own worth and all you deserve through your gift. You helped me this New Year's Eve more than you know,

303

because yesterday at the ball I changed the whole run of my life and proposed to my beloved fiancée, of a very important family, and she's said yes, and so I'll be married after Lent.'

'I wish you and your future wife,' I said, 'every happiness.'

'Well, you drink to it.'

I couldn't refuse, and had a drink, but asked to be excused any more.

'All right,' he said 'only you tell me where you live and what your Christian name is, patronymic and surname: I want to be your benefactor.'

I said:

'I'm called Vasilii, son of Konon, and my surname is Laputin, and my workshop is just here, next door, you'll see a little signboard, it says: "Laputin".'

And as I was speaking I never noticed how all the guests suddenly seemed to kind of explode at my words and double up with suppressed laughter, while the gent I mended the coat for all of a sudden swiped me across one ear and then across the other, so that I fairly tumbled off my feet. Then he pushed me towards the door with his knee and bundled me out.

I couldn't understand a thing and ran for dear life.

Back I came, and my wife asked me:

'Quick, Vasenka, tell me how my luck has served you?'

I said:

'Now, Mashenka, don't you start questioning me about details, but if it goes on as it has begun, I'd rather not live by your luck. The gent gave me a hiding, my angel.'

My wife got very agitated—what, why and what for, and all that kind of thing; and of course I could tell her nothing because I knew nothing myself.

But while we were talking about it all, suddenly there was a noise in our lobby, a banging and a crash, and in walked my benefactor from Number One.

We both jumped to our feet and looked at him, while he, all red and worked up—with wine too, I suppose—held in one hand the *dvornik's* axe, with a long shaft, and in the other the splintered board which displayed my cheap little sign stating my poor trade and my name: 'Old Clothes Mended and Turned. Laputin.'

10

"In came the gent with the splintered signboard and straightway flung the bits into the stove, while he said to me: 'Get dressed—hurry—you're coming for a drive with me—I want to make your life's happiness. Otherwise I'll smash you and your wife and all you've got here—like those boards of yours.'

Well, I figured, it was no use arguing with the brute, better have him out of the house as quickly as possible before he did some hurt to my wife.

I dressed hastily, and said to the wife: 'Bless me, Mashenka!' —and away we drove.

We went to the Bronnaya, where there was a famous estate agent, Prohor Ivanovich, and the gent straightway asked him:

'What houses have you for sale, and in what part of the town —price about twenty-five to thirty thousand roubles, or a little more?' It was in paper currency, of course, in those days.

'Only, I want a house,' he explained, 'that I could have straight away, and could go into at once.'

The agent took out a copybook from a chest of drawers, put on his spectacles, looked at one page, then at another, and said:

'There's a house that will suit you in every way, but you'll have to add a little.'

'I can go a little higher.'

'Well, it will cost you up to thirty-five thousand.'

'That'll do me.'

'Very well, then,' he said, 'we'll get the matter through in about an hour, and you'll be able to occupy it tomorrow, because a deacon choked with a chicken bone at a christening in that house, and died, and because of that no one is living there now.'

And this is the very house we are sitting in—you and I. They said that the dead deacon walks about here at night and makes choking noises, but that's all nonsense and no one's ever seen him while we have been here. My wife and I moved in the very next day, because the gent transferred it to us as a gift; and two days later he came along with some half a dozen workmen and a ladder and that signboard which talks as if I were a French tailor.

They came and nailed it up and went away, and the gent said to me:

'There's one thing,' he said, 'that I command you: never you dare to alter this signboard, and you're to answer to that name.' And all of a sudden he bellowed:

'Lepoutan!'

I answered:

'Yes, sir!'

'Good lad,' said he. 'Here's another thousand roubles for you for household junk and what not; now, mark well, Lepoutan— you do as I order you, and all will be well with you; otherwise . . . if you start calling yourself by your old name or what—God help you if I get to hear of it. . . . As a preliminary I'll beat you to pulp, and then I'll have the law on you and take back the gift. And if you do as I want, you've only to tell me what else you need, and I'll let you have it.'

I thanked him, of course, and told him I'd got no more wishes and couldn't think of any, except one—if he would be pleased to tell me what all this meant and why I was given the house.

But this he would not tell me.

'That,' said he, 'is something you don't want to know; only remember this: henceforth you are called "Lepoutan" and that's how you stand in my Deed of Gift. Keep that name: you'll find it will pay you.'

11

"So we were left to set up home in our own house, and every-thing went very well with us, and we reckoned that it was all through my wife's luck, because we could not get a real explanation of it from anybody for a long time, but one day two gentlemen happened to be running past here, and suddenly they stopped and came in.

My wife said:

'What can I do for you?'

And they replied:

'We want to see Monsieur Lepoutan himself.'

I came out and they looked at one another and both burst out laughing at the same time and began speaking to me in French.

I excused myself for not being able to speak the lingo.

'And how long,' said they, 'have you been under that signboard?'

I told them how many years that would be.

'That's it. You know,' they said, 'we remember you and we've seen you before; there was a certain gent you mended a dress suit for on New Year's Eve for a ball, and then, because of it, you had to suffer a bit of unpleasantness at the hotel.'

'You are quite right,' I said; 'there was an incident like that, but I'm only most grateful to the gentleman and through him I became a man, only I don't know his name or surname, because he wouldn't tell me.'

They told me his name—and his surname, they added, was Laputin.

'How do you mean—Laputin?'

'Of course,' they said: 'Laputin. Don't you know why he's done all this for you? He didn't want to see his name on the signboard.'

'Now fancy that,' I said. 'You know, to this day we had no idea what it was all about. We've been making full use of his benefaction and yet felt as though we were all in the dark.'

'Nevertheless,' said my guests, 'it hasn't helped him much. Yesterday,' they said, 'he struck another bad patch.'

And they told me a bit of news that made me feel very sorry for my former namesake.

12

"Laputin's wife, to whom he proposed in the patched-up dress suit, was even more touchy than her husband, and she adored show. Neither of them was particularly highly born—their fathers just made a pile of money on contracts—but they sought acquaintances only among the nobility. In those days, we had as Commander-in-Chief in Moscow Count Zakrevsky, who himself, it was said, was only of the Polish gentry, and the real gentry, like Prince Sergei Mihailovich Golitsyn, didn't rate him highly; but the rest were flattered to be received in his house. The wife of my former namesake also pined for his honor. Only, God knows why, nothing came of it for a long time, but at last Mr. Laputin found a way to make himself agreeable to the Count, and the latter said to him:

'Come and see me, brother; I'll tell them to admit you, you just tell me what your name is, so that I don't forget.'

The other said his name was Laputin.

'Laputin?' said the Count. 'Laputin. . . . Wait, wait now—Laputin . . . I seem to remember, Laputin. That's someone's surname.'

'Quite so,' the other said. 'Your Excellency—that's *my* name.'

'Of course, of course, that is your name, brother, only I seem to remember something . . . there seemed to be some other Laputin. Perhaps it was your father, Laputin?'

The gentleman replied that his father had been a Laputin.

'That's why I seem to remember it. . . . Laputin. It may have been your father. I have a very good memory; come along then, Laputin—come tomorrow if you like; I'll tell them to admit you, Laputin.'

The other was overjoyed, and the very next day went off to see the Count.

13

"But Count Zakrevsky, though he did say he had a good memory, on this occasion slipped up a trifle and said nothing about receiving Mr. Laputin.

The latter came dashing up.

'I'm So-and-so,' he said, 'and I wish to see the Count.'

But the doorman would not admit him.

'Orders,' said he, 'to admit no one.'

The gentleman tried arguing this way and that. 'I haven't come of my own accord,' he said, 'I've come at the Count's invitation.' But the doorman was not to be moved.

'I've orders,' said he, 'to admit no one, and if you're on business, you go to the office.'

'I'm not on business,' the gentleman protested, 'but a personal friend; the Count must have told you my name—Laputin; you must have got muddled.'

'The Count mentioned no name to me yesterday.'

'That's impossible; you must have just forgotten the name—Laputin.'

'I never forget anything, and this name I could not forget if I tried, because my own name is Laputin.'

The gentleman fairly flared up.

'What do you mean—you're a Laputin yourself! Who taught you to call yourself by that name?'

But the doorman said:

'No one's taught me anything—that's our name, and there are any number of Laputins in Moscow, only the rest are all of no importance: I'm the only one who's got on in the world.'

And while they were arguing, the Count himself came walking down the steps and said:

'Of course, that's the one I was thinking of, he's also a Laputin, and another scoundrel. And you come another day, I'm busy just now. Good day.'

Well, naturally, there was no question of any visit after that!"

309

14

Maître Tailleur Lepoutan related this with an air of quiet sympathy, and added as a finale that the very next day he came across the great Laputin himself, whom Vasilii Konych had reason to regard as his benefactor. Konych was passing along the Boulevard with some work at the time.

"There he sat," he said, "on a seat, as sad as sad. I wanted to slip past, but the moment he saw me he said:

'Hullo, Monsieur Lepoutan! How goes it?'

'By the grace of God, and with your help, very well. And how would you be feeling, sir?'

'Couldn't be worse; I found myself in such a mess-up.'

'I've heard of it, sir, and was glad you at least abstained from touching him.'

'I couldn't touch him,' he said, 'because he is not a free-lance artisan, but only the Count's flunkey; but what I want to know is this: who bribed him to offer me this insult?' "

Konych, in his simplicity, proceeded to console the gentleman:

" 'I should not look for bribery in it, sir. There are indeed lots of Laputins in Moscow, and there are some very honest ones among them—like my late grandad, for instance: he used to peddle felt soles all over Moscow.'

And no sooner had I said it than he ups and swipes me with his stick right across my back. . . . I streaked away, and haven't seen him since. I only heard that he and his wife went abroad to France, and there he lost all his money and died, and she put up a monument over him; only I heard say, she picked one up second hand, with the same name as on my signboard: 'Lepoutan.' So we found ourselves namesakes again, after all."

15

Vasilii Konych ended his recital, and I asked him why he did not want now to change his signboard and write on it his own, legal, Russian name?

"Well, why should I, sir? Why should I stir up all that business which started my luck? It would only do harm to the district."

"How could it do harm to the district?"

"Why, of course: my French signboard, everyone knows it to be just so much splash, but it's given all our district quite a different atmosphere, and the neighboring houses are now in quite a different class."

So Konych remained a Frenchman for the good of the inhabitants of his back alley, while his proud namesake rotted away uselessly under an assumed name at Père Lachaise.

The Harvest without Seed

RUTH SCHAUMANN

WHEN the great cold came, the plague died out. Only five inhabitants were left in the tiny market town, three old people and Simon and Colette. At first it seemed astonishing to them that they should be still alive, but after a time they thought no more about it. Then, all in one week, the three died of weakness, old age and cold. Simon buried them and inherited their meager sacks of bread and the little barn cottages in which the dirt floor could be seen through the layer of reedy wheat. And the man and wife subsisted on this.

Rheims was not far away. On still days the sound of the cathedral chimes echoed in the empty farms. From their door, the couple could see the gigantic body of the church towering above the distant city walls like the serrated spine of the leviathan, and they marveled at the many voices which came pouring out of it.

It got farther and farther into the winter. The cold increased and Simon began to wonder if they should not leave the desolate town and move to the city. But Colette, who was with child, dreaded the journey. She also feared that it might be fruitless, for she had heard about one of the now dead villagers who had fled with several others to the city at the beginning of the epidemic. They had barred the huge gates to them, had sounded the alarm and had threatened them from the towers with bows and arrows, just as though the handful of fugitives were a whole army of Englishmen, marching upon the city with banners and deadly weapons. So great was the fear of the plague, that most dreadful of visitations. And the wanderers returned and were

312

received by those things from which they had fled, death and a common grave.

And the cold mounted. Rats and mice took possession. Simon looked over his store, once, and then again and again. It was growing no bigger. The scuttering, gray creatures helped with the consumption. Without saying a word to Colette, he put a little sack of grain under his cot against the time of bitterest need. And he slept on it.

From Rheims the bells were ringing in the Advent. Only a few notes carried over to them. The frost broke up the song making it sound thin and meaningless. Simon and Colette did not listen to it any more. They ceased to care about anything. Like two forlorn birds, they sat by their hearth and tended the fire; for they had little left but this. What meaning did Advent have for them? Spring would have been much better, but it was still a long way off.

Seven days went by. The bells rang out from Rheims a second time. Another week passed and they pealed for the third time. It was not so cold that day. There was a lingering sweetness in the tones. Having traveled from far away across the fields, they had more longing in them than high up in the city. Colette listened. But Simon stopped up the last cracks in the door with straw. He said that the cold was still coming in. Colette forgot the sounds. The child within her stirred. She wondered if it were a boy, and another kind of faraway look came into her eyes.

The week came to an end. On Saturday, during the noon hour, there was a loud knocking at the door. Simon pulled the stuffing out of a tiny crack. Something was assisting him from the other side. Through the chink he could see nothing but shaggy hair. He felt warm breath on his face. This was no human being, it was surely the devil. He cried out in a frightened voice, "Go away, go away!" But the shaggy being pressed closer to the door. The straw-stuffed slits all emptied with astonishing rapidity and the cold came through like the points of sharp swords. Simon saw two gigantic ears twitching outside the cracked door and at the same time he heard a gentle human voice asking to be let in. But still he hesitated. Then he heard the braying of an ass and his last fear was banished. He slowly opened the door. It must be a peddler, he thought, with a she-ass to sell. He still had some hay. It would provide milk for him and Colette, and the peddler would continue on his way.

Cheered by this thought, he looked at the new arrival. It was

a man, as he had guessed, with a donkey. It was not a she-ass, however, but a riding animal, scrawny and exhausted, though somewhat restored at the moment, after its plucking and crunching at Simon's stuffed door, which from the inside offered it still more of the wretched nourishment. Simon shooed the animal away.

On the back of the ass sat a woman. She was very pale. Whether with weakness or with cold, Simon did not care. Disappointed in his hopes, suffering from the cold, frightened by the pallor of the woman, he turned a deaf ear to the pleading words of the man, who was holding the donkey by the bridle. "We have nothing. Go to Rheims, there is a very fine granary there. Look at my threshing floor. There is nothing in it but a thin layer of oats."

He shut the door of the house, went into the barn and pulled up the planks of the floor. The man looked in. "It will be enough for us all," he said confidently. "God will provide for four with what he provided for two." In the back of the barn lay a bundle of dry weeds. The ass brayed happily.

"Go away, go away," said Simon, for it seemed to him that man and animal were taking possession of all that he had with their grateful eyes. "There is nothing. Your wife is sick. Don't bring the plague into my house." The woman on the ass sighed. The stranger looked at him thoughtfully.

"So you will not allow us to stay?"

"No," said Simon.

The donkey flipped his ears several times straight up into the air, but they did not stay there. He patiently let them flop back again and turned away. The man let go of his bridle and went out after him, as meekly as the animal. The woman had drawn her cloak up around her face. She glided down the street like a blue hill. The top of her head grazed the branches of the bare, low-hanging fruit trees. They quivered like harp-strings and gave out the same kind of silvery sound. But no shiny needles of hoarfrost came sprinkling down. That was very strange. Simon looked after them. The indifference with which they had departed astonished him. These people must have been turned away often. He went back into his cottage.

Colette was lying back in her straw armchair, a melancholy look on her face. She asked what it had all been about. "A man, a woman and an ass—that's all." Simon went over to a bin and came back with a few stalks of juniper which he tossed onto the fire. A sharp, acrid odor sprang up like a lean dog and penetrated every corner of the room. Colette made a wry face.

"Why the plague weed?"

"The woman was sick."

"Why didn't you tell her to stay?"

"I want to keep us alive, you, Colette, and I and the third who hasn't come yet."

"It isn't always the plague," said Colette, and she realized how weak she was. From between the boards came the squeaking of hungry mice. The burning juniper died out leaving a trail of strong smoke. Colette coughed. It would soon be dark. The two of them lay down to sleep. A snowstorm came sweeping over the village. It rattled around the barn and the trees could be heard moaning in the blast. In the darkness Colette suddenly asked, "Is it far to Rheims?"

"Two hours in good weather. Do you want to go there?" Simon smiled to himself, for it was nice and warm in his sack of straw.

"Not I." Colette's voice sounded as though she were accompanying someone in her thoughts. The storm raged on. Simon fell asleep.

About midnight he awakened. He could no longer feel Colette's breath on his right cheek. He called to her softly, then more loudly. As though from far away he heard a moan. Like a mole in the winter darkness of his hole, he began to grope his way through the room amid the smoke, the warmth and the dim, cloudy shapes of the familiar furniture. He picked up a stick of kindling wood from the hearth and was soon holding its burning end over Colette's face. She was crouching between the brightly decorated chest and the cupboard in which he kept his farming tools. Her head was bowed and her face was twisted with pain. The plague, thought Simon, and cursed the woman on the ass. Colette, awakened by the sound of his hoarse voice, opened her eyes. She smiled through her pain. He realized that his wife was not ill, that the child would not be long in coming. The storm had died down, but the cottage was filled with Colette's cries, sometimes high, sometimes low. Simon assisted her, clumsy and trembling. She gave birth in the gray dawn. It was a boy.

Rejoicing, Simon laid her on her bed. Then he went into the barn to gather up some oats with which to make a little porridge to strengthen the new mother. There was more snow in the yard and jutting up here and there were planks which had not been there the day before. The boards from the barn door! The wind had been sweeping through the granary all night and there was not a grain on the threshing floor, not a single grain. Simon turned pale beneath his rough, tanned skin. He had shown the granary to the stranger and afterwards had forgotten to bolt the door securely. He cursed the visitor and once again searched every corner of the threshing floor. It was entirely empty. Even the bundle of weeds had been carried off by the wind. Now nothing was left but the little sack of grain under his bed. It would do them for a day or two. In the dim light of dawn Simon trudged back to the house.

His wife was sleeping and the child in her arms was breathing deeply as though it were asleep. He went over to his cot and began poking about. He shoved to one side the rustling hay and straw and plumped the old feather pillow down on top of them. Why was the sack so flat? Why was it so light? Through big holes in the cloth, empty husks came trickling out in a golden stream, but they made no sound as they hit the floor. The mice had stolen their last food right from under his body. A sack full of holes and a heap of pale husks were all that he possessed. And Colette must eat! He wanted to awaken her to tell her of their misfortune, but he was stopped by the sight of her face. Even the warm rays of dawn which were shining through the little pane of glass lent scarcely any color to its whiteness.

He could hear the pealing of bells. They were ringing in the cathedral of Rheims. They sounded very near. It was Sunday. Well, he would go there and knock on all the doors and ask for bread for his wife who had just given birth. He placed a jar of melted snow beside Colette. The child gave a tiny cry without opening its eyes. He threw on his scalloped coat and went out. Across snow-covered fields and frozen ditches he ran toward Rheims. The bells were still ringing.

He reached the gates of the city in three hours. Bathed in perspiration from his run, he stood steaming like a messenger's horse before the huge gate. The bridge had been let down half way and was hanging suspended above his head like the mighty wings of a wooden angel. He leaped up into the air like a dog to catch hold of it, but it was too high for him. He called up to the towers. His voice, what with the running, the fear and the cold, was nearly gone. When he opened his mouth to call the sound was scarcely audible and did not carry up to the battlements. Secure within itself, an ark of peace, the city stood there, as though there were nothing beyond its walls. A pale sun lit up Rheims for a moment, then the little warmth from the sky died out. The chimneys of the city began to smoke more vigorously. It seemed to Simon that he could distinguish all kinds of smells and could see many varieties of food, as though the walls were of glass and transparent. In this strange way he also saw those who were eating and drinking, but none of them saw him. He looked about him. The plain was empty. Should he dig for roots? The icy snow beneath his worn-out shoes did not yield, no matter how hard he jabbed at it with his feet. He knew that the frozen whiteness was shoe-deep and below it was the frost-bound earth. He shouted again. A raucous cry, like that of a raven forced its way out, froze and fell on the wall like a tiny bullet of hail. Through the peephole, a warder looked down across the moat. Simon was shouting something about the drawbridge, the gate and bread. The man did not understand him. He only saw the wildly agitated figure clad in the red scalloped coat of the peasants of the town which had been ravaged by the plague. This terrifyingly haggard form, with its cracked cries, was to him the personification of the plague. He disappeared from the hole, Simon waited. The gate did not open, the drawbridge did not come down, mist rose from the moat. A noise from within his body startled him. It was hunger. But over the wide, white fields was a house, and in it lay his wife. And there was nothing there to fill his need. Simon raved and raged and trembled. Mice, wind, the groans of the woman in labor, the donkey leader and the pale face of the riding woman all floated through his mind. Then he burst into tears.

Something like the sound of little hoofbeats seemed to pass by him. Was the ass too haunting his despairing mind? Then, not far away, he saw coming from the opposite direction the man, the ass and the woman on it. Silently, three patient shadows, they had slipped past him and he had not seen them. Had they been turned away from the city too? But why were they still wandering about aimlessly? For the next village on that side was four hours away. Simon no longer had the strength to make the journey. How could the ailing woman get there? He called out to tell them this. The man stopped, the donkey stood still, the woman turned to look at Simon. She was even more frail than she had been the day before. Simon came over to them.

"Wouldn't they let you into the city?"

None of them answered.

"Where are you going now?"

"Wherever God wills," said the stranger.

"My wife has given birth to a child," said Simon accusingly. "The storm swept out my threshing floor, the mice have devoured my grain."

The man nodded as though he already knew about it.

"Now I can no longer put you up," said Simon, and he realized that he should have done so yesterday.

"Colette and I will starve, and our little son will die before our very eyes. Was it for this that he came into the world?"

The woman on the donkey looked down at him sadly. She was different from Colette, but beneath her breast, her coat swelled out as though she were carrying something there. Simon thought of his wife before she had given the child its life. He

319

became frightened. Where will this woman be able to bring forth her child? "We must all starve," he said dully.

"You shall reap without sowing," replied the stranger. It sounded very comforting. The ass tugged at his reins, he began to move. The man walked ahead, the woman pulled her cloak high above her breast. Simon went on his way. He left the city behind him without making any further attempt to prevail upon the tower warder to let him enter. His hands were empty, he was bringing no bread to Colette.

"You shall reap without sowing," he said to himself. He could very well understand that there might be no harvest even if one did sow. This other he did not understand. He should have asked the man what he meant. It was not too late even now. He turned around and ran after the group which was moving at a resolute pace over the frozen desert of snow. Perhaps the man knew of some place where there was a hidden store.

He ran on, the darkness increased, but he could not overtake the travelers. He raised his voice, he heard the donkey snorting, but he could not seem to make any of them hear him. He forgot that he was getting farther and farther away from his own home in which his wife was lying in fear, hunger and darkness beside the burned-out hearth, with the child sucking at her empty breasts. He hurried on and fell down. He had stumbled over the stump of a tree. He must think this thing over. "To reap without sowing!" Behind it, it seemed to him, were concealed rivers of grain and mountains of bread. He started running again, obsessed with this one question. In the gray twilight he had still been able to distinguish the people. Now they had vanished into the blackness. He came to the forest. The snow helped him by its feeble glow to see his way among the trees. Everywhere, it seemed to him, he could hear the hoofbeats of the ass and the sound of the pilgrim's staff as it thrust aside the bushes. But when he reached the place from which these sounds had come, there was nothing to be seen. He was tired. He wanted to rest for a little while. The snow in the wood was warmer than it had been in the fields. Stars appeared overhead between the treetops. First they looked like hard sparks, then frozen kernels, then they became warmer and bigger like a heart when pride melts. In their midst there was one empty place. To the countryman, gazing up at them, it seemed that right there, there should be a star which would rule all the others. But the place remained black and the others were gathered around it like flocks around a spring from which no water is coming. Simon sat down. These two things, the star that was not there and the harvest without seed kept going over and over in his head. To his untutored peasant's brain, the struggle with words and thoughts was exhausting. He felt that he must sleep, he was already sleeping, had been sleeping for a long time. He felt his heart melting out of his body and coming out under his chest, and the cold touched it and it hurt.

Simon woke up terrified. His heart was not outside of him. It was pounding within him as though with excitement. Had he really been sleeping? He looked up through the branches. In the midst of the heavenly host was flaming a gigantic star filling all the darkness of the firmament. Simon thought of the long forgotten words of the old priest who had presided over the village church before the plague had snatched him and his congregation away. "And a star shall rise over all ages and all peoples and a child shall be born . . . " Wasn't tonight the night of the birth? Simon beat his breast, his heart was pounding painfully. Oh star of this night! I am a sinner and in darkness, but you are the glory and the majesty.

He took a few steps. A smell of cinnamon and marjoram, mingled with that of rosemary and the violet-colored thyme that wild hares love so much, floated toward him, a wave of spring and summer together. And there was a clearing between the trees like a lonely song which bursts forth in splendor all by itself. Blades of wheat swayed in the gentle wind, the clover bloomed, and there was a wild apple tree in blossom. A tree to

321

the left of it bore cherries, as red as drops of the holy blood. Twined about the wheat was a vine, heavy with grapes, and the grapes were full of juice. But all around the clearing the ground was covered with snow.

Here was the harvest without seed. Simon went down on his knees. Had the pilgrims stopped to rest here before he came? Oh, how well their Lord cared for all His creatures! He reached for the wheat. It fell into his arms and formed itself into sheaves. Hesitantly he plucked some of the fruit, praying as he did so. Then, filled with awe, he left the place. The sweet fragrance around him faded away.

Simon came out of the forest. The cold of the fields surrounded him once more. Before him, already far in the distance, three moons were moving away, shining with a gentle radiance. One was a little way ahead, about as high as a man, one was a little above it, and near this one, almost merging with it, was the third. But this was the biggest. "Jesus, Mary and Joseph," sighed Simon and he crossed himself in his soul, for his arms were full. And he found himself very close to his village. He seemed to have gone in a circle and was standing before his door. He found Colette lying in untroubled sleep, the child nestling against her warm, unconscious body. But behind him fresh snow was falling which covered the place where the miracle had been. And the strong, bright star stood among the others in the middle of the night.

TRANSLATED BY JANE BANNARD GREENE

The Baron's Two Francs

FRANÇOIS COPPÉE

THAT CHRISTMAS, as the winter was very severe and the socialist press was vociferating with redoubled invectives against the rich, Baron Mufelbach gave one hundred thousand francs to the poor of Paris. One hundred thousand francs. Certainly, that's something, and it must not be forgotten that the Baron is the most "solicited" man in France. On the other hand, don't go overboard, please, about his generosity; for the Baron's fortune is enormous, scandalous, obscene. His father only left him a miserable fifty millions, which once wrung from old Rothschild the heartfelt cry "That poor wretched Mufelbach! I thought him better off." But we must be allowed to suppose that the mother of Mufelbach kept her eye on the figure 4 while pregnant, as her only son, sole heir to the name and to the famous banking house, quickly quadrupled his patrimony.

However, Baron Mufelbach's fate is not, on the whole, a happy one.

To begin with, he enjoys very poor health. Owner of one of the most famous "chateaux" of Medoc, he can only drink milk and Vichy water, and if, at dinner, he is imprudent enough to ask for a second helping of filet de sole, he will be tattooed and tortured by eczema for at least two weeks.

You would, I feel sure, feel sorry for him if you happened to catch the envious gaze with which, pressing his nose against the windowpane of his splendid office, he watches the cab drivers in the pub across the street, shoveling away plates of beef and cabbage, and pouring down quarts of liquor.

Nor has the Baron a happy love life. His wife, an Englishwoman whom he married almost from affection—she only had five millions, a mere fleabite— became an invalid shortly after her first child. Having dragged out a miserably semi-invalid existence for a number of years, she left him a widower at forty, with a big good-for-nothing hulk of a boy, almost a moron, with a huge birthmark on his left cheek, who has just been demoted to the ranks, after a nasty scene with his major.

Not naturally a fly by night, the Baron was, however, unable to settle down, as he would have liked to do, with a steady girl, for the most disinterested females came to have, by the mere fact of his acquaintance, a revolting rapacity. Now, aging, he was almost completely continent, disgust having disposed of desire.

He isn't a bad man, only an insensitive one. Very much solicited, indeed, very much exploited, he lets himself be duped. He gives a lot, but without pleasure or regret, with absolute indifference, since he is sure his limitless cash will never run out. A sedentary Jew, he yet is like the wandering Jew, who always had five cents in his pocket, but with this advantage over Ahasverus, that it is not five cents, but five millions that he always finds at the bottom of his pocket, and of course with the interest, when the market is steady.

The Baron is always making money, in spite of himself as it were, and effortlessly, simply because he has always had so much, and because now he has more, and in the future he will always have more still. He finds it perfectly natural to attract gold, as the magnet attracts iron, merely by the power of his capital. He has read all the economists, and those serious jokers have taught him that money is nothing else but the combination of intelligence plus hard work. Since he is a profoundly modest man, the Baron is not at all sure that because he is one of the richest men in Europe, he therefore should be one of the most intelligent and hard working. Still and all, it seems to him perfectly normal and legitimate that his thousand-franc bills and gold pieces should multiply and increase like rabbits in a warren. It would astonish him very much if you told him that there was something indecent and immoral in the spectacle of a fortune as monstrous as his.

All the same, he is not an animal. He knows envy exists, and that one must be on one's guard against it. And just the other day, after reading the gutter press, leaning with his elbow on the pillow, waiting for the result of the glass of Hungarian Epsom salts which his doctor insists upon his taking once a week, and after having had, in the face of so many revolutionary prophecies, the vision of a furious mob breaking open his safe, invading his hotel, breaking windows, smashing pictures, and carrying off his head at the end of a pike, the Baron thought that the moment had come to throw a sugar cake down the howling throat of socialism; and he sent—as he does periodically now and then—his wad of thousand-franc bills to the Public Welfare, intending to make up the sum by making a corner (which he had been preparing for some time) in Chicago hams.

Once more, let me repeat, one hundred thousand francs is a large sum, and Baron Mufelbach was not displeased with the effect he produced. Naturally, the leftist press didn't carry any mention of his generosity, but it went across big in the government and in the society papers. Though in discreet and restrained terms, without too much "blather," as that wouldn't have been at all to the taste of a man who was a subscriber to the *Révue des Deux mondes* and the *Journal des Debats*.

Well, just this morning, Christmas Eve, the Baron woke up pretty crochety. His liver was playing up, his stomach a bit queasy, and he was aware, having just looked at his tongue in his shaving mirror, that it was strangely yellow. He really felt that to be so bilious after having done a good act was pretty discouraging.

However, he sat down at his desk, in front of a masterpiece by Rembrandt, for which he paid a small fortune, and which does not interest him at all—for he is quite unable to appreciate the deep and intimate poetry of this picture of an old Dutchwoman, where the whole of an existence is revealed, and a whole society, a whole background, and which tells you such details as to what time this lady said her prayers, and at what time of year she did her laundry. All of a sudden, a visitor was announced, who brought the thanks of the Administration for the Baron's generous gift.

It was an old dandy who showed up, with some silver in his mane, and some wrinkles from overindulgence round the gills and around the eyes. He was buttoned up, from the word go, in the classic business suit.

In the face of this superb specimen of the human race, the ultra-rich financier, insignificant and crouching in his armchair, with his sick headache, his bald pate, his livid complexion and his silly little whiskers, looked simply like some miserable creature who had just gone broke.

Suddenly, the Baron became curious. He interrupted, with a gentle gesture, the flowery gratitude of the facile speaker.

"Could you give me some information?" he asked. "One hundred thousand francs—how much does that make for each poor person?"

Evidently, the magnificent government official found the question rather vexing. He reddened slightly, ashamed of the answer. "Well, Sir, we have, here in Paris, yes, listed with the welfare agencies, about fifty thousand indigent persons. So we gave them two francs each."

"Two francs," said the man who had millions, without betraying, either by his voice or look, whether he thought that sum too much or too little.

Then he added, still impassible:

"Fifty thousand indigent people, labeled and assisted as much . . . In spite of the savings banks, of the insurance companies, of so many preventive societies, fifty thousand. It really is a lot."

"You've put your finger right on the spot" exclaimed the handsome city employee. "The carelessness, the thoughtlessness—the unbelievable imprudence of the people . . . There is the true secret of their misery . . . "

And he would have launched out into a whole speech had not the financier, who knew there was a line of people waiting to see him in the outer office, and who husbanded his minutes, risen as a sign of dismissal.

Acting on his doctor's advice, and in the interest of his digestion, Baron Mufelbach went out on foot every afternoon, and took a constitutional for an hour.

On that day, as usual, he wandered about, aimlessly, shivering under his greatcoat in the December fog. His usual sadness was increased. "Two francs," he muttered over and over, with an ironic smile. What a drop of water in the sea. That's all it produced, his royal alms. Now he wasn't surprised any longer at not getting any pleasure out of his gift. One hundred thousand francs to the poor of Paris—get this down, you dear philanthropists who are always preaching charity in season and out of season, that makes two francs a head, that is to say, not a thing. What assistance could two francs bring to any miserable unfortunate? You must agree that it is ridiculous, derisory. And note that in all Paris there are barely twenty people in a position to give a hundred thousand francs, even if they wished to do so. Will twenty times two francs per person end pauperism, or advance the social question one step? Laughing softly to himself under his breath, the Baron trotted along in the dense fog.

He had arrived in a thickly populated suburb, where the shops were all lit up and gay with Christmas decorations. In the butchers' shops the roasts were wrapped in gaudy paper, in the grocers', the display of goods was dazzling. And the toy shops were crammed with sleds and toy boats, and what glorious colors —what lots of tinsel and gold paper!

Impeded in his hygienic exercise by the ever denser crowd, Baron Mufelbach walked slowly now, behind two poor women; one was very old and in rags, bent double; the other was hardly better dressed, but was younger—in her forties—and carried herself upright, with a little girl of about five or six clinging to her skirts.

And, without meaning to, the Baron overheard this bit of dialogue:

"Is it true, Mrs. Jules, that this morning they gave you two francs up at the Welfare?"

"Yes, indeed, Mrs. Fournier. It appears that some very charitable gentleman—they did tell us his name, but I've forgotten it—an aristocrat, a nobleman, or what, gave hundreds of thousands of francs."

"And if I may ask, without being indiscreet, what are you going to do with your two francs, my poor Mrs. Jules?"

"Dear Lord, why I'm going to buy some coffee and sugar. I'm fed up, you know, with the high cost of living. And what about you, Madame Fournier, is your old man more reasonable these days?"

"Don't mention him to me . . . last pay day, Saturday, he went on a spree again, and I didn't get even one third of his earnings. Without the hock shop and my credit at the baker's, I don't know how I could possibly make ends meet until the end of the month."

The Baron was listening casually to this conversation. Indeed, it was pretty stereotyped. Poverty? Yes, it's very sad. But what can be done about it? Millions upon millions could be dropped into such a bottomless pit. All the same, with those two francs, the old woman will have her coffee for a few mornings. That's always something.

But now the little girl tugs at her mother, in front of a toy shop. "Oh, mummy, the lovely dolls."

The mother tries to drag the child away, tries to shut her up with "Come along, now, Margaret . . . You know perfectly well that, this Christmas, I can't give you a thing."

But Mrs. Jules had stopped also. She looks, first at the hungry, longing looks of the little girl, then at the sad eyes of her mother.

And then with a smile so good, so humble that it seems, as it were, to float over her toothless mouth, she says in an almost timid voice:

"Look there, Madame Fournier, look at that one, with the yellow frock—that one is real pretty, and it costs just two francs. Do let me buy it for Margaret . . . You have been so good to me. Ever since the beginning of this winter, who was it who gave me the coal for my stove? I won't have any extras, that's all. Or rather, you invite me to coffee, when you can . . . "

Well, that's a bit thick to be sure, and at first the Baron was simply staggered. Here it certainly was, the mad improvidence of the poor, of which the city employee was talking just now. It seems to Baron Mufelbach as if he had just bought one hundred thousand francs worth of dolls. . . .

But when the group disappeared into the crowd, the little girl walking ahead clutching in her arms the handsome lady made of cardboard in her yellow dress, the man of millions, who, after all, is definitely neither bad nor stupid, reflected a bit, and fell into a profound gloom. He remembered the delighted air of the old lady when she bought the doll. He realized that it gave her great pleasure to pay down her two francs, while it gave him none to give his great wad of greenbacks. His vast alms, drily given, from convention, from a vague sense of duty, perhaps also a bit from fear, now seemed to him pretty mean, and in the addled brain cluttered with a gold merchant's accounts, this truth gradually stood out clearly, that a benefit is a pretty feeble thing if it does not entail a sacrifice, and that—by some mysterious law of compensations which makes human misery tolerable—it is only for the poor that charity is a pleasure.

TRANSLATED BY ANNE FREMANTLE

Tom a' Tuddlams

SABINE BARING-GOULD

I

ALL THE western border of Yorkshire, from Derbyshire to the sources of the Tees, is a region of mountains and moors. The scenery is very wild in places—rugged, picturesque, varied, and everywhere beautiful.

In parts of this region it is still unusual for a native to be known by a surname. Indeed, he is generally doubtful whether he possesses one, and has to consider and consult authorities for it when he gives in his name to have his banns called. Every one in each of these dales knows every one else, and every one's pedigree, and it is by their pedigrees that each man and woman is known, much as in Wales, where every one was an *ap* some-one, and in Normandy of old every man was a *fitz*. For instance, in the parish of Kebroyd, in these Western Hills, there were, no doubt, at least two Johns and two Marys. One man would be John a' Dick's and the other John a' Jake's; and each Mary would, in like manner, be recognized and distinguished by the name of her father. But as it sometimes happens that there may be in the same place two Johns, both sons of Richards though of different Richards, to differentiate them the grand-fathers of each are called in, and one becomes John a' Dick's a' Harry's, and the other John a' Dick's a' Jake's. But sometimes the designation of a man is not by a patronymic, he takes the territorial name when he is the owner of and permanent resi-dent in a small farm or cot. This was how Tom a' Will's a' Joe's came to be called Tom a' Tuddlams. Tuddlams is not an euphonious name; but no name but one sounded sweeter in the ears of Tom, for Tom was proud of Tuddlams—prouder, maybe, than the Duke of Devonshire is of Chatsworth, or the swallow is of its well-plastered nest. Tom loved Tuddlams because Tuddlams had come to him in a time of great distress and doubt where he should go, and had come to him quite unexpectedly.

I have said that no name but one sounded sweeter in Tom's ears. The one name more grateful to him than even Tuddlams was that of his wife Jewel. "Jewel" was the name by which she was christened, but "Jewel" was shortened on the vulgar tongue into "Jule;" and she was known throughout the neighbourhood as Jule a' Nort a' Nowheer, or, more laconically, as Jule a' Nobbudy. This meant that she did not belong to the parish of Kebroyd, nor to any of the parishes immediately impinging on Kebroyd, into which public opinion allowed the young Kebroydians, when seeking mates, to look for them. Every one beyond that arbitrary line was esteemed as "nobody" and "nort" (naught), and the whole British Empire outside the same line was "nowheer," (nowhere). If Tom had wanted a wife, why did he not wait till he came into the parish and then look about him? Tom had not waited till his uncle died and he had inherited Tuddlams, and settled in to take a "skeen" (look) round and choose a housewife where his home was to be. He had married an out*landish* lass, of whose ancestry nothing was known and whose birthplace none had seen.

Tom's ideas were not cast in the same mould as those of the people of Kebroyd. He had seen the world—that is, a good deal more of it than they—and he was impatient at their narrowness and prejudices.

Tuddlams was a small, low farmhouse, built of limestone blocks that had turned gray with old age. The fells rose behind it, covered with heather, on which one waded knee-deep, and when one waded, started grouse. A dip in the hills carried the drainage away to the Skelf; little converging becks rose on the sides of Scalefell and Houghfell and united in a ravine below the farm, where they formed a brawling, foaming stream of some pretence. Tuddlams lay in a scoop or basin of the moors, high up, sheltered from fierce winds, unless they blew up the valley from the south-east.

Tom had led a roving life. His father had been an unsuccessful, discontented, disagreeable man. He had gone away from Kebroyd early in life, and had wandered from town to town in quest of work. Tom's father, Will a' Joe's, as he was called in his native place, Bill Greenwood as he called himself out of it, never stuck long to one trade. He tried wool-combing, he tried cutlery, he tried dyeing, weaving, he even for a short while cultivated liquorice at Pontefract; he went on a coal barge on the Calder canal, quarreled with his trade when he did not quarrel with his employer, and, finally, helped to make Devil's dust in a shoddy mill at Ossett. The Devil's dust got into his lungs, and cast him on his bed in a galloping consumption. On his death-bed he threatened to prosecute the nurse who attended on him, and he argued politics with his doctor till a fit of coughing came on and he broke a blood-vessel, and died slapping at his son who ran to hold him in his arms.

His wife had died some years before, glad, poor woman, to leave a life full of change and privation, and only sorry to be obliged to leave behind her her little boy to drift about the world where that spinning, eddy-headed husband of hers carried him.

After his father's death, Tom found work in a mill, and remained at his post for several years, steady, patient, exact in doing his daily task, and doing it always well. He was a quiet, reserved fellow, who did not make many friends, because he did not seek the society of his fellows, and he had acquired in his drifting life the art to live to himself. But though he had few friends he had no enemies, for he was harmless, and ever ready to do what was kind to those who needed assistance.

As he went to his work every day and as he returned from it, he encountered a girl who worked in another factory. This girl was Jewel, a tall lass with fresh complexion and clear honest eyes, with hair like amber, but covered with a scarlet kerchief, after the habit of mill girls. Also, like the rest, she wore a white pinafore, and carried her dinner in a tin can. She was usually attended by a brother, a poor deformed boy, with one shoulder higher than the other, and a twisted spine. This lad, almost daily, attended his sister to the factory, and went to meet her as she returned when "the mill loosed."

Tom took to pitying the cripple, made him little presents, and gained a smile from Jewel. An acquaintance thus began, slowly ripened, and Tom thought the happiest moments of the day were those to or from his work, and the most miserable occasions those when he got away too late or too early to walk with Jewel. Tom, however, was not aware that he loved her, till a time of distress came on Ossett, and Jewel was thrown out of work.

Among the hands the greatest distress prevailed. Hundreds were discharged from the mills. Then it was that Jewel lost her work.

Tom became uneasy about her. He looked around for her, but could not see her. He feared she might suffer want, that she would be forced to leave Ossett, and go elsewhere seeking work —that Wakefield, Dewsbury, Leeds, might engulf her, and that then it would be impossible for him to trace and recover her. Then, and then only, did he wake to discover how much in love he was. A couple of weeks passed, weeks of torturing anxiety to Tom. He could endure the uncertainty, the suspense, no longer, so he went to the house where she lodged with her brother, and rapped at the door. As he stood on the steps listening for her foot, waiting for her call to enter, he heard the tones of a fiddle within, playing—

"Christians, awake! salute the happy morn
Whereon the Saviour of the world was born!"

Christmas was coming, but was not come. What a sad Christmas it would be to many in Ossett! thought Tom. Happy was he to be still in full work. He tapped again at the door, and went in. No candle was burning, but there was a fire of coals shedding a red glow over the "house," as the main downstairs' room of a cottage is designated in Yorkshire.

By the fire sat Jewel, doing needlework, bending forward to see by the flames, and so the light danced over her amber hair. On a low stool sat the deformed, half-witted boy, fiddling.

"Jule," said Tom, "art thou out o' work?"

"Eh! I am, Tom."

"And how beest thou keeping body and soul together?"

"They hou'd together without keeping, like man and wife."

"Why, lass! Jim addles (earns) nowt. Hast thou any savings out o' which to feed him and thee?"

"The savings be all emptiness, Tom."

"Look thee here, lass," said Tom Greenwood. "I'm in work mysen, and the strong ought to help the weak. If thou'lt let me help thee, thou must take me altogether—me, that is, for the sake o' my savings."

Jewel considered a moment, then said—

"Who takes me must take Jim, too. I've to fend (care) for him, poor lad; there's no one else."

"Never another word, lass; I've a broad back, and I'll carry the whole bag o' tricks."

That was a queer courtship, and a doubtful start on the journey of life, made doubly doubtful after the banns had been put in, by Tom getting his dismissal from the factory where he worked, not from any fault of his, but because there was no work more to be done in it till trade looked up.

"Jule," said he dolefully, "now I'm out o' work too, so we sha'n't lose nothing by honeymoon holidaying. We can't be worse off together than we are apart, so we'd better link our hands and hearts."

"Very well, Tom: thou know'st best."

That was a dismal wedding on Christmas Day. They had no new clothes, a sorry dinner, and no wedding trip, though they kept, perforce, holiday. Hungry and poor they went to church;

hungry and poor, but full of love, and rich in hope, they began their united stream of life.

I I

Tom had some savings, but not much. Jewel had none at all. How could she? At the best of times her earnings had but barely provided for her own and her brother's necessities. Six shillings —at piecework sometimes eight, never ten—per week, worsted reeling. How had she managed to support herself and brother on from six to eight shillings a week? She had often tried to get Jim to do some trifling task which might add something to the little store, but he was too unreliable, too feather-brained, to remain long at anything; and all her efforts were unavailing. Yet, he was always sorry that he had disappointed her, and cried piteously over his own shortcomings. But he was as incorrigible as a drunkard. He could not stick to regular work. And yet he earned money in his own way, though a way not approved by his sister. Jim, like so many who are half-witted, had a singularly developed faculty for music, and he could play with rare delicacy and feeling on his violin. No one who heard his performance without seeing him would believe that he lacked brain: he threw so much expression into what he played, and played with such refinement of feeling. His skill on the violin led him to play in the "folds" or mill-yards to the workmen during their dinner hour; and those who heard him gave him halfpence. Sometimes he went, when invited, into the public-houses. His sister had urged him with fervour not to allow himself to be enticed into the taverns; but Jim could say no man "nay," and he went in, played, received money and drink, and now and then staggered home tipsy.

But now this small rill of income dried up. The hands were no more flush of money, the folds were empty, and Jim might play to the idle, but he received no pay in return.

"Whatever is to be done?" asked Tom disconsolately. "We must go elsewhere."

335

"But whither shall we go?" asked Jewel.

A rap at the door, and a letter flung in by the postman. The question was answered. Tom's uncle was dead—Uncle Nick, about whom he had scarcely heard—thought less. Uncle Nick had been a small landowner—a yeoman on a very small scale—at the head of the Skelfdale, at Tuddlams, in Kebroyd parish. Uncle Nick was dead, and left no sons or daughters to inherit Tuddlams after him, so Tuddlams fell to his nephew. This is how Tom a' Will's a' Joe's came to be Tom a' Tuddlams at the age of twenty-three.

A proud and happy man was Tom Greenwood—proud above all to have a house of his own in which to place his dear Jewel, to be its mistress and queen. Jewel looked about her.

"I'm glad—I'm fain glad," she said. "It must be two miles from a public-house, and there'll be no trouble about Jim."

"Is that the chief good o' t' place in thine eyes?" asked Tom, a little disconcerted.

"It is one, and a great one," answered Jewel.

But every pleasure has its attendant annoyance, and Tom's delight and pride in his home were damped, and his temper nettled, when he heard his wife—his Jewel of jewels—lightly designated by all the neighbours, acting under a common impulse, "Jule a' nort a' nowheer."

It cannot be said with truth that Tom received a cordial welcome on his arrival in the parish. In the first place, he had married a foreigner.

" 'Tis a pity," said some, "that he should have took that lass Jule a' nort a' nowheer! 'Tis like putting new cloth into an ow'd garment, or new wine into ow'd bottles, clean contrary to Scripture. It is as bad as Moses casting down and breaking the Ten Commandments."

Then, in the next place, Tom was regarded as a sort of renegade. His father had left Kebroyd and gone east, to the big towns, and roystered there, and had never returned to his native village, not even there to lay his bones. Tom had not been born in the dale, but at Huddersfield. However, though not born and bred under the shadow of Scalefell, he could not be counted a stranger, for he was Tom a' Will's a' Joe's a' Jake's a' Nick's—his genealogy was better known than that of Noah, and he was, in right, as he was in fact, inalienably, undeniably, Tom a' Tuddlams.

Tom speedily settled into his little farm. He kept on in his service old Matthew, the man who had been with his uncle, Nicodemus—Nick a' Joe's a' Jake's, as he was called. The old man's advice and assistance would be invaluable to him, ignorant of the mode of conducting the operations on a farm. Tom had Yorkshire energy and self-assurance, and had inherited some of his father's versatility. In a very short time he was sure, to use his own expression, he would "frame." The life he had led since his early childhood, instead of making him restless, had filled his soul with a longing for rest. The incessant change in his father's condition, now in receipt of good wages, then with nothing, had made him hunger for a stable position, in which he need not be looking forward with uneasiness to the future. To have a house not rented, but his own; to have earth under his feet in which he could take root, certain not to be upriven and displaced, this was to him the most perfect happiness that could fall to his lot. It had come to him quite unexpectedly, for he had never thought of, certainly never reckoned on, Uncle Nick's acres. He had never inquired whether his uncle was married, whether he had children. He had never visited him. He had not thought of applying to him when out of work and in distress.

Tom loved, admired, almost worshipped Jewel with a deeper love, admiration, and religion every day. Tom had not had his heart unlocked as a boy. His mother had died early, and was to him only a pale and characterless reminiscence. His father had bullied him, had shown him little affection, or had shown what affection he bore in an unpalatable fashion. No one else had shown him any regard, and he had been brought in contact

337

with no one to whom he could cling. Consequently Tom had grown to man's estate without having really loved anyone, and now that he was married, and possessed both a house and a wife of his own, his heart overflowed with love for both. He had, it is true, acquired also a brother-in-law, but Jim did not inspire him with much affection. Jim was the fly in his cup of happiness, chiefly because he exacted of Jewel so much attention and caused her so much anxiety.

Silly Jim might have done a hundred useful things on the farm, if he could have been kept to his work; but if he was set a task, he began to execute it eagerly, then tired, and deserted it. Jim tried Tom's temper. He could not believe that the poor lad was not responsible for his actions; he believed that Jewel spoiled him by allowing him to have his own way, by not being stern with him, and forcing him to adhere to his work till it was done. Tom had, without knowing it, a strong sense of the beautiful, and Jim was so ugly, so untidy and misshapen, that his appearance was offensive to the eye. Tom came to dislike the boy, and he had some difficulty in concealing his aversion from the sharp eyes of his wife. But though he tried to hide his distaste, and believed he had effectually covered it, Jewel perceived it. It distressed her; it disappointed her. Her first duty was to Jim, who had no one else in the world to care for him; and, she argued, she had given Tom fair warning, when he had asked her to take him, that she would not go to him without her helpless brother. It was a pity—Jim was the spring of trouble that began to cloud—only a little, but still a little—the clear current of the life and love of Tom and Jule.

Christmas was at hand—the first Christmas since Tom had taken Jule, the first anniversary of their wedding day.

"Oh!" thought Tom, "if some excuse or contrivance could be got to send that fool, Jim, out of the way, what a happy Christmas we should spend! I'll get him a mask and send him a-mumming."

Italian, 15th century. Angel Appearing to the Shepherds

But—"Tom," said Jewel, "we're bound to have" (*i.e.*, we must have) "a Christmas-tree."

"Tree! Why!—there are no bairns, lass."

"But there is Jim; it will give him so much pleasure. And then, lad, I want to find some'ut as'll keep him at home and away from the mummers, and the carrolers, and the ale and spirit drinking—poor bairn, poor bairn! Thee'll get me a tree, wilt thou not?"

Tom shrugged his shoulders, and the corners of his mouth twitched; but he said nothing.

"Thou doesn't grudge me a tree?" asked Jewel.

"I grudge thee anything!" he exclaimed. "Nay, I grudge thee naught. Why, lass, if thou'd a fancy for Tuddlams without me, thou should have it, and welcome."

"I don't want Tuddlams without thee. Tuddlams and thee goes farrantly (comfortably) well together. But to go back to Jim. It is a pity that the beck is being dammed up to make a reservoir for the towns below—it brings a parcel of navvies and rough chaps up near us, and they draw Jim to them, what with his curiosity to see what they are doing, and what with the fiddling, in which they encourage Jim."

"Oh, Jim, Jim—always Jim!" said Tom impatiently. "Thou hast no thoughts for nobody or nothing, but only Jim."

"And why shouldn't I? He's my brother, and a poor silly, misshaped creature, with no will to earn his living, and no looks that nobody should like him. If I didn't care for him, who would? He's my own flesh and blood; and if there be ony truth that man and wife are one flesh, then he's now just as much thine as mine to fend for. I told thee—I never concealed it one moment—that he who took me, took Jim, too."

She was hot. A fire sparkled in her eyes, and her hand trembled as she scoured a kettle.

"I didn't mean offence," said Tom.

'Then go out and get the Christmas-tree."

"Yes—for Jim."

III

Tom went out and fetched first his pick, then his shovel.
There was a small plantation behind the house—a belt of larch,
spruce, and Scotch pines, that had been put in by Uncle Nick
a few years before his death. They had not made much growth,
for the situation was cold; still, they were sturdy, green trees,
well rooted. Several could be spared, as they had spread and
incommoded one another. The larch had shed its leaves, the
Scotch boughs turned up, clad in spines all round, but the spruce
would serve the required purpose.

Snow had fallen, and had to be shovelled away, but the
ground was not frozen. Tom chose a tree, and then began to
clear the snow from about it, Tom was not only fond of, he
was proud of Jewel. He wondered at her cleverness. She fitted
into the house as if the house had been made for her, like a
set of clothes. She fell into the duties as if they had been familiar
to her from infancy; she seemed to know by instinct what should
be done in a farmhouse—she who had lived in a cottage in a
row all her girlhood! But, love and admire her as he did, he could
not love Jim; and he felt jealous of the poor idiot because the
boy occupied so large a share in the thoughts and affections of
his wife. Men are said to be most selfish animals, and Tom
was no exception; he was very selfish in this one particular: he
wanted his wife to think, and consider, and work for himself
alone. He was not a man to analyse his feelings, and he was
therefore supremely unconscious that he was jealous. The boy
annoyed him—he disliked him; but he did not attempt to
account for his repugnance.

"Jule wants the tree for Jim. Shoo" (she) "never for a
moment thought I might like it. I never had a Christmas-tree in
my life—no, never. Father wasn't the man for that. He never
thought of one. Why shouldn't I have my tree? I suppose I'm
to find the tree, and the trouble, and the candles, and the gim-
cracks, and the gilt nuts and apples for that Jim. And I know

that Jule is knitting him a muffle for his throat, and warm gloves, and stockings, and shoo hasn't a thought for my comforts no more than for my pleasures. Why should not Jule think that I might like a tree? 'Tisn't the tree itsen," said Tom, impatiently driving the pick into the ground—" 'tis the consideration. Why, if Jule were to light a tallow-candle-end in the lantern, and say it was done for me, I'd kiss her and be pleased. And now, here I be digging and pulling up a tree only for Jim. She said it—'only for Jim.' 'Tis unhuman."

He was unjust; but is not jealousy always unjust? Does it not always jaundice the eyes that they see falsely, black spots dancing in clear air, and lines crooked that are perfectly straight?

Was it possible that Jewel could for a moment entertain the thought that her husband, a man standing six feet, with hair on his face with a gruff voice, aged twenty-four, very nearly a quarter of a century old, a landed proprietor, could fret for a Christmas-tree? If he had considered the matter impartially, he would have perceived that he was making himself ridiculous. He vented his ill-humour on the roots of the spruce; he hacked through them. "Of course," he said, "I'm expected to spoil one of my beautifullest trees—just for Jim!" Then, after another peevish dig at the roots, he growled, "But I won't. Why should I spoil my tree, that Uncle Nick planted, just for that lout? I'll dig all round it, and have it up roots and all, and plant it again when Jule has done with it. I won't have even a spruce spoiled for Jim. He ain't worth it; a fiddling idiot!"

Just as he had got the tree up—a pretty, well-built tree about three feet six inches high—he heard a cough behind him, and turning, saw Matthew by the hedge.

"Aught fresh, old man?" asked Tom.

"Over-fresh," answered Matthew, laconically.

"What do you mean? Am I wanted?"

"Eh! I should just think you were."

"What has happened?"

"Fine laikes wi' Jim."

"What has Jim done now?"

"There's nort like a fellow seeing the unpleasant through his own eyes."

Tom threw down his pick and shovel, and, grasping the little fir-tree just above the root, walked to the house, after signing to the man to bring in the tools after him.

As he came in at the back door, and stood holding the same, knocking the snow off his boots, he heard voices in the front kitchen or "house."

Carrying the tree, he pushed through the door, and saw a couple of men standing in the room, broadshouldered fellows, and Silly Jim cast at their feet. Tom looked first at the men, then at his wife for an explanation. Jewel was sobbing.

The case was not one that needed much explanation. Jim had been down to the reservoir, had fiddled to the navvies there employed, had been treated by them to gin and water, and had been made tipsy.

The men had brought him up, and they looked at Jewel and Tom with a pleased and also expectant expression. Their consciences told them they had done a good thing in bringing Jim home, and said no word of reproach to them for having brought him to a condition in which he was unable, without assistance, to reach his home. The glory of a contented, approving conscience beamed in their rough faces. A good deed always deserves, and almost demands, a reward, and the two navvies in their warmth of self-satisfaction waited for the feel of money in their palms and the offer of brandy neat, or, at least, ale and cake, as refreshment after their exertions.

Tom took in the situation at a glance. Of course he must reward the men, though little deserving. He signed to Jewel to bring out the cake and the "haver-bread" (oat scones), and to put butter on the table, whilst he filled a jug with beer.

"Sit you down," he said sulkily to the men. "There's a shilling a-piece for you, and it is the last I'll spend in this way. The lad would not be drunk unless you'd given him the liquor. I'll teach him not to go near you again."

He said no more till the men had done eating. The haver-bread is oatcake thin as biscuit, baked on a griddle, and hung up on strings in the ceiling. The men ate heartily, voraciously; bread, cake, and butter flew, and they drank the ale as though they had drunk nothing for twenty-four hours and had fed on herrings and salt pork. Then they drew their hands across their lips, and each, thrusting his plate before him, said, "I'm full;" and one said condescendingly:

"I don't think, now, as I've iver enjoyed myself more, not even at a hanging."

Tom said nothing. He waited till the men were gone, then he called angrily to the boy:

"Get up!"

Jim was somewhat recovered; the jolting of the journey, and the time it had taken, had combined to somewhat sober him, and he obeyed. He had a great mouth, like that of a fish, and he grinned at Tom; but the grin died away as he saw the expression on Tom's face, and the boy had sufficient mother-wit to understand what that meant. He began to whimper.

"Come, Jim, get to bed," said his sister, going up to him. She was engaged clearing away the remains of the men's meal. "Do, to please your Jule."

"Give me a drink first," pleaded Jim.

Tom said roughly, "Stand up!" and he caught the lad by the collar of his coat and pulled him to his feet. Jewel was back in the kitchen.

"Jim," said Tom, "I won't allow these goings on. Thou'rt not going to bring discredit on my house, and unhappiness on thy sister, and stir me to anger, not if I can help it. If thou doesn't learn mastery over thysen, I must teach it thee. Look here, Jim. Dost thou see this tree? 'Tis a Christmas tree Jule made me go and dig up for thee. A Christmas tree hung with apples and nuts is for good chaps, and not for bad. It's not for them that bemean themselves, and make beasts o' themselves, as thou hast a' been doing. I don't wish to give thee a hiding, lad, but I must, to teach thee what thou must not do. And so—I'll make thee taste o' this tree o' knowledge of good and evil, wrong way on, sour end, afore Christmas comes."

And with that he brought the Christmas tree whishing, slashing, crackling, about the boy's back. It did not hurt him. It could not hurt him. Tom knew that very well. It made much noise, and there was a great deal of it, but it could not raise a welt in his skin anywhere. Tom did not design to hurt him, only to frighten him, as a parent chastises his young child with a newspaper. But the shrieks that Jim uttered, the leaps, the writhings he made, would have led anyone to suppose he was being scourged with scorpions.

Jewel rushed from the back kitchen into the room, and stood for a moment paralysed with horror; then, with a cry of wrath, she rushed on her husband, her cheeks flaming, her eyes flaring, and wrenched her brother out of his hand. She trod on the end of the spruce, and, clutching it, tore the root away from his grasp.

"How dare you!" she gasped.

Jim staggered back, howling and sobbing.

"How dare you—you coward! you base, mean coward!" she cried, facing her husband, without a spark of love in her face, without a token of relenting in her tone. Her blood boiled, and every scrap of control she had over her tongue was lost. She was like a tigress defending her cub.

"Jule," said Tom, "be reasonable. Jim must be punished if he does wrong."

"But not by you!" gasped Jule. "Not by you. Is this what I and my poor brother are to expect in your house?"

"I have not hurt him."

"You have. Do not add a lie to your wrong. Cruel and false— that is what you are! I curse the day that ever I came under your roof! I curse the day that ever I saw your face—if this is what is in store for me and Jim. Come to me, Jim; come to your sister.

She will take care of you, and defend you with her arms against brutal men. And—I tell you this, Tom; if ever you dare—you dare —you dare"—she quivered with rage, she panted for breath, she stamped her foot—"if ever you dare lay hands on my own poor afflicted Jim again, I'll carry him in my arms, and run away, and leave you forever. Thank God, I have hands, and can earn my living. It may be only six shillings a week, but I'd rather live on crusts with Jim, and drink water, and toil eight, or nine, or ten hours a day than stay here to be slavedriven by you—you, a strong man, beating a defenceless, helpless innocent!"

Tom was speechless with astonishment. In a moment his loving, his true Jule was converted into a savage, hostile virago.

To reason with her was impossible. She was not in a condition to listen to reason. She was not herself; she was as one possessed.

"Jule," said Tom, looking sadly at the Christmas-tree that lay on the floor, "if I have done wrong, I am sorry; but I think I am not to blame."

"No," said she scornfully; "men will never allow they're to blame. It is we—we feeble lasses—who're in the wrong."

He went up to her.

"Jewel, I do not understand thee."

"I am sorry I have not spoken plain.

She threw herself into a chair, and folded her arms.

"Jewel, forgive and forget. Give me thy hand, lass. This be Christmas eve, when there should be 'peace on earth and good-will among men,' most of all in a home between man and wife."

"No," she said; "there shall be no peace between us, no good-will."

Then he turned, opened the door, and went out.

I V

Tom a' Tuddlams left the house. He walked away down the valley without any clear idea whither he was going or what he wanted to do. He left the house because he could not breathe in it; he could not endure it, whilst his Jewel was in this new

346

and wondrous mood. He had been married for one year, a year less a day, and had been perfectly happy—so happy that he had sometimes felt that he could not bear an accession to his happiness. Jim, as already said, had been the fly in it; but a small fly, only a gnat floating in a very brimming cup. And now that gnat had tilted the goblet and poured forth all its contents! Tom had been so happy that he now felt his disappointment, his misery with double poignancy.

How cruel, how wicked, how unjust Jewel had been! He had not hurt that odious, yelping idiot, he had not meant to hurt, only to scare him. He had chastised him for his good— to deter him from again drinking with the navvies and becoming drunk. Jewel was spoiling the boy; she remonstrated with him, but remonstrance was thrown away on him: he was not rational, he must be made to feel, like an ass or a dog, when he did wrong. Jewel would, in the end, be the sufferer unless Jim were corrected and disciplined.

He walked fast, his feet stamped in the snow, he set them so hardly, firmly, as he trampled his way down the valley. The simmering wrath in his heart rose and boiled over. Let her go! He clenched his hands and teeth. Let her go! How dare she insult him by such words as to call him a coward and a liar! A coward —he a coward! he laughed out. He knew his own heart, his strength of purpose. He, a liar! He, who would be torn to pieces rather than speak a word that was not true! Tom stood still: he was trembling with emotion—with wrath. His knees smote together. He was thinking how he would deal with the man who spoke to him as his wife had spoken. But there was the terrible rankle of the words: he could not resent them, for they were spoken *by his wife*. Those dear lips he had so often kissed, that heart in which he thought he reigned sole and altogether— they had poured forth the wicked words which entered into him as a searching knife cutting his heart.

He came to the reservoir, then to the dam; at that point there was a tavern recently built, and opened for the entertainment

347

first of the navvies engaged on the works, and then was to serve for the refreshment of the visitors who came to fish and boat in the reservoir, or Scalefell lake, as it was called.

When Tom came opposite the door of the tavern, he halted. A strong impulse came on him to go in, sit with the navvies there, drink, smoke, laugh, sing songs, and tell tales, and forget his misery. He was conscious of his utter loneliness. He had shown himself indifferent to the society of the neighbours, because he was perfectly satisfied with that of Jewel; and now that Jewel had turned on him, and stung him, he was alone, he had no friend. But the impulse to enter and drown his grief was but momentary. He was angry with Jim for going there, he had chastised him for drinking, and should he do the very thing he had objected to in the idiot?

He shook his head and walked on.

"Yes," he said, "there is some excuse for the fool, but none for the sane man!"

And then, strangely, the wheel of his mind went round and his mood altered. He had been accustomed to his father's bad humours, had made allowances for them, and had schooled himself to patience under them; and now the old discipline began to tell on him, and his wrath faded away. What gave his mind the turn were those words he used about Jim, as he went past the tavern. He began to think of Jim, and he admitted to himself that Jim was not seriously to blame. Then he thought how that Jewel had not been in the room when he laid hold of the boy and struck him with the Christmas-tree. Jim had howled ear-piercingly. Jewel came in, frightened by the cry, and thought her brother had been more hurt than he really was. After all, it was natural that she should take the side of her brother—that she should defend the weak and suffering. What would he have had? asked Tom of himself. Would he have had Jewel stand coldly by and tell him how many cuts the lad was to receive? No, that would be unlike Jewel. No, by ginger! he would not have endured that in Jewel! Why, that would have been worse than her firing up at his laying his hand on the boy. There was something grand, womanly, in Jewel defending Jim—Jim, who had no other protector in the world but she. There was really something noble in the way in which she threw in her lot with the poor, fond creature; she was ready—she said it—rather than that he should be maltreated, to leave her comfortable, beautiful home, and trudge back to a factory town, and work again in a worsted mill and earn her six shillings a week, which she would freely divide with her brother. Give up Tuddlams! Tom considered. Really, Jewel was a wonderful woman; he had never hitherto realised her greatness of soul.

And then Tom remembered his own train of thought as he dug up the tree, how jealous he had been of the poor idiot, how absurdly vexed he had been because the tree was destined for Jim and not for himself. "Why, Lor!" said Tom, standing still; "all the trees in the plantation are mine. Tuddlams is mine, so are the fields and the pastures, so are the sheep and the cow, and the gray mare. Everything is mine. Shoo couldn't give me what was my own! Shoo simply axed me to give that darned boy one out of the hundred or two hundred, or may be five hundred, trees in my plantation, and I begrudged it him! Gor! what a chap made up of selfishness I be!"

But, although Tom a' Tuddlams thus debated with himself, and extenuated Jewel's fault, and stood her advocate against his outraged feelings, he only half convinced himself that she was in the right and he in the wrong. He threw the cloak of forgetfulness over her bitter words. Yet they worked their way through, scratched and bit and tore their way through, and were again before him in all their unkindness and injustice.

"I suppose there was wrong o' both sides," said Tom uneasily. "I'm sure there must ha' been wrong on mine." He had had no experience of women's anger, of female temper, and he did not know how long the storm at home would last; whether, when he went home, he would find Jewel subdued with self-consciousness, in tears, and ready to kiss and make up the breach, or whether the evil temper were still tossing and threatening, possessing and unexpelled.

"There can be no harm in my bringing her summat," he said. "It is Christmas eve, and I'll give her a Christmas present, and —by George I will!—I'll get a packet of yellow, and green, and red, and blue tapers for the tree. Shoo'll be fain at that, and ready with her forgiveness."

He was now in the village of Kebroyd. When I call it a village, I do it a dishonour; it was one of those hobbledehoy villages that are almost towns and yet not quite towns. There was no gas in the streets.

As Tom entered Kebroyd he saw a cluster of men and women about a cottage, and beside the door, on a table, stood a man haranguing.

"A political lecturer, or a teetotal or a ranter chap," said Tom; but on nearer approach he heard:—

"Going, dirt cheap! What! for this beautiful looking-glass no higher bid than one shilling? I'll tell you what it is, the gentlemen don't want to look at their faces, and so they won't bid, and as for the ladies, they are provided already, and think the most beautiful of mirrors are the eyes of their admiring husbands and lovers. But, nevertheless, I urge you not to be shy of making a bid. Why, this looking-glass cost 15s. 6d., if it cost a penny, when it was new. Real mahogany, and not a scratch, and —see the size of the glass. It is too ridiculous, only one shilling. Thank you, marm, eighteenpence. Are we to strike it down to you, marm, for that absurd sum? Two shillings. This gentleman with a red tie" (he was a navvy) "has bid another sixpence that he may be able to tie a stylish bow every day when he goes out courting."

An auction was in progress. The occupants of No. 14 Reservoir Road had failed, and were leaving, and their furniture was being sold before the house.

"I daresay," proceeded the auctioneer, "many of you ladies have been disappointed in your looking-glasses. The knobs on

which they swing have a tendency to come off, and the screw
gets loose, and when you want to look at your beautiful hair
and eyes, then the mirror is swinging so that it shows nothing
but your toes. Now I beg you all to observe how—thank you,
marm, half-a-crown—how, I was going to say, how easily this
turns on its pivots, and how it always stands at the angle at
which you want it. Three shillings, yes—going for three shillings.
Now, let me see, this is Christmas eve; I'm sure for certain there
are some of you who want to make a Christmas present to your
wives or sweethearts. There's nothing a woman likes better than
a looking-glass. It is meat and drink to her. Let us suppose you've
had a domestic breeze or a lover's quarrel. Do you want to make
it up? To lay the storm? Buy the looking-glass, and present the
lady with it; and you will see the waves go down and become
smooth as though oil were poured on 'em. Eh? sir!"

"Three and six."

"Three and six you are, sir. I beg pardon, is it Tom a'
Tuddlams? Tom a' Tuddlams it is. Tom a' Tuddlams has bid
three and six for a mirror for Jewel a' Nort a' Nowheer, and a
more beautiful and smiling and sweet face than hers to look
into it is not to be seen. Or, do I stand corrected? If any gentleman thinks he knows a beautifuller one, let him bid four shillings,
or forever hold his silence."

"Four shillings".

"Right—four shillings; now, sir?"

"Four and six," said Tom.

"Five shillings."

"Five and six," said Tom.

And at five and six the mahogany swinging looking-glass was
struck down to him.

Tom went on into the village and visited the grocer's shop,
where he purchased some coloured tapers for the tree, and nuts
and oranges, and sweetstuff; and also some little tin or lead
ornaments to hang on the tree and make it glitter.

Thus supplied, with his pockets stuffed, he put a bit of cord around the mirror, fastened it to his large pocket-handkerchief, where it passed over the wood, to prevent chafing, and so slung the great looking-glass across his back, and trudged up the glen homewards to Tuddlams.

The trouble was gone from his mind now, the weight from his heart. Now he was bringing home to Jewel a beautiful Christmas present, which would delight her, and prove to her that he bore no ill-will for the cruel words she had launched at him.

He chuckled as he strode along. He thought how pleased she would be. He pictured her waiting impatiently for him, longing to make up the little quarrel, of her flying to his arms and clinging to him, and cuddling into his breast with sobs of penitence and of love, as he opened the door when he came in.

He was rudely undeceived.

As he came expectantly into the house, Jewel started up—

"Tom! there! this comes of your cruelty! Jim is run away and we cannot find him. What have you got there? A looking-glass! What folly and waste of money! Put it down and run—see if you can find where Jim is."

V

Yes, Jim had run away, and taken his fiddle with him. At first Jewel had not thought much of his disappearance. She had sent old Matthew down to the reservoir; but Jim had not gone in that direction. Night had fallen and the boy was not returned.

There was nothing for it but to search for him. He could not be left straying about the fells all night. He would be dead before morning.

"You must go after him," said Jewel. "Put on a great-coat and take a lantern—Jim must be found."

"You do not know in which direction he has gone?"

"Matthew said he saw footprints in the snow going towards Arncliff."

Tom saw that it was necessary that Jim should be pursued.

Matthew was too old to do that. He must go after the boy himself.

"The night will be bad; there's a bank of black cloud over Houghfell full of snow, ready to shake out its feathers."

"Then, make haste," urged Jewel. "If the snow comes on thou'lt not be able to trace him."

She took a shepherd's pouch and put into it a flask of brandy, a box of lucifers, and a second candle.

"If he is lost," said Jewel, "I will never forgive thee. Unless thou had ill-treated him, he'd never have run away."

Tom heaved a sigh—he was disappointed; still he made an excuse for Jewel. She was alarmed for the safety of her brother. His heart was heavy when he went forth in the night with the lantern in quest of the missing lad.

The tracks noticed by Matthew as diverging from the road were a little way down near a stone called the "Loaf," from a fancied resemblance to one.

Matthew accompanied him thus far. "I thowt," said the old man, "he'd a' gone after liquor and fire, and not up into the fells, which shows he's more of a fool than I believed."

The old man offered to accompany his master in the search, but Tom declined his assistance. "In the dark one pair of eyes are as good as two," he said. Then holding the lantern to the snow, he followed the traces. "Mind the pot-hoyles!" shouted Matthew. The Yorkshire moors are dangerous, in parts, to traverse by one unacquainted with them, and even dangerous to go over by one who knows them, in the dark, for in addition to the usual risks of loss of way, there is the special peril of falling into the so-called "pot-holes." These are natural shafts descending into the bowels of the mountains, often of great depth, and all gaping with assurance of certain death to anyone who should incautiously fall into their treacherous jaws.

The mountains are built up of limestone, and in the limestone are numerous caverns running horizontally, through which, at one time, streams were discharged. But all the caverns are not

353

horizontal; some are vertical, caused by the fall of the crust above a subterranean vault, but the water has worked its way to a lower level, and now runs out at a considerable depth beneath the deserted and dry channel, or else the shaft has been worked through some fault in the limestone by a descending stream, and it precipitates itself into the well that engulfs it and conceals its further course.

If Jewel had but greeted him lovingly, put her arms about his neck, and entreated him, as he loved her, to go in search of her brother, Tom would have started on his quest with alacrity and a hopeful heart; but her reception had been chilling. She had taken no notice of his looking-glass, as she had been too much engrossed in her anxiety, and her ill-humour had not spent itself: she charged her husband with having driven the poor fool forth—perhaps to his death.

If Jim were to die, to fall into a pot-hole, to sink in the snow, Tom feared that Jewel would never forgive him—that it would totally destroy his married happiness. To escape such a contingency, it was necessary for him to find Jim, and this urged him on as much as his desire to help the unfortunate, half-witted creature.

Jim's course had been erratic. He had gone along without any notion whither he would direct his steps. His traces led in a zigzag course, now up the hill then at a slant to the north, then they turned downwards, to where there were rocks, among which Tom lost them.

He was obliged to search long before he could pick up the trace again. He looked up at the sky. The clouds were black above, but then his eyes were dazzled with the glare of the lantern on the snow, and he could not tell whether they had spread and were about to discharge their burden.

He stood still and shouted. He waited; he received no answer. He shouted again and again in vain. Then he went on, bent, holding the lantern to the snow, following the course of the steps. Suddenly he stared and shrank aside. There was a broad, black, snowless disc near at hand. He held up his lantern over his head. It was a pot—he believed, but dared not approach nearer. The traces of the boy led along the verge. A foot to the right would have precipitated him down the abyss.

"There is a providence over bairns and fools," said Tom. "If God were not bound" (going) "to save him he'd have gone down there. But—wherever can I be?" When he had passed the dangerous spot he stood still to consider. He was out of his reckoning altogether. He had not the smallest notion where he was. He had gone on, looking intently at the traces, without considering whither they led; and, indeed, the night had become so dark that he might have lost himself soon had he not been thus preoccupied. "Let me see," said Tom, "there's Hull Pot, and there's the Ox Hole, and there's Scale Pot, and the Boggarts'. Well—whichever of all these was it that I've gone by?"

He went on, shaking his head.

"I'm flayed" (afraid) "I've lost mysen," said he.

"There'll be nowt for it but when I've found him we must come back the same way."

He considered.

"I must be certain not to go down the pot-hole with him here." He took out a red pocket-handkerchief and threw it down on the snow. "There, when I come to that, I'll remember to walk more cautiously, because we'll be close to the pot."

Again he stopped and walked on; and now saw flakes of snow sail lightly as eider-down into the flare of the lamp. First a solitary flake, very large; then several; and, after a minute or two, the snow came down fast and thick.

"Now I'm beat," said Tom. "In a varra few moments all the foot-taps will be covered over, and how shall I find my way on after Jim, or, missing him, find my way back? That was a bad hour for me when I dug up the Christmas-tree; if I hadn't had the tree I shouldn't, maybe, have whacked him with it. And now we shall both be lost on the fells all along of it. However, it is no use considering; I must go on after the lad while I can mark where he's set his foot."

There was little or no wind. In the still, dark night the flakes came down thickly; they came into the depressions made in the old snow, blurred their edge, and began to choke them up. Fortunately, the boy had dragged his feet heavily, as if weary; and so had drawn a furrow; and this furrow was traceable for a while. It went in the same random doubling, zigzag, purposeless way as before. Where a dark rock had appeared, the boy had made for it in the dusk; and then had turned away from it again, finding it to be only a rock affording no shelter.

The way became steep, steeper; a sharp, scrambling ascent—to what could it lead? Then came a slip or shoot of snow where the boy had gone down; and below a trampled mass, where he had rolled about, struggled up, and at length gone on again. Whither? Tom hunted about and could not find. There was a tract of rubble on which no footprints could be distinguished, and what snow lay on it was dotted on the lumps of stone.

What was Tom to do? He began to be uneasy about himself as well as Jim. He had been walking a long time; how long he could not tell—he had lost the count of time. He had gone a long way; how far he could not tell—the direction had changed so often. He might have crossed the neck between Scale and Hough fells and be in Lancashire, or he might be near his home; he could not tell. He put the lantern behind him, and covered his brow with his hand, and looked through the night and falling snow to see if he could distinguish anywhere a light. If he saw a light he would make for it—it might be his home; if not it did not matter—he would ask for help, and a party would scour the moor for the poor lost boy.

Not a light could he see. Had there been an illumined window a mile away he could not have seen it, for the snow thickly descending formed an impenetrable veil.

"Blow that Christmas tree—that's done it!" said Tom, and suddenly turned. He heard something far above him—a shrill strain. In his sudden turn he struck the lantern with the lappel of his coat; it went over and bounded down the steep—for a moment as a flying rocket, and then was dark.

"Here's a worse go than all!" groaned Tom. "Now I'm without lantern, and whativer in the world shall I do?"

Then, again, above him, he heard the same weird, shrill sounds—the strain:

"Christian, awake! salute the happy morn,
Whereon the Saviour of the world was born."

"That's Jim!" shouted Tom; "and like his mad ways: fiddling in a winter night—in the snow—lost."

He resumed the scramble, guided by the sound, and soon found himself against the face of a rock. Still he could hear the notes of the violin more now to his left, and he groped his way slowly, cautiously along, now almost sliding down or falling over a projecting stone, till his hand pressed against nothing, and here the strains sounded so articulate and loud that Tom was sure he was close to the boy.

"Jim!" he called, "are you under shelter?"

"Eh, be that thee, Tom?"

"Yes—come after thee. Where art thou?"

"In a sort of a hoyle."

"A cave?"

Tom felt with his hands and feet, then he groped his way forward; the boy had ceased fiddling.

"Go on playing, Jim; I can see nowt."

Again the instrument twanged.

"It is a cave thou art in. Is it large?"

"I dun' know."

Tom put his hand in the pouch and produced the candle and the match box. He struck a light and kindled the tallow candle. He was obliged to hold his hand over the flame, for there was enough air stirring to blow it out if unprotected, and thus imperfectly he reconnoitred the place.

357

Jim had taken refuge in a small cave in the face of a limestone scar—a cave rounded and smoothed with water, but dry. It ran some way in. As Tom looked about, he saw that there was dry fern and heather piled up against the side. Others before Jim had gone there and had used it for shelter—perhaps from sun or wind—and had collected material to make soft cushions.

"Why, Jim," said Tom, "we're in luck's way. I've a light and here's fuel. We'll have a fire, lad; I'm sure thou'rt cold."

"Eh! I am, Tom. I fiddled to keep my fingers warm."

Tom put a light to the bracken, but it was damp and would not readily burn. He swealed the tallow over it, and at length coaxed it into a blaze; then it flared up, and he looked around. The light and the smoke alarmed some birds or bats—he could not make out which—in the recesses. They fluttered and danced about, and then, as the smoke became thicker, rushed forth.

"It's boggarts!" said Jim; "that's why I played a hymn. I heard them before you came."

"They are gone now, Jim."

Tom considered what was to be done. There was a possibility of rescue, if he could keep the fire burning; it would guide searchers to the spot where he was. But, supposing no searchers came out or came that way, and Jim and he had to remain there till morning, they would need the fire to keep them from being frozen.

"Jim," said Tom; "we must have more heather. Where can we get it?"

"There's that near the mouth of the hoyle," said the boy. He crept out, and soon returned with some heather. There was plenty without that could be ripped up.

"That will do, Jim," said Tom; "anyhow, for a bit." Then he took the brandy flask and uncorked it. "Open thy mouth, lad." He gave him a draught of the spirit. "Now keep by the fire and warm thy limbs. I'll fend the fire."

Tom sat over the glow, raking it together, adding fresh fuel as required, and did not speak. He was now thinking of Jewel. He knew that she must be anxious about him, and in great distress. What would she do when she found that he did not return? She would send down to the reservoir for some of the navvies. Jewel had her wits about her, and would not lose her head in an emergency. "She don't lose her head," murmured Tom, "but she's got a way of losing her temper."

"I say"—Jim interrupted his train of thought— "thou won't take away my fiddle, wilt thou?"

"I—I?—no!"

"Jule said thou wouldst if I got fresh. That's why I runned away."

"That is why you ran away," repeated Tom. "Not because I beat thee?"

"No," the boy giggled; "thou didn't hurt much. But I hollered and Jule came up. Thou won't take away my fiddle?"

"No—certainly no."

The boy was satisfied, and said no more.

Then again Tom sank into a train of thought. So Jewel had been scolding and threatening Jim; and it was her doing that he had taken flight.

But this consideration did not occupy him long. He was relieved by it. It would simplify the reconciliation. He was cold, very cold, for the frosty, snowy air breathed in from the entrance. The fire was a poor affair. He must husband his material, burning a little dry heather along with some of the wet and fresh, so that there issued from his fire more smoke than flame. Still, he must be thankful to have any fire. Occasionally he put on some bracken to produce a flare, in the hopes of attracting attention. The smouldering damp heather did not emit much light. Then he went to the entrance of the cave and looked out. The snow was not falling as thickly. In half an hour it might cease altogether, and then through the darkness he would be able to see lights. That would be a comfort; though he could not venture to leave where he was till the day dawned. Lights at night are treacherous. They may be very far off, and gulfs and impassable rivers may intervene.

Tom came back to the fire, Jim had sunk beside it, and was asleep. The flicker of the fire was on his pale face. Tom leaned over to observe it. Poor boy, he was to be pitied, not blamed. As Tom looked, he saw that the upper portion of the lad's face was very like Jule's—the same forehead and delicately-drawn, gold-brown eyebrows. What long lashes Jim had! In his sleep the feebleness was effaced from his countenance, and there was a delicacy in the features, and even a beauty, which was not perceived when he was awake. "How like Jewel! How like Jewel!" said Tom, and his heart grew soft and warm and loving within him towards the poor boy.

"He'll take cold. He looks deadly white," said Tom, and he pulled off his great-coat and laid it over the sleeper. "Poor Jim! I wish I'd noticed before he hadn't his overcoat."

And, as he drew off his warm garment, he noticed by a flicker of the fire a long amber thread—long, a yard long—caught in the rough cloth.

"One of Jule's hairs," he said, and took it and twined it round his finger, and kissed it and smiled, and held it to the light, and kissed it again. "Dear Jule! dear Jule!"

VI

A shout! Tom started from his reverie, threw on a handful of dry fern-leaves, and ran to the entrance.

Men with lanterns were below, apparently a long way down, and they called, and he replied. Then Tom ran back into the cave and roused Jim, who with difficulty rallied his scattered dream-laden wits; and Tom noticed that when he opened his eyes and great mouth, at once all likeness to Jewel disappeared. He was again ugly and loutish. But Tom had a pity for him, and a love he had not felt before. He had felt what it was to have to care for a poor, helpless creature; and he had seen in the dull face the underlying likeness to her who was dearest to him in the world.

He helped the boy to his feet.

"What is't, Tom? Thou'rt not going to take away my fiddle?"

"They are come," said Tom eagerly. "Come along; they are here."

"They—they'll leave me my fiddle? I won't go unless thou swears to me that I shall keep it."

The clouds of sleep and of suspicion were not off the boy's brain, and Tom had to be patient with him.

Presently, up the steep ascent came some of the searchers, scrambling.

"Whatever brought you up here?" they asked.

"I do not know where I am."

"In Arncliff."

What! in the great grey crags above his own house? Tom was amazed. He had wandered strangely. He could be down at home now in ten minutes. It took twenty to reach Arncliff from his door, but half the time to descend.

"There comes the moon," said one of the men. As he spoke the disc of the moon rose above Sowton down into a space of clear sky, painting white and ghostly the fringe of snow-cloud that hung across the sky from north to south. The cold light flared over the moors deadly white, palled in snow.

Below, the lights of those who had come out in quest of Tom and Jim seemed, by contrast, not yellow, but orange. Below, beyond was something—no, someone. Surely not Jewel!

It was Jewel, indeed—come forth in the track of the men who were seeking her husband and brother. When Tom saw her he flung out his arms and away he went down the steep descent, plunging through the snow, shouting, sliding, recovering his balance, and then bounding over a snow-capped stone.

Presently one of the navvies nudged his fellow and said:

361

"It's not Jule a' Nort, but Jule a' Tom's, and Tom a' Jule's: they seems to belong to each other and to none beside."

"If they are so glad to see each other again," said the man addressed, "and we've had the finding and the bringing together, we shall be tipped handsome for our trouble, and be given to drink."

"Eh! to be sure," said Tom, who overheard the remark, made purposely as an aside to be overheard. "Drink and meat and cheese you shall have. 'Tis Christmas eve. Peace on earth and good-will, and the making-up of quarrels and the patching of strife, and the sowing again of love in the field where weeds had sprung up and nigh choked the corn."

Then the whole party went to the farm, where a blazing fire filled the "house" with warmth and light and laughter. The white plastered walls, the ceiling, the floor, flushed as with pleasure at the return of the master; and the crickets were shrilling behind the jambs and back of the great fireplace, as if they also were rejoicing that he was not lost on the wold, but come home again. On the table were the trifles Tom had bought for the Christmas-tree; sparkling tin ornaments that twinkled gleefully, and oranges that asked to be eaten, and nuts that cried out to be cracked, and the great Yule candle, which every grocer in Yorkshire sends on Christmas eve to his customers, expecting to be lighted. And, more, beside the fire was a great pan of fermity—wheat and currants mixed with water and milk, and stewed—ready to be eaten, for on Christmas eve every Yorkshire Christian makes his supper off fermity. Now was the time for Jewel to show her powers, and she showed them, and the long deal table was rapidly spread and laden, the bowl of fermity was placed smoking on it; cheese, and "cake" (bread) and butter, and oat-scones, cold beef, smoking potatoes, and jugs of home-brewed ale—everything that was needful to furnish a good Christmas eve supper was ready to be attacked in a very short while, Jewel getting all ready whilst the men and Jim and Tom crowded about the fire to thaw themselves, and melt off their boots and breeches and coats the snow that still clung.

Then Jewel set the Yule candle on a brass candlestick, and planted it in the midst of the table, and bade—

"Come, lads, you as have a mind to 't, fall to."

Not one was indisposed to do so, not even those two who had previously partaken of Jewel's hospitality. Their appetites had not been satisfied—only stimulated, and they ate now as lustily, as omnivorously, and as long as the rest. Verily, a navvy is like a caterpillar, that eats its own weight in four and twenty hours.

When supper was over, and every bowl and plate and dish had been cleared, the wonder was that bowl and plate and dish had not been eaten as well, with the steel two-pronged fork and the knife to boot, as pickle and Yorkshire relish to the rest; and the cauldron, and the saucepans, and the stone ale-jars on top of the rest as stomachics and digestive pills, and the red-hot coals off the hearth after them again, as stimulants to torpid livers. Then the men groaned, and thrust back from the table, and Tom said:—

"Let's all draw about t' fire, and have some hot brandy and water, and a bit of fun."

The suggestion of the master of Tuddlams was complied with, with equal alacrity to that displayed when the call came to table from the mistress.

Then they lit their pipes and held their steaming glasses, and Tom said—

"To begin wi', lads:—

> " 'The King of Agripp
> Built a varra great ship,
> Ann' at the one end
> His sweet daughter did sit.
> If I had to tell her name,
> I shu'd be varra much t' blame.' "

"But thou'st told it for all, lad," shouted one of the navvies, Ben by name.

"How so?" asked another; "I didn't hear it."

"He has, though—i' t' third line. Her name were *Ann*. I can cap that, though:—

> " 'As I were going over London Bridge
> I saw a man stealing pots,
> And the pots were his own.' "

"Yes," said Weatherall, another man. "Thou'st told that too often, Ben. The pot-steals were his own, and he was putting the steals" (handles) "on the pots."

"Right," said Ben. "Black and breet, and runs without feet."

Then Jewel, looking into the circle by the fire, answered, as she carried the dish with the beef-bone away, "A flat-iron." She halted in the doorway to the back kitchen, and asked:—

> " 'A houseful, a hoyle' (hole) 'full,
> An' I can na' catch a bowlful.' "

Then said Tom, "It's t' same as I am blowing out betwixt my two lips now—reek" (smoke), and he sent forth a long spiral puff of tobacco smoke into the air above him.

"Come, tell me this," said Tom:

> " 'The King of Northumberland
> Sent the Queen of Cumberland
> A bottomless vessel to put flesh and blood in."

No one could divine the answer, so Tom sprang up, ran after Jewel, caught her round the waist, drew her into the circle before the fire, held out her hand on one of his, divided the rosy fingers, and pointed to the wedding-ring. "Do you see, lads? A ring o' gou'd. It's Christmas eve!" Then to Jim: "Strike up a dance, lad, and me and Jule shall dance in Christmas day."

The men cleared a space, thrust back the table; some jumped upon it, and seated themselves thereon. Ben caught up Jim and the stool together, and heaved him up on the table, where he could fiddle as from a gallery. The boy was in his element now. He struck up a waltz, and played first slowly, but gradually quickened his pace.

Jewel had hesitated, shrunk away at first; but the strong arm of Tom was about her, and his heart was beating against her shoulder. He put his chin on her head and drew it against his breast. She moved it away to utter a word of remonstrance, and looking up, her eyes met those of her husband, and such a flood of love streamed from them, that her heart gave a leap, she forgot her objection, rested her head where he had drawn it, and danced with him. The navvies clapped their hands, and sang or trumpeted through closed lips the air of the waltz, and kicked the table to the time.

Then Jim played "heel and toe," and Tom and Jewel danced that; and Ben on the table, who set up to be a wag and a clown, began to throw out his legs, heel and toe, as he sat, and to torture his body and face and arms into grotesque postures, and to emit absurd noises. Also Weatherall got the iron empty kettle, in which the hot water had been boiled for the grog, and put it between his knees, and hammered on it as if it were a gong or a drum.

Suddenly Jim changed the tune to a polka, and the two wheeled round faster and even faster. Jewel's face was on fire, her neckerchief had fallen, and as she danced she entangled it with her feet, and danced over it, and caught it in her shoe, and kicked away her shoe and the kerchief together. How well they danced! How they whirled and kept the tread! Her skirts flapped past the fire and made it blaze up with the sudden draught, then they were flung round the legs of Tom as he spun along. Her hair came loose behind, and she disengaged her hand to put it up; but down it came, and, as the amber tresses flew about with the firelight on them, the men jumped off the table and up from their stools, and came capering, dancing around them, catching the end of her locks, circling round the circling pair, and then—stopped short; for, from outside came the song of the carolers:—

"Christians, awake, salute the happy morn,
    Whereon the Saviour of the world was born."

Tuddlams was the last house they visited that night, and already the grey dawn was showing.

VII

"Well," said Jewel on Christmas day, "this is the first time that I've not been able to go to church at Christmas. I don't feel any other than a Jew or a heathen; and you know why I cannot go. I daresay there will be no blessing on the coming year, as I've not asked it this day."

"But, Jule," argued Tom, "why should you not go to church, if you wish, this evening?"

"This evening! Thank you—in the night and cold. I had enough of going out of a bitter winter night after you last night. No, thank you! I have not been able to go to church this morning, so I suppose I must be a heathen."

"But, Jule——"

"It is all your fault. I couldn't pray if I went to church after last night. I should shame to be seen by decent folk. What did you take me for—to make me dance, to pull me about before all those men? Do you think I married thee to practise to become one of them little figures that go round on a barrel-organ?"

"I thought thou liked it, Jule."

"I like it! Thou never asked me."

"Jule," said Tom, anxious to change the topic, "haven't thou looked in the pretty mirror I bought thee yesterday?"

"Mirror!" exclaimed Jewel. "You brought it here to insult me. You made me dance before all those men, til my kerchief came loose and fell off and then my shoe went away, and last of all, my hair came down, and there were all of them dancing and capering round about me, holding on to the ends of my hair. I never was so ashamed in my life! And you, my husband—you who ought to protect and care for your wife—you expose her to this shame." Jewel began to cry. Tom was alarmed. It was a bad sign when she began to address him with "you" instead of "thou."

"And when you've almost danced every rag off my back, you say, 'Go and look at thyself i' t' glass.'"

"I did not say that, Jule!"

"I saw thee look it in thy eyes. And all those men staring at me, and me with scarce a stitch o' clothes on."

"Jule, you had lost a shoe, that was all."

"And my kerchief."

"But that you only put on when you went out of doors after me."

"Do you call it naught having my hair all down, and the hair-pins sanding the house-floor?"

"Jule," said Tom, "I wish thou'd look in thy new glass I bought thee now, and thou'd see thy beauty gone; thy eyes aren't bright, thy cheeks are red, and thy lips——"

"Oh, I know I'm a fright in thy eyes. I never was much, except just for a week or two, and then thou wast ready to cast me aside. No, I will never, never look in that glass. Some day, when thou'st lost me, thou canst ask some other lass—some one with a pretty face, whose eyes are bright, and whose cheeks are lilies and roses, and whose lips are worth kissing and full o' smiles—thou canst ask her to look in it—I will not. Keep it for her."

"Thou art tired, poor lass," said Tom. "And because thou'rt tired, thy temper is ruffled."

"Of course I'm tired. How should I not be tired? First, I have to be rambling over the wolds and fells after thee, because thou can't bide at home."

"Eh! Jule! I went after Jim at thy bidding."

"That may be so; but what made Jim run away?"

"Thou didst flay" (frighten) "him with making him think I'd take away his fiddle."

"It was not that. It was because he was in dread for his life. Thou didst poise" (kick) "and beat the poor lad."

"You are unjust, Jule."

"I know I'm all that is bad in thine eyes. Other folk may think better of me. I wish I were dead! I wish I were dead! I'd like to cast myself into the reservoir, or down one of the pot-holes, to be out of my wretchedness and away from thee."

"From me, Jule?"

"Eh! I've had enough of thee, after last night, putting me to shame before all those men, after thou hadst beaten nigh to death my poor brother. Oh, that ever I married thee! That ever I did! I curse the day!"

"Jule! Dost thou mean this? Hast thou ceased to love me?"

"Long ago. I hate you."

He heaved a long sigh; stood thinking.

"Very well, Jule. I'll trouble thee no more."

He was gone.

VIII

Jewel dished up the roast beef, and saw that the plum-pudding was ready in the pot to be dished up when noon struck—the hour of the early dinner in the farmhouse, but Tom did not appear. She waited till half-past and then sat down with Jim and ate her Christmas dinner in gloom, and with a tear of vexation gathering in her eyes. When evening closed in, snow began to fall thickly.

"Now, Jim," said Jewel, "Tom brought in a beautiful tree yesterday, and nuts, and oranges, and candles; but we could not have the tree on Christmas eve, so let us amuse ourselves together with dressing it, that we may have it on the evening of Christmas; and, Jim, I've knitted six pairs of the most beauti-

ful warm socks for Tom, and he knows nowt about it, and will
be pleased when he finds that sort o' apple hanging for him on
t' tree."

But after the tree was made ready with all the beautiful con-
trivances provided for its adornment, Tom did not come. Jewel
went to the door, and looked out into the snow that fell in
blinding fleeces, large and fast.

"Wherever can he be?" she asked.

At dinner-time she was angry, because she thought he stayed
away to annoy her; now she became uneasy, thinking he was
staying away too long. Annoyance might be carried too far, well
—the night was bad, and to trudge home through the deep snow
would be a labour—up hill, too, for no doubt he had gone to
Kebroyd. Perhaps he had gone to church; in that event he
would not be home till late. The night would be pitch-dark, the
moon did not rise till late; he had not the lantern with him.
Well, he would have a tedious and unpleasant walk. She was
glad of it, the more tedious and unpleasant the better. It would
serve him right for staying away. She would not give him the
socks now. As he did not come home in time, she would have
the Christmas-tree without a present for him, and so punish
him. He would feel that, and he must be made to feel uncomfortable if he gave his wife occasion to be anxious.

As the night drew on and Tom did not return, Jewel became
alarmed; but she was far from supposing that he had taken
mortal offence at her words.

"I did speak a bit sharp," she argued with herself; "but men
don't mind that. They've their consciences thick-skinned as
rhinoceros hide, and unless one speaks sharp they don't feel.
I'll give him the six pairs of socks when he comes home, and
he'll forget all about what I said. Men ha'n't got much o' memories."

She had removed the socks from the tree; now she hung them
on it again.

Ten o'clock struck and Tom had not returned. Jim was nodding by the fire, wearied with not having had proper rest the night before.

Jewel went to him and touched him.

"Is t' tree alight and ready?" he asked, starting up.

"No, Jim. We shan't have it till Tom comes back. He is out. He went down to church at Kebroyd, and the snow has come on so thick, and he not having a light, has thought best to stay there. He'll be home i' t' morning"—she spoke what she hoped and believed, or tried to believe—"Jim! go to bed, lad, thou needst sleep."

It was unlike Tom, always thoughtful, leaving her in uncertainty. Why had he not made an effort, got a lantern from an acquaintance, and made a push to get through the snow? If he could not come himself, why did he not send some one to tell her he was detained?

She slept as little that night as she had slept the night before. All next day snow fell, and the moors were deeply buried. There had not been much wind, so there were no heavy drifts, but the white sheet lay pretty evenly, and very deeply over everything.

Jewel consulted Matthew next morning. He had not seen his master. She despatched him to the reservoir, and, if he heard nothing of him there, to Kebroyd. After several hours spent by Jewel in suspense that would not let her remain quiet in the house, Matthew returned. No one that he could learn had seen or heard anything of Tom a' Tuddlams on Christmas day.

Not a trace, not a report of his having been seen reached Jewel on that day, or after.

Then Jewel remembered Tom's last words to her—

"My love shall drink good-bye to me,
An' I'll drink like to him."

Did he mean that seriously? Did he mean a long good-bye? Her heart stood still at the thought. But though Jewel began, reluctantly, to fear that Tom would not return, she was very far from supposing that she had driven him from his home. She racked her brains to think what had become of him. She supposed that after the quarrel had broken out again on fresh grounds, he had flung away in a huff, and had, perhaps, gone over the moor and lost his way—perhaps had fallen into the reservoir, perhaps into a pot; there were quaking bogs on those moors to engulf the wanderer who treads incautiously upon them. She turned faint at the thought that he might be dead.

Some one suggested that he might have gone to Ossett to see some of his old acquaintances there at Christmas. She wrote to a friend there to inquire, and learned, so far as her friend could find, he had not been seen in Ossett. Old Matthews asked whether it was the way of Tom to go for a spree to one of the big towns, because old Uncle Nick did that occasionally, and drank for a fortnight till he had spent all his money, and then came back.

The fortnight had passed and Tom had not returned. January passed and still no tidings of Tom. No tidings all February. The Christmas-tree was put in its pan, outside the house; there was earth with the roots, and the old pan had holes in it. The tree would live. As for the tapers and gewgaws, Jewel thrust them out of sight in a drawer.

In March came a thaw—a rapid thaw—and the white world, in a day and a night, under pouring rain and a westerly wind, became black.

A few days after the thaw, old Martha a' Samuel's—an aged very poor woman, who was thought to be a witch, who blessed white swellings, and took away warts, and discovered lost articles, and removed spells—came one day to Tuddlams holding a red kerchief in her hand.

"Dost 'a know this?" she asked of Jewel.

"Yes," answered the mistress of Tuddlams; "yes; where didst thou find it?"

"I found it at the very edge o' the Boggarts' Well Hole, one end caught in a bleg" (bramble) "bush, or it might have been washed or blown away."

"At the Boggarts' Well!" Jewel's head swam. She put her hands to her temples.

"Eh! to be sure. And if that be thy man's, how came it there?"

Exactly—how came it there? Jewel could not speak.

"To my mind," said the old woman, "it seems that Tom a' Tuddlams must have gone that road, and what with the snow and the darkness coming on, he may have slipped and fallen down into t' pot-hole. But the bleg, wi' its thorns, caught the handkerchief and held it. He wouldn't cast a good handkerchief away. He lost it somehow. And how came it caught by a bleg unless he was falling, and it held to the kerchief as were sticking out o' his pocket?"

"The pot must be searched."

"Eh, dear life!" exclaimed Martha. "However wilt thou do that? Why, if thou goes nigh it, and listens wi' thy ear over t' hoyle, thou canst hear water running and roaring far below. If a chap was to fall in, he'd be swept away—the Lord knows where —for nobody yet has found out where the water comes to daylight that is heard running below the earth in the Boggarts' Well."

"I'll ne'er believe it! I ne'er will!" cried Jewel, wringing her hands. "It would be too dreadful; and my dear, good Tom! The Lord is merciful! He would not suffer it."

"Then where be he?" asked Martha.

Jewel threw herself down on the bench beside the table, laid her arms on the table and her head on her hands, and burst into a storm of tears.

"I cannot bear it!" she cried, choking with sobs; "I cannot bear it! If I only knew where he was! But not to know if he be alive or dead!"

"Not to know," said old Matthew, who came in, "whether he mayn't be still on the spree in Halifax, or Huddersfield, or Sheffield. Why, bless thee, he was brought up i' towns, and this was too lonely for him. He'd money i' his pocket when he disappeared. Take my word for it, he's laiking at one o' the towns where he used to be wi' his father when a boy."

"Oh, Matt!" she cried, "I'll give thee brass" (money) "if thou'lt go to Doncaster, and Pontefract, and Sheffield, and Huddersfield, and Ossett—wherever I can call to mind that Tom has been in former days—and axe if he has been seen there."

"Nay," answered the old man, "I must look after the farm, and I should never know how to begin that road. Get some younger man to go. There be Ben, the navvy. They've just about finished the new reservoir, and the water is to be let in to-day and out o' the oud one. Then Ben's occupation will be gone. Send him. He's a shrewd chap."

A rap at the door, and in came Ben himself.

"Mistress Jule a' Nort a' Nowheer," said he, "thou must come down directly to t' reservoir. The water ha' been let out o' t' oud pond, and a dead man ha' been found i' it; but the eels ha' played the deuce wi' his face, and nobody can make nowt out o' him, except by the clothes, and them as does must be his kin. Come along and see if it be Tom. Whomsoever he be, t' folks as drink water out o' this reservoir ha' been drinking soup for some time made out o' dead man and oud clothes."

Sick at heart, wild with misery, horror-struck at the discovery, Jewel went with the man, and was led into the parlour of the little tavern, where the corpse was destined to lie till the coroner had come and sat on it, and an intelligent jury had decided who he was and how he came by his death.

Jewel came away with face livid and eyes dilated with horror. No, no; it was not he. It could not be he. She could identify nothing. The hair was the same colour as that of Tom or near about, but the clothes were not his—at least, she thought not. No, no; that was not he.

Accordingly the coroner and jury sat on the dead man and pronounced that he was unknown, and that the occasion of his death was unknown. Nevertheless, a strong impression remained in the minds of the people of Kebroyd that this was the body of Tom. For—they reasoned—one man disappears, and a body is found, and nobody knows of a second man having been lost— it stands to reason that the corpse belongs to the man we know was lost. As for Jule, poor thing—well, it's natural she should cling to hope that her husband is still alive.

There were times, night—long sleepless nights—when Jewel doubted whether this were not really the body of her husband. It was true that she could not identify the clothing; but that had been sodden in water and mud, and was so disfigured and discoloured that she might have been deceived. The hair—the hair was the same colour. But no! Those were not his boots. She could swear he had no boots such as were worn by that horrible corpse. No; that was not Tom—unless he had changed his boots somewhere.

Then, on other nights, she thought of his red handkerchief by the Boggarts' Well which lay on the flank of Scalefell. How could it get there unless he had been there? How could it be caught in a bramble spray, unless it had been caught from his pocket as he lay on the ground? She would rather think of him drowned in the reservoir than carried underground by the mysterious stream whose exit was unknown. Again, at other times, mostly at night, she considered the suggestion of old Matt. Was it likely that he had tired of the loneliness of Tuddlams, tired of *her*, and gone away to a more stirring, gay life, such as he had, or might have known, of old? Oh, rather than that, in the Boggarts' Well—rather the drowned man found in the reservoir —rather dead than alive and unfaithful to her.

The summer passed.

Jewel, with the assistance of Matthew, carried on the farm with prudence.

No tidings of Tom, except a letter from her friend at Ossett, that someone had said he had heard somebody say that Tom had been seen somewhere. But next week came a letter from the same friend to say that it was a mistake. Someone had heard somebody else say that someone very like Tom Greenwood had been seen somewhere.

Autumn passed, and the suspense was the same. The uneasiness, the unhappiness of Jewel grew greater, instead of diminishing. And now a new name was given her—"Jule All Alone."

IX

Such is the perversity of mankind, Jule acquired the title of "Jule All Alone" just as she ceased to be all alone, for in September she became the mother of a dear little son, who was christened Thomas, and who was destined to be the future Tom a' Tuddlams, or Tom a' Tom's a' Will's a' Joe's. Consequently Jule was not alone; yet she was in another sense more alone than ever, for she felt doubly desolate in having a child without a father to show it to, think of and care for the little one. She tried to trace the likeness to the old Tom a' Tuddlams in the face of the young Tom a' Tuddlams, and fondly fancied that she found it.

One day, shortly before Christmas, old Martha, the witch, arrived at the farm; she had come to remind Jewel, by her presence, that on the former Christmas she had received a widow's dole.

Jewel bade the old creature be seated by the fire, and she showed her the babe.

"Eh!" said the hag. "I've brought him salt, and an egg, and matches. As thou didst' not bring t' bairn to my house, I've brought t' puddening to t' bairn." * Then, when the three gifts had been disposed of, with thanks from the mother, "Si' there, lass," said the old woman, "I've brought the weeds and onfas," and she offered her some blue woollen threads. Thou must wear these about thy neck all the time thou'rt nursing t' bairn."

Jewel accepted the threads.

---

* These three gifts are made to every child when visiting a house. It is called, in some places, "Puddening." Sometimes silver—generally a threepenny-piece is added—or takes the place of the matches.

"Whativer thou does," said the old woman, "don't let t' bairn see into a looking-glass afore he's a year old."

"What would happen?"

"Thou'd best not ask," said Martha shaking her head. "But there, Christmas eve is coming, and if thou wants to know how to be sure where thy Tom is, whether he be alive or whether he be dead, I can tell thee how to discover."

"Dost thou know anything. Hast thou heard?" Jewel gasped, her colour went, then flushed her cheeks, then she again became deadly white. "Oh, Martha! if thou knowest aught, tell me."

"Nay, lass," replied the hag, "it's none for me to tell thee. It is for thine own sel' to find out."

"But how can I find out? I've been trying every way I can think of all this twelvemonth, and not a word about him can I hear. I cannot tell if I'm a widow and my bairn an orphan, or whether Tom be alive. He may be ill somewhere—I shall go mad if I do not know."

"I tell thee, lass, it is for thee to find out."

"How can I, Martha? Tell me the way."

"Hast thou never heard o' looking i' t' glass on Christmas eve at night? On Christmas eve the spirits of the dead are all about in the wind, and if thou looks i' t' glass, and thy husband or thy true love be dead, thou'lt see him looking over thy shoulder; and if he has been drownded, he'll be dripping with water; and if he's been burned, he'll be all in flames; and if he's been killed wi' a knife, thou'lt see t' wounds bleeding."

"And if he is alive, and elsewhere, and—and—happy and has forgotten his home?"

"Then thou must say t' Lord's prayer three times again, thou'st said it already three times, and lighted the Yule candle. If he don't come then, then thou sayest t' prayer over three times again, and backwards, and then thou'lt force him to come and show hissen, just as he is."

"And if——"

"And if he's been untrue to thee, and forgotten thee, then thou'lt see his face over one o' thy shoulders, and the face of that other over thy second shoulder."

Jewel shuddered and covered her eyes. "I had rather know nothing than risk it."

"Nay, lass, there's no risk. And, there—I'd forgot. Thou mun take a sprig o' mistletoe and set it over the mirror, and then light the Yule candle. An' thou must be alone, and nobody must disturb thee or know aught about it."

She thought about the suggestion of Martha all the day on Christmas eve, and when evening came, she had made her mind to the adventure. As she nursed her babe, she stooped over it, and whispered in its ear, "To-night thy mother shall know all, and whether thou'rt a fatherless bairn or no. It mun be, it mun be! I cannot bear the doubt any longer."

When the darkness had set in, Jim was troublesome; he was fidgeting about the house, going up stairs and then coming down.

"What is it, lad? What dost thou want?"

"Jule," said the boy, "I'm looking for Christmas. Matt said I mun have my tree to-night."

"Tree!" exclaimed Jewel, then thought. "Aweel, lad," she said, "there's the tree still living and green, outside the door, that Tom took up last Christmas. Thou canst have that, and in yonder drawer are tapers and sparkling things, and thou canst take them out, and do what thou likes with them, only—" she said emphatically—"thou mun be quiet, and not disturb me. Si' there, t' baby has gone to sleep, and I'll lig" (lay) "him i' t' cradle, and don't thee disturb him whatever thou dost. I'm going upstairs, and don't thee come up, mind."

Jewel had procured a sprig of mistletoe, and this she took in her hand. She took in the other the Yule candle sent her by the grocer at Kebroyd. It was green. She went upstairs to her room in the dark.

Now Jewel recollected the looking-glass that Tom had

377

brought her that same night a twelvemonth ago, and which she had put aside on a shelf, with a towel thrown over it. She had never looked into it since he gave it her.

She struck a light with one of the matches the hag had given to the babe, and with it kindled the long green Yule candle, which she set on a candlestick upon the dressing-table. Then she went to the shelf, withdrew the towel, and, taking the heavy swing mirror, placed it on the table. With a strong pin she affixed the sprig of mistletoe above it. The green candle she set beside the looking-glass.

This day—twelve months ago! Jewel knelt down before the glass and turned it, so that, looking up, she could see her own face in it, and also—when it appeared—that other face she desired, yet dreaded, seeing. No, that would not do. She could not bear the glass thus. She turned it up again, so that kneeling she could not see into it, but must rise to her feet and stand before it to see what she sought.

Then she knelt, and waited a moment.

How hushed the house was! Jim hardly stirred, so engrossed was he with his treasures.

She said the "Our Father" in a low and tremulous voice. Then she paused.

This day—twelve months ago!

She remembered how angry she had been with Tom about the tree, about his beating Jim. Yet—had he not acted rightly? The boy must be broken off the trick of going among the navvies and drinking spirits. Did the chastisement hurt him? Jim had himself told her it did not; he had howled to awake her sympathy and provoke her interference. What had she said to Tom? She remembered now every word—every cruel, cutting word. She remembered the look of pain that came in his face as she spoke. What—what were the words he then said? She recalled them now—now for the first time: "Jewel, forgive and forget. Give me thy hand, lass! This be Christmas eve, when there should be peace on earth and good will among men, most of all in a home between man and wife."

And what had been her answer?—

"There shall be no peace between us, no good will."

Jewel put her hand to her brow and wiped the cold drops of sweat that ran over it. Then she stood up, trembling as she rose, and looked into the mirror, and saw her own face, white, with the sweat-drops forming on the brow, and the eyes, large, full of fear, and with dark rings about them.

That was all she saw—herself.

Then she remembered that she had said the Lord's Prayer but once, and the apparition did not appear till it had been repeated thrice.

She knelt once more, and slowly, and with a broken voice and trembling lips, said "Our Father" again.

That night—a twelvemonth ago!

Tom had gone forth, after she had spoken so unkindly, and had brought her this mirror, and the little candles and tin ornaments for her tree; he bore her no ill-will, though she had spoken so cruelly to him. Then she had not thanked him, but sent him forth after her brother. Oh, he had been well-nigh lost on that snowy night, along with her brother; but he had saved Jim. Without him Jim would never have been recovered. He would have slept in the cave and died as he slept.

How had she acknowledged what he had done for Jim and for her? He had been merry that night, and she had yielded at the time to the spirit of joviality that sprang up; but next morning had regretted it, being angry and ill-humoured because tired, and had vented her ill-humour and anger on her husband.

She staggered to her feet once more, and again looked into the glass, and saw herself, and herself only.

She struck her head with her hand.

"I am distracted! I have forgotten! I have said the prayer but twice."

Then she fell on her knees again.

That night—two years ago!

Two years ago! Why then she was a poor millgirl, almost starving, and seeing her brother nearly starving, too. Then Tom had come and offered to stand by her in her need; and two years ago tomorrow they were made one. What would have happened to her had not Tom then come to her aid? There had been nothing for her—or at least for Jim—but the workhouse; and it would have been misery for her to have to part with that poor silly brother. Tom had kept Jim by her. Tom had been very good to Jim for her sake, because he loved her; and how he loved her now she saw plainly. On six shillings a week she had maintained her brother and herself, so scantily; and now she and Jim lived in plenty; but Tom, who had brought them into the land that flowed with milk and honey, Tom was cast out from it, cast down, may be into death, by her hand, by that hand he had taken to lift her out of poverty.

Though she was shivering with cold and fear, yet a rush of blood mantled her brow and cheek, and dyed her neck, and in her shame she laid her head on the ground. Then she heard her blood beat like hammers in her ears; there was a bounding of pulses in her temples, and noises as of tramping feet behind her, on the stairs, in the room.

With a cry of terror and shame and yearning unutterable, she leaped to her feet, and looked once more in the glass and again *saw herself*.

Yes, she had seen herself that night as she had never seen herself before. And in her agony of self-remorse and longing for pardon she cried out:

"Oh, Tom! oh, Tom! oh, Tom!"

And suddenly at the word, saw his face looking over her shoulder in the glass.

She stood frozen to the spot; her heart ceased to beat. She could not speak. Her wide, distended eyes were riveted on the mirror; and lo! there was a third face reflected there, looking over her other shoulder. Her bosom heaved with a spasmodic sob. A cloud came over her eyes but cleared again, and she saw that other face was the face of her babe.

"Jule!"

With a cry she turned.

In the mirror under the mistletoe were three clasped together.

X

How long did they thus remain, those three, clasped together? Not long, for the babe protested.

"Oh, Tom! oh, Tom! where have you been?"

"In Lancashire."

"Lancashire!"

No one had for a moment dreamed of his crossing to that side of the fells.

"And what hast thou been doing?"

"Never mind, lass: working and waiting, and wishing to come back to thee."

"Why didst thou not come?"

He hesitated awhile, then he said:

"I thought it best to keep away a bit."

"And how didst thou hear of the babe?"

"As I was coming here I spoke to Matt, and he told me. When I entered I saw the cradle, and took up the bairn; and then I came on to see thee, upstairs. Jim said thou wast here."

"Oh, Tom! I am fain thou'rt back. Yea, lad, it were right. I'm glad thou went, and I'm glad thou'rt come. Tom, I'll never drive thee away again, I've seen that to-night I never knew before— I've seen my Real Self."

Then they heard Jim calling and they went down the stairs, holding hands, and holding the babe between them; and as they passed through the door into the room, their eyes, that had been in the dark, were dazzled by the light, for Jim had kindled all the tapers on the tree, after he had set them up; and now he caught his fiddle from the nail where it hung, drew the bow across it, and began to play—

"Christians, awake! salute the happy morn
Whereon the Saviour of the world was born."

And, as he played, the carolers from Kebroyd, who had come up to Tuddlams, burst forth in the song:

"Christians, awake! salute the happy morn
Whereon the Saviour of the world was born."

382

For the Time Being

W. H. AUDEN

NARRATOR

Well, so that is that. Now we must dismantle the tree,
Putting the decorations back into their cardboard boxes—
Some have got broken—and carrying them up to the attic.
The holly and the mistletoe must be taken down and burnt,
And the children got ready for school. There are enough
Left-overs to do, warmed-up, for the rest of the week—
Not that we have much appetite, having drunk such a lot,
Stayed up so late, attempted—quite unsuccessfully—
To love all of our relatives, and in general
Grossly overestimated our powers. Once again
As in previous years we have seen the actual Vision and failed
To do more than entertain it as an agreeable
Possibility, once again we have sent Him away,
Begging though to remain His disobedient servant,
The promising child who cannot keep His word for long.
The Christmas Feast is already a fading memory,
And already the mind begins to be vaguely aware
Of an unpleasant whiff of apprehension at the thought
Of Lent and Good Friday which cannot, after all, now
Be very far off. But, for the time being, here we all are,
Back in the moderate Aristotelian city
Of darning and the Eight-Fifteen, where Euclid's geometry
And Newton's mechanics would account for our experience,
And the kitchen table exists because I scrub it.
It seems to have shrunk during the holidays. The streets
Are much narrower than we remembered; we had forgotten
The office was as depressing as this. To those who have seen

The Child, however dimly, however incredulously,
The Time Being is, in a sense, the most trying time of all.
For the innocent children who whispered so excitedly
Outside the locked door where they knew the presents to be
Grew up when it opened. Now, recollecting that moment
We can repress the joy, but the guilt remains conscious;
Remembering the stable where for once in our lives
Everything became a You and nothing was an It.
And craving the sensation but ignoring the cause,
We look round for something, no matter what, to inhibit
Our self-reflection, and the obvious thing for that purpose
Would be some great suffering. So, once we have met the Son,
We are tempted ever after to pray to the Father;
"Lead us into temptation and evil for our sake."

They will come, all right, don't worry; probably in a form
That we do not expect, and certainly with a force
More dreadful than we can imagine. In the meantime
There are bills to be paid, machines to keep in repair,
Irregular verbs to learn, the Time Being to redeem
From insignificance. The happy morning is over,
The night of agony still to come; the time is noon:
When the Spirit must practice his scales of rejoicing
Without even a hostile audience, and the Soul endure
A silence that is neither for nor against her faith
That God's Will will be done, that, in spite of her prayers,
God will cheat no one, not even the world of its triumph.

CHORUS

He is the Way.
Follow Him through the Land of Unlikeness;
You will see rare beasts, and have unique adventures.

He is the Truth.
Seek Him in the Kingdom of Anxiety;

You will come to a great city that has expected your return
  for years.

He is the Life.
Love Him in the World of the Flesh;
And at your marriage all its occasions shall dance for joy.

Christmas Is Here
A CATHOLIC SELECTION OF STORIES AND POEMS

Edited by Anne Fremantle

One of the most important facts about Christmas is the way in which it is received—as many ways as there are human beings. This fine new book is mainly a collection of stories about how different people in many lands receive the great news of Christmas Day, for it is always *news*. The lovely woodcuts and engravings that appear with the text echo the main theme with the simplicity and devotion of an earlier Christian age.

Here is a lasting Christmas gift for the entire family, one that will be opened and re-read with pleasure throughout the year. Selection of text and pictures is by Anne Fremantle, whose usual discriminating good taste makes this an outstanding book of its kind. As an editor of *The Commonweal* and author of many articles and books, for one of which she received the coveted Christopher Award, she has drawn upon her wide acquaintance among the literatures of the world for the best of Christmas reading. Many of the selections will be new to the American reader, some appearing in especially made translations, others coming from little-known English sources.

There is something for every mood. Primarily, of course, the special religious atmosphere of the holiday season, but there are also all the ingredients of good reading—sentiment, fantasy and adventure, realism, great poetry. And, not last, the comic spirit—speaking in the most British of accents, as in the delightful stories of Saki,

continued on back flap